D1242652

NAVAL SURGEON

Peter St. Medard, by an unknown artist. The portrait must have been painted after the summer of 1802, perhaps somewhere on his Mediterranean cruise, because the United States Navy Surgeon's uniform he is wearing was authorized by the Secretary of the Navy on 27 August of that year. (Courtesy of the late Esther Gilbert. The painting is now in the U.S.S. *Constitution* Museum, Boston.)

NAVAL SURGEON

Life and Death at Sea in the Age of Sail

J. WORTH ESTES

SCIENCE HISTORY PUBLICATIONS/USA
Canton, Massachusetts
1998

First published in the United States of America
by Science History Publications/USA
a division of Watson Publishing International
Post Office Box 493, Canton, MA 02021

© 1998 Watson Publishing International

Library of Congress Cataloging-in-Publication Data

Estes, J. Worth, 1934–
    Naval surgeon : life and death at sea in the Age of Sail / J.
    Worth Estes.
        p.   cm.
    Includes bibliographical references and index.
    ISBN 0-88135-194-6
    1. St. Medard, Peter, 1755–1822.   2. Surgery, Naval—United
    States—Biography.   I. Title.
    RD200.S8E88   1997
    616.9′8024′09—dc21
    [B]   97-31845
                                                                          CIP

Designed and typeset by Publishers' Design and Production Services, Inc.
Printed and bound by Thomson-Shore, Inc.
Manufactured in the U.S.A.

For
Bill Wieting and Ed Pelikan
physicians, naval officers, and long-time friends

Contents

APPENDICES

INDEX

Preface and Acknowlegments

THE STORY of this book began one autumn night in 1979 when I arrived at the library of the U.S.S. *Constitution* Museum, near the pier in the Boston Navy Yard where "Old Ironsides" is berthed. I had been invited there by Jo Gladstone, then a producer for PBS, as a medical consultant for the development of a slide-tape show about medical care on the ship during her first major victory over the British in the War of 1812. While waiting for the rest of Ms. Gladstone's advisers to arrive, I began looking around the small library, and then into the large, flat drawers that fill the island in the middle of the room.

One of the drawers contained a large leather-bound volume labeled *Physical and Chirurgical Transactions of Dr. Peter St. Medard on Board the U.S. Frigate New-York*, dated 1802–1803. Almost as soon as I began leafing through the neatly ruled pages containing the name, age, rank, date, diagnosis, treatment, and eventual outcome of every case that came under Dr. St. Medard's care, I realized that I had stumbled upon a sort of Rosetta stone that would allow me to explore the day-by-day treatments prescribed by a doctor trained in the eighteenth century. Most important of all, the data promised to facilitate answering a question my earlier research into the medical practices of that period had not permitted: *why* did physicians prescribe all those remedies which, we know today, could not have specifically benefited their patients?

That was only my first stroke of good luck. The second came when I was able to recruit Carole P. Kiler, R.N., then a graduate student in American and New England Studies at Boston University, to construct an analogue of the modern medical record for each man—and one woman—in *New-York* from Dr. St. Medard's daily clinical notes. Her painstaking transcriptions onto McBee Keysort cards, one set for each patient (this was done before any of us had a computer on every desk), formed the backbone of the entire study.

My third encounter with serendipity occurred when Captain Serge Rateau volunteered to pursue some biographical questions about Dr. St. Medard that had eluded me completely. His key role in the story of my story is outlined in the Notes to Chapter One.

Indeed, I have met with continuing good luck during the seventeen years since I found the St. Medard manuscript—chiefly in the form of the generous assistance I received from many people. At the top of my list is Elizabeth B. Andrews, a collateral descendant of Dr. St. Medard. She had given his manuscripts from his time on *New-York* to the *Constitution* Museum because St. Medard had been the surgeon on "Old Ironsides" on her first major assignment, during the Quasi-War with France. Miss Andrews and I have had a long, and pleasant, correspondence over the years. She brought several other St. Medard documents to Boston for me to see early on, and most recently sent me two very large packets of his remaining letters in her possession. Whereas Captain Rateau's work permitted me to reconstruct Dr. St. Medard's early years, Miss Andrews's manuscripts permitted me to round out the life of this member of the first generation of U. S. Navy surgeons.

At the urging of the late Mark D. Altschule, M.D., I presented a summary of my findings at the Naval History Symposium at Annapolis in 1981. That led, over the years, to the contributions of knowledge and pertinent references by virtually all members of the wonderfully generous community of students of the early navy whom I met there and at meetings of the North American Society for Oceanic History. Foremost among them is Professor Christopher McKee, Grinnell College, who out of the clear blue sky sent me his extraordinarily careful biography of Edward Preble, as well as copies of his biographical data cards on the officers who served in *New-York*. He has also reviewed an early draft of this book; any remaining errors are my own. An equally generous contributor was the late W. M. P. Dunne, who sent me, again out of the clear blue sky, a copy of the extraordinarily detailed operational history of *New-York* that he had compiled for other purposes. Similarly, Harold D. Langley sent me lists of pertinent documents in the National Archives. Thus, not only generosity but spontaneity have distinguished much of the assistance I've received from naval historians.

Others who have helped in a variety of constructive ways include: Dean C. Allard, Médécine Générale and Mme. P. H. Bonnel, Mrs. Linn P. Brown, Jr., Howard Browne, Philip D. Curtin, William S. Dudley, Ira Dye, William M. Fowler, Jr., Gerald L. Geison, Toby Gelfand, Professor Jean-Pierre Kerneis, Frederick C. Leiner, Esq., Tyrone G. Martin, William J. Morgan, Eric Nellis, Philip Chadwick Foster Smith, Virginia Steele Wood, and librarians all over the country. Peter V. Sterling, who was director of the U.S.S. *Constitution* Museum when I embarked on this project, provided a great deal of assistance and encouragement, as well as some of the museum's facilities. Nicolle Coffin and Isabelle Mintz helped me translate some of the more difficult French correspondence.

The late Miss Esther Gilbert, another collateral descendant, kindly permitted me to photograph and publish her portrait of Dr. St. Medard while it was on exhibit in Boston; she later gave it to the U.S.S. *Constitution* Museum, along with the doctor's lowboy. The Earl Gregg Swem Library of the College of William and Mary kindly granted permission to quote from the letters of James Barron and William Lewis. I am further indebted to the many curators, librarians, and dealers in maritime fine art who have tried to help me find a picture of *New-York*, even if the search has been fruitless. Still, I would not be surprised if one did turn up some day, after lying in someone's attic, or perhaps even hanging over an inherited Federal sideboard, for the past 190 years.

Finally, I continue to be indebted to my old friends Philip Cash and Richard J. Wolfe for their patient answers to my unending bibliographic and historical questions, not to mention their encouragement. My work would have been impossible without them.

*   *   *

Because I had come upon an unusual opportunity to reconstruct the day-by-day work and medical thinking of a physician trained in the eighteenth century, I decided to use, whenever practical and useful, his own words, taken not only from his own journals and letters but also from those of other men on his ship; nothing would have been gained by simply paraphrasing them in condensed form. However, I have modernized his punctuation and capitalization, as I have those of other participants in his story. Similarly, I have included full texts of pertinent naval regulations, to delineate the extent to which the Department of the Navy and its predecessors were concerned with their crews' health. Dr. Medard tried to fulfill all the expectations embodied in such directives, but until now these regulations have not been gathered into one place.

Finally, I debated long and hard with myself over an appropriate format for citing the sources used in this study. In the end, I concluded that it would be unnecessary (and certainly messy) to cite hundreds of individual entries in Dr. St. Medard's *Transactions*, much less the multiple contributions of all the various manuscript personal journals and letters used, since all are identifiable by their present location and dates; worse, the nearly 350 manuscript letters in Miss Andrews's possession are not catalogued. Consequently, I have written bibliographic essays for the end of each chapter. Even in the absence of individualized footnotes, they will permit interested readers to find any item cited in the text, as well as the sources of my more sweeping generalizations, although Appendix II will have to be used to find the dates pertaining to individual patients.

J. Worth Estes
11 November 1996

Prologues at Sea
1755–1801

Chapter One

Prologue in the French Slave Trade

STONE TOWERS have guarded the entrance to the harbor of La Rochelle, on the stubby peninsula where the Sèvre Niortaise empties into the Bay of Biscay, since the late fourteenth century. Medieval and rococo buildings in which much of the city's business has been conducted for several centuries line the inner harbor and the town's narrow streets. Hippocrates, Galen, Avicenna, and other ancient physicians still look down from the facade of an elegant seventeenth-century town house, proclaiming that its builder, Nicolas Venette, had earned his substantial wealth as a physician. Indeed, much of the old part of the city looks as it did a week before Christmas, 1773, when young Pierre St. Medard was accepted as a surgeon into the French merchant marine, unaware that he would soon become a citizen in a country that had not yet been formed, and under whose colors he would eventually take arms against his native land.

Pierre was born nearby on 12 March 1755, in the small town of St. Georges on the northern end of the Ile d'Oléron. The largest island on the west coast of France, it stretches twenty miles into the Atlantic Ocean between Rochefort to the east and La Rochelle to the northeast. Well populated in Pierre's youth, each of its six parishes comprised many villages. Because its surface is flat, the islanders worked at farming, wine-making, and salt extraction, but their chief occupation was fishing. Indeed, their maritime tradition sent many young men into the King's Navy and the merchant marine.

The earliest known Saint Médard, lord of Salency and a bishop of Noyon in the sixth century, became a spiritual patron of agriculture, especially viticulture, both of which were important to the economy of the Ile d'Oléron. He is also said to have been invoked by people suffering from toothache and migraine. There is no evidence that Pierre was descended from the saint or his family, but some of Pierre's relatives were sea surgeons. One, Joseph St. Medard de Duart, of Aix, passed his surgeon's exam in 1738, while Charles Samuel St. Medard, from the Ile d'Oléron, was surgeon on a merchant ship headed for the French colony of St. Dominque when it was taken by a British ship in 1745. Young Pierre would have a nearly identical experience 30 years later. After returning to France and the merchant marine, Charles Samuel went to India to seek his fortune. When Pierre's father, a merchant, married his mother in 1735, one of Pierre's uncles—perhaps Joseph or Charles Samuel—was recorded as a "master surgeon." Yet another Charles St. Medard (who may have been a brother of Pierre), from l'Orient on the mainland, passed his surgeon's exam in 1774, and Pierre's uncle, Jean Georges St. Medard, was a surgeon at Rochefort. Pierre had at least two sisters, Victoire and Eustelle, who never left St. Georges, and an older brother, Samuel. Although Samuel became curate of the town's church, a Chevalier de la Légion d'Honneur, and, in 1813, bishop of Tournai, in Belgium, he, too, shared his family's interest in medical matters: in 1807 his *Mémoire sur la Vaccine* earned a silver medal from the Comité pour l'Extinction de la Petite Vérole (Committee for the Eradication of Smallpox).

It is not certain why Pierre chose a medical career in the merchant marine, but the family tradition was strong and may have led him in that direction. His commitment to surgery—his social position may not have been high enough to permit pursuing a career as a physician, one usually reserved chiefly for the élite in eighteenth-century France—would have provided ample opportunity to broaden his practical experience at sea, and assured his income ashore. Or, perhaps he simply sought adventure.

In addition to the local medical tradition of sending doctors to sea, the Oléronais had provided care for sick sailors since at least the Middle Ages. For many years most of the ships that visited the island were coasters. Then, as seamen began to bring exotic diseases home from new lands and colonies, quarantines and lazarettos began to appear along the French littoral. Moreover, by the seventeenth century naval warfare had made military service at sea more hazardous than ever before, prompting the establishment of a forty-bed naval hospital on Oléron, but it was largely the risk of dying from contagious diseases, like typhus ("ship fever") and scurvy, then associated with filthy living conditions on Royal Naval ships, that prompted young French men to go to sea on merchant ships. Even so, they contracted malaria, yellow fever, and schistosomiasis in the West Indies, cholera in Asian ports, and venereal diseases virtually anywhere. Mortality rates in the merchant marine averaged about 5 percent among seamen on the routes to the French West Indies, and 15 percent on French slave trade routes to west Africa; in the sixteenth century mortality had been as high as 50 percent on the far longer routes to the Far East, but it had fallen to about 20 percent over the following two centuries.

There is no evidence that Pierre St. Medard attended the premier naval medical school and hospital (where one of his cousins had studied) that had been established in 1722 at Rochefort nearby on the mainland. It seems probable that he first learned his profession, from the age of 14 or 15, as an apprentice, perhaps to his uncle Jean Georges, who would have been paid a fee for the usual three-year course. Many years later Pierre said he had worked at a royal hospital in France, perhaps the small one on the Ile d'Oléron. He probably underwent a further year of training at the Hôpital Général St. Louis, which still admits patients at La Rochelle. Such civilian "general hospitals," which comprised only about 9 percent of all French hospitals at the time, functioned much like modern hospices, intended primarily for the confinement—actually, the segregation—of abandoned children and the indigent, and of patients who had been rejected by other hospitals, usually because they suffered from clearly contagious illnesses. Pierre may also have taken surgical courses at La Rochelle's École de Chirurgie, established in 1677 on the rue St. Côme, named for the patron saint of surgeons. The curriculum of that institution, as at Rochefort, included standard subjects such as anatomy, osteology, physiology, surgery, hygiene, obstetrics, pathology, and therapeutics.

Presumably, as was true at the Royal Naval medical school at Rochefort, St. Medard learned the common surgical techniques of the day, such as opening abscesses and superficial cystic tumors; cauterization; gastroraphy (i.e., suturing abdominal wounds); paracentesis (i.e., draining abdominal fluid in severe cases of ascites); repair of hernias, fistulas-in-ano, and arterial aneurysms; urinary catheterization and

5

removal of bladder and urethral stones; trepanning (cutting through the skull with a circular saw, usually to relieve intracerebral pressure caused by a penetrating injury); tracheotomy and extraction of nasal polyps; reduction of dislocations and fractures; amputation of arms and legs, fingers and toes; and cataract extraction. He would also have learned how to blister, as well as the several techniques of bleeding, including scarification, cupping, and leeching, along with current theories of medicine and the treatment of non-surgical illnesses, and about appropriate diets for men at sea. The greatest emphasis was, of course, given to emergency surgery.

The Naval Ordonnance of August 1681, as strengthened by Louis XIV in 1717, required that merchant ships with crews of 20 to 50 men carry one surgeon on board if they sailed beyond the customary coastal routes, or if they carried slaves as cargo, or two surgeons for larger crews. Surgeons who aspired to go to sea on long-haul vessels of more than fifty tons had to pay five livres to be examined by two master surgeons, but only three livres to be qualified for service on the lighter vessels used in the coasting trade. The regulations also specified that surgeons keep a record of their professional work at sea, for submission to the Admiralty, along with a certifying statement from their captains, upon returning from each voyage.

In 1772 the Parisian physician Jean Colombier proposed that clinical changes in the condition of hospital patients be recorded every two hours on a chart kept at the bedside. He cited an English model, probably Francis Clifton's 1731 book, *Tabular Observations Recommended as the Surest Way of Improving Physic*. Colombier pointed out that such patient charts would facilitate medical students' learning. Although Clifton's suggestion for keeping systematic patient records was not widely adopted by English-speaking physicians, such records were standard at the Royal Infirmary in Edinburgh, where students also maintained informal but highly detailed progress notes on patients in the teaching wards for the further instruction, through practical example, of other students. Eventually, French, British, and American military establishments would find clinical record-keeping to be useful for making manpower and other logistic predictions.

On 17 December 1773, after completing his surgical training at the age of eighteen, Pierre St. Medard applied to the Admiralty office at La Rochelle for acceptance as a sea surgeon on long-haul voyages—primarily to the French West Indies, especially to St. Domingue (now

Haiti), the French western end of the island of Hispaniola. He underwent oral examination by two master surgeons that day, on the most
common afflictions of seamen "dans les voyages de longs cours,"
including abscesses, superficial wounds, fractures, dislocations, and
ruptures, as well as on standard treatments from operations to ligatures, bandages, plasters, unguents, balms, and the full range of drugs,
including their therapeutic properties, their doses, and their hazards. A
day later, on 18 December, his application was approved. The eighteen-
year-old surgeon must have felt that Christmas was really worth cele-
brating that year, for he knew he would have ample opportunities for
employment.

In 1774, twelve ships sailed in the "triangular trade" out of La
Rochelle alone. They carried French manufactures to exchange for
slaves brought by local chiefs to West African coastal towns between
modern Sierra Leone and Angola, and then on to their most profitable
market, St. Domingue. One of the most productive of all European
colonies in the 1770s, it received the largest number of French slave
ships, and over 75 percent of all the slaves sent from Africa to all French
colonies. The demand for slaves for working the sugar fields there
never let up because their life spans were short under the inhospitable
working conditions on Caribbean islands, not to mention diseases to
which they had never been exposed in Africa. Ship captains could
anticipate that the transatlantic voyage from Africa to the Caribbean
would require about two months and an average of 240 liters (68 gallons) of water, and 40 kilograms (88 pounds) of food such as beans, rice,
and sea biscuit for every slave and sailor on their ships. For the final leg
of the triangular route, Rochellais captains loaded their ships with
indigo and sugar to sell when they returned home.

This was a lucrative and respectable business in late eighteenth-
century France, one that could also provide valuable professional experience for young surgeons. In 1776 alone, for instance, 69 French slave
ships left French ports for West Africa. Not only did their surgeons
look after the health of the crews both on board and during the months
they spent on shore in tropical climates, while still in Africa they were
expected to examine and treat, if necessary, the wounds that local
chiefs made with silver blades when branding people being sold into
servitude in the New World. On the westward run each surgeon was
responsible for maintaining the health of between 200 and 400 slaves
at sea. The average mortality rate among them was less than 10 percent

in 1774–75, a figure that captains needed to keep at a minimum, although the average death rate among their crew members averaged 11 percent, and could be as high as 17 percent.

Pierre St. Medard's first voyage as a surgeon was on the slaver *Saint Paul*, 180 tons and carrying four guns. She left La Rochelle on 24 April 1774 with a crew of 37 commanded by Captain Paul Hardy. St. Medard served as second surgeon under Pierre Latapie of Lourdes, who earned 60 livres per month. The novice surgeon is described on the Rôle d'Equipage as nineteen years old, of average stature, and with chestnut-brown hair; his wages were 35 livres per month.

It is not known when *Saint Paul* reached her first destination, the major slave trading post at Cabinda, on the coast of Angola. She disembarked the cargo of 304 "nègres" that she had picked up there on the north coast of Hispaniola, at Cap Français (now Cap Haïtien), then the capital of St. Domingue, on 7 May 1775, just over a year after leaving La Rochelle. If the crossing was completed in the usual time of two months, Captain Hardy must have remained in Africa many months while collecting his human cargo and enough food and water for the transatlantic leg of the voyage. It is not known if any of the slaves under St. Medard's care died on the westward trip, but one "novice" seaman died, of unrecorded cause, in the French hospital at Cap Français ten days after *Saint Paul* arrived. She departed on 16 July, and sailed into La Rochelle on 29 August 1775, after an absence of fifteen months and six days. When the crew were paid off nine days later, their second surgeon should have received about 530 livres.

St. Medard left La Rochelle again a little more than three months later, on 9 December, in *Duc de Laval*, 200 tons, four guns, and a crew of 50 men under Captain Jean Pellier. Pierre was again second surgeon under Pierre Latapie, but the junior surgeon's salary had been raised to 40 livres per month. Their first destination was Badagri, near Juda (now Ouida, in Dahomey), on the Côte d'Or, where the only two deaths among the ship's crew occurred while the ship was taking on its new cargo. After stopping for several weeks at Principe Island in the Guinea Gulf, to take on food and water and to refresh the slaves, *Duc de Laval* arrived at Cap Français on 22 September 1776. Ten days later the ship's local agents advertised 430 blacks for sale. On 2 December she sailed for home, where she arrived on 24 January 1777, but Pierre St. Medard was not aboard—he seems to have elected to stay at Port-au-Prince, where he was paid off about 9 October.

It is not clear just what he did in St. Domingue during the months he remained there. Often second surgeons stayed behind to attend to slaves who had been disembarked, although the human cargo shipped on *Duc de Laval* was said to be in good condition when it arrived. But a stay on the island could also provide a surgeon with opportunities for a lucrative private practice, and perhaps for making his own investments. Later letters from Dr. St. Medard's agents in France and St. Domingue suggest that he had invested in the island's sugar production; a 1795 letter from his agent in France hints that the doctor may lose his assets there as the newly reconstituted government tries to achieve republican perfection. The reputed existence today of a sugar plantation called St. Medard some miles from Port-au-Prince further suggests that Pierre might indeed have invested in the primary local business, sugar. Further business opportunities had opened by then, inasmuch as the outbreak of the American Revolution in the spring of 1775 had encouraged smugglers who had been illegally supplying French arms and West Indian rum to Americans in exchange for tobacco and rice. Moreover, many Americans were living in St. Domingue, and their compatriots' rebellion was being trumpeted in French newspapers there. Thus, St. Medard may have first become familiar with Americans and their cause while he was in the West Indies.

It is not known just when or how he returned to La Rochelle, but it was probably via Bordeaux or Nantes. At any rate, on 13 January 1778 he left France again as the only surgeon, at a salary of 50 livres, on *Le François*, 260 tons, 11 guns, under Captain Jean Étienne La Fontaine, manned by a relatively small crew of 25. Although the ship was customarily in the French triangular trade, the nature of her cargo on this run was not recorded at La Rochelle, but it did not include slaves: this time St. Medard was headed not for west Africa, but directly for St. Domingue.

Three weeks later, representatives of France and the new United States of America signed the treaty of alliance and commerce which automatically made France an enemy of Great Britain. Because both the French and the British navies actively sought to disrupt the other's slave trade from then on, it is not surprising that the next time we hear of *Le François*, she and two other ships have been captured by the British tender *Dunmore* on 12 April 1778, off the coast of Virginia, before the French merchantman had turned south toward St. Domingue. Two days later the four ships joined a convoy of prize ships that, on 22 April, arrived at New York, then occupied by the British. *Le François* was condemned there, but it is not known whether she netted her captors her insured value of 40,000 livres empty, or that of her cargo, worth 73,101 livres.

St. Medard, and probably his fellow officers and other shipmates, were imprisoned for about six months in H.M.S. *Jersey*, a dismasted 64-gun ship of the line anchored in Wallabout Bay, where the Brooklyn Navy Yard would later be established. Indeed, the French prisoners may have been among the first to enter the new prison ship. By the end of the war, the British would have committed at least 16 derelict hulks to prison duty at New York, but *Jersey* was the most notorious of all. Contemporary estimates that she housed as many as 1,000 to 1,200 prisoners at once seem exaggerated to some modern historians. But maybe the estimates are accurate.

It is probably true that the prisoners incarcerated in *Jersey* were treated brutally by their captors, and poorly fed with largely rotten food, that the stench of both the living and the dead was unbearable, and that the numbers of deaths from dysentery, small pox, and yellow fever were inexcusable. British commanders justified their treatment of the American prisoners as no more than the rebels deserved: their independent belligerent status was not recognized in Whitehall. For instance, the House of Lords refused to improve the lot of American prisoners, especially their diet, on the specious grounds that prisoners were mostly inactive and did not require as much food as others did.

Because the British did not recognize American independence, there were no protocols for exchanging British and American prisoners of war. Nevertheless, prisoners were exchanged, although the process was never regularized beyond the basic equation of one for one, and the Americans seldom had enough British prisoners to balance that equation and justify an exchange. However, probably under pressure from the French naval forces recently arrived off New England, whose belligerent status could not be doubted, Captain La Fontaine of *Le François* and most of his men were exchanged for the same number of British prisoners of war held by nearby American forces, under a cartel agreed to on 24 September 1778 by the Comte d'Estaing, Vice-Admiral of France and commander of His Majesty's forces in America, stationed at Boston, and Rear-Admiral James Gambier, commander of

His Britannic Majesty's naval forces in North America, who was at New York. Not all of the French crew were exchanged, however; two sailors from *Le François* died in a prison hospital ashore.

Pierre St. Medard and several other French prisoners were sent to Boston on the British schooner *Pembroke*, which arrived there on 6 October, not quite six months after their capture, and other men from *Le François* arrived over the next month. Upon disembarking at Boston, St. Medard and eight other French officers "refused to give their names" to the local French consul, perhaps because they did not wish to be repatriated. Thus, traditional French enmity for the British probably combined with whatever enthusiasm they may have had for the American patriots' cause to produce a new infusion of French volunteers into the ranks of the Continental forces. This was certainly true for Pierre St. Medard who, at the age of 23, was about to contribute his professional services to his new country.

NOTES

This chapter would not have been possible without the enthusiastic research contributed by Captain Serge Rateau, of Boulogne-sur-Seine, and formerly of the French merchant marine. In February 1984 he wrote to the U.S.S. *Constitution* Museum in Boston, seeking a photograph of the portrait of Pierre St. Medard (hereinafter PSM) which had recently been displayed there, and which has now joined the museum's permanent collection. Because modern merchant ships do not ordinarily carry doctors on board, their officers, including the captain, are charged with their crews' health at sea. Captain Rateau's interest in maritime medicine was further stimulated by his membership in a naval medical history society. The director of the museum forwarded the captain's letter to me, and I sent him a copy of my first paper based on PSM's work and a slide of the portrait. I also sent along some unanswered questions about PSM's life in France, which M. Rateau volunteered to try to answer for me. On 30 June 1984 he sent me a series of carefully collated notes, complete with maps, pictures, and photocopies, true copies, or summaries of official documents, all of which provided an outline of PSM's early life; on 9 December 1984 and 1 April 1985 he sent the results of more inquiries he had made. It was a great pleasure to meet M. et Mme. Rateau for dinner in Rouen while we were travelling in western France five years later.

The details of PSM's birth, and of his parents' marriage, are in the St. Georges parish register; his brother's biographical epitaph is still visible in the church graveyard. M. Rateau described the geography and occupations of the Ile d'Oléron for me in some detail. Because naval and hospital officials at Rochefort could not identify PSM in their archives, we conclude that he learned surgery at La Rochelle; because his training was in surgery, not medicine, it is unlikely that he studied at the other major hospital of the town, the Hôpital St. Barthelmy, which was devoted chiefly to what we might call internal medicine today. His acceptance as a surgeon by the Admiralty office is recorded in the Archives du Départment de La Charente-Maritime in La Rochelle. M. Rateau also sent me a copy of the 1717 regulations for maritime surgeons, and a typical surgeon's certificate, dated 23 July 1768; most of these certificates have not survived because they were issued to the surgeons, and archival copies were not retained.

Documents for the three French slave ships on which PSM sailed from 1774 to 1778 are in the Archives du Départment de La Charente-Maritime (docketed as B 259), the Archives du Port de Rochefort (docketed as 6 P 27, 6 P 28, and 6 P 31), the Archives Nationales, Paris (F 2 B 5, *Commerce aux Colonies*), and the Bibliothèque Nationale, Paris (Cote 4° L c 12 17/19 et 20/22, "Affiches Americaines," in the *Gazette de Saint-Domingue*, for 13 May 1775, 22 July 1775, and 28 September 1776). M. Rateau also cites a book, *Le Commerce de La Rochelle au XVIIIè siècle.* The Public Record Office at Kew provided evidence that *Le François* was taken by *Dunmore* (ADM 52/1719, ADM 51/828, cited in a letter from T. R. Padfield to Capt. Rateau, 12 June 1984). M. Rateau found the manuscript *Rôle des prisonniers françois debarqués á Boston le 6 [Octobre] 1778* in the Archives Nationales (series F, under series F2/95). Additional details of the capture and release in Boston are in *Antilles et Etats-Unis d'Amerique, 1778-79, . . . prises et prisonniers*, microfilm B 4/151, also in the Archives Nationales. Curiously, Boston newspapers in the fall of 1778 did not mention the arrival of the French prisoners, although they passed on similar information from newspapers in other American cities. Keith P. Hertzog presents a useful overview of the impact of the war on the slave trade in his "Naval operations in West Africa and the disruption of the slave trade during the American Revolution," *American Neptune* 55 (1995): 42–48. PSM's investments in the West Indies are discussed in letters from his agents at Ambissany, 21 August 1792; M. Cairoche, at Newport, 7 May 1794; M. Ménoire, at Bordeaux, 14 Thermidor, 25 Vendemiaire [1795], and 5 August 1792; at La Rochelle, 10 August 1807; and a letter from PSM to his agent at Martinique, 22 May 1821; all are in the collection of Elizabeth B. Andrews (hereinafter cited as the EBA collection; for more on it, see the Notes to Chapters Two and Twelve).

The French slave trade is described by Philip D. Curtin in *The Atlantic Slave Trade: Census* (Madison: University of Wisconsin Press, 1969), pp. 163–203; the mortality for the slave ships is on pp. 277, 283.

It is regrettable that the documentation that accompanied PSM's application for membership in the Massachusetts Medical Society in 1811 was not retained by the Society. Still, the curriculum vitae he furnished at the time (in the Boston Medical Library, B.Ms. b75.1 / MMS f.168) is consistent, as far as it goes, with the independently constructed outline presented in this chapter. His incarceration in *Jersey* is attested in a letter he wrote on 29 May 1820 to Smith Thompson, Secretary of the Navy (Officers Letters, Microcopy 148, roll 24, National Archives).

Supplementary information about other eighteenth-century St. Medards who were maritime surgeons was kindly collated for me from his research in the marine archives at Rochefort by Professor Jean-Pierre Kerneis, chair of anatomy and physiology of the faculty of medicine at the University of Nantes (letter dated 22 October 1981). Records of at least six voyages that Charles Samuel St. Medard made to East Indian ports such as Mauritius and Pondicherry are among merchant marine abstracts dated from 1748 to 1755 on FNA reels 14 and 15 in the International Marine Archives now at the Old Dartmouth Historical Society Whaling Museum at New Bedford, Mass. Information about the saint from whom the family took its name was sent to me 2 April 1982 by Howard Browne, M.D., who collects such information; more is found in Gordon Jones's notes to Cotton Mather's *The Angel of Bethesda* (1724; first published at Barre, Mass., by the American Antiquarian Society, 1972), p. 380. Eighteenth-century La Rochelle is well illustrated in Jean-Louis Rieupeyrout, *Connaître La Rochelle* (Bordeaux: Editions Sud-Ouest, 1988).

The outline of French maritime medical training is drawn from Muriel Joerger, "The structure of the hospital system in France in the Ancien Régime," trans. by Robert Forster and Orest Ranum, in *Medicine and Society in France* (Baltimore: Johns Hopkins University Press, 1980), pp. 104–136; Jacques Payen, "Les Frères Périer et la pompe à feu de l'Hôpital de la Marine à Rochefort (1783)," *Revue d'Histoire des Sciences* 22 (1969): 66–69; Alain de Bozec, *Histoire de l'École de Chirurgie de Rochefort* (Bordeaux: G. Taris, 1959), pp. 20–22; Jean Torlais, "Manuel des opérations de Chirurgie par M. Du Puys, Premier Médecin du Roy, à l'Hôpital de la Marine de Rochefort—1757—Manuscrit," *Histoire de la Médecine*, numéro spécial (1958): 138–144. The following excellent surveys are in Pierre Pluchon, ed., *Histoire des Medécins et Pharmaciens de Marine et des Colonies* (Toulouse: Editions Privat, 1985): Philippe Masson, "Expansion maritime et santé," pp. 15–43; Marc Gentilini and Jean-Pierre Nozais, "Expansion coloniale et santé," pp. 45–65; and, Bernard Broussolle and Philippe Masson, "La santé dans la Marine de l'ancien Régime," pp. 69–87. The following works of Toby Gelfand were equally useful, especially on medical record-keeping in eighteenth-century France: "From guild to profession: the surgeons of France in the eighteenth century," *Texas Reports on Biology and Medicine 32* (1974): 121–134; "Medical professionals and charlatans: the *Comité de Salubrité enquête* of 1790–91," *Histoire sociale—Social History 11* (no. 21, May 1978): 62–97; "A clinical ideal: Paris 1789," *Bulletin of the History of Medicine 51* (1977): 397–411; and, "Gestation of the clinic," *Medical History 25* (1981): 169–180. Another positive evaluation of French military and naval medical education is found in Thomas Neville Bonner, *Becoming a Physician: Medical Education in Great Britian, France, Germany, and the United States, 1750–1945* (New York: Oxford University Press, 1995), pp. 54–58. For medical record-keeping at Edinburgh, see the pioneering study by Guenter B. Risse, *Hospital Life in Enlightenment Scotland: Care and Teaching at the Royal Infirmary of Edinburgh* (Cambridge: Cambridge University Press, 1986), pp. 43–56.

For prisoners of war held by the British, and in *Jersey* in particular, see: Charles H. Metzger, *The Prisoner in the American Revolution* (Chicago: Loyola University Press, 1971), pp. 203–240, 281–304; William M. Fowler, Jr., *Rebels Under Sail: The American Navy during the Revolution* (New York: Charles Scribner's Sons, 1976), p. 260; and Gardner W. Allen, *A Naval History of the American Revolution*, 2 vols. (1913; rprt. ed. Williamstown, Mass.: Corner House, 1970), II, pp. 621–636, 644.

Chapter Two

Prologue in the Continental Navy

PIERRE ST. MEDARD disembarked at Boston just as the town was beginning to recover from the British occupation of 1775–76, and to take an important role in the maritime war against Britain. Supplying privateers commissioned by the new state of Massachusetts, as well as Continental and French warships, was helping to revive the local economy, devastated by the flight of over half the Bay Town's 16,000 inhabitants since the war began. Moreover, the enemy still controlled access to other American ports from Rhode Island to South Carolina.

It is not known when the young French surgeon anglicized his name to Peter, or how he spent his first months in Boston. Perhaps he used some of them to improve his English language skills, although he never mastered English spelling. He was certainly establishing connections with visiting countrymen, with the local medical community, and with the extended maritime community that surrounded the peninsula on which most Bostonians lived, the kind of community he had left behind. Indeed, in December 1778 nearly the entire Continental Navy—the frigates *Warren, Boston, Alliance, Queen of France, Providence,* and *Deane*—was in Boston Harbor, along with a couple of Massachusetts cruisers and ten large privateers.

However St. Medard was acclimating himself to his new surroundings, he was also preparing to head back to sea. Sometime before June 1779 he chose to exercise the skills he knew best when he entered the naval service of his new country in the 28-gun U.S. frigate *Providence*, commanded by Abraham Whipple, one of the more successful captains in the Continental Navy. He may have found St. Medard an eager volunteer among the pool of local surgeons if only because the expatriate needed a source of income. At that time captains were responsible for recruiting their own surgeons, who were often difficult to entice into the service and away from their more lucrative practices on shore. St. Medard was given the rank of Surgeon's Mate, rather than Surgeon, perhaps because he had not yet been examined as to his fitness to practice his profession at sea, as Congress had required as early as 30 September 1776; it seems unlikely that a second surgeon, at higher rank, would have been assigned to a ship as small as *Providence*.

She had been languishing at Boston from the time she arrived in December 1778 until Congress sent specific orders, accompanied by funds for outfitting her, and until she could be readied for sea again. Finally, on 18 June 1779, Whipple led a squadron that also included the sloop *Ranger* and the frigate *Queen of France* out into the North Atlantic, under orders to plunder British merchantmen homeward bound from Jamaica. After *Boston* joined the small American squadron a month later, they picked off at least nine eastbound British vessels between Newfoundland and Virginia without a fight, much less casualties. Even if the British did recapture three of the prize ships from Whipple, the remaining six yielded over $1,000,000 in prize money for the captains, officers, and crews under his command. Because naval surgeons were allowed a share equal to that of Second Lieutenants (four shares, compared to a ship's captain's six and a first lieutenant's five), St. Medard's share from this single cruise, possibly a few thousand dollars, may have given him a modest degree of financial security.

In November the Boston Navy Board assigned him to the 32-gun U.S. frigate *Deane*, commanded by Samuel Nicholson of Maryland. The 550-ton frigate, built in Nantes to the order of the American commissioners in Paris, had been named for Silas Deane to recognize his role at the Continental Congress in creating his country's new navy. Still, because the frigate could not leave Boston until instructions and funds arrived from Congress, St. Medard probably spent much of the next year ashore trying to establish a medical practice in the town.

That effort may not have met his expectations. The ratio of doctors to population, a good clue to the degree of competition for patients' dollars, had never been lower throughout Massachusetts. This was highly important to physicians, since the practice of medicine alone was almost never sufficient as a sole source of support. Most New England physicians had to rely on other sources of income, a possibility not readily open to the newly arrived French surgeon. Moreover, any income from his West Indian ventures and his father's estate in France appears to have been put in escrow by agents there, for fear of being intercepted by the British. Worse, the war was wreaking havoc with the new country's tenuous economy in general. All these factors probably encouraged St. Medard to try to capitalize on his maritime medical experience in the navy.

Congress had been concerned with the health of its sailors early on. On 28 November 1775 it adopted a set of "Rules for the Regulation of the Navy of the United Colonies of North-America" that was derived from British regulations promulgated in 1731. The two sections that most immediately affected seamen's health and their care were:

> Article 16: A convenient place shall be set apart for sick or hurt men, to be removed with their hammocks and bedding when the surgeon shall advise the same to be necessary: and some of the crew shall be appointed to attend and serve them and to keep the place clean. The cooper shall make buckets with covers [for disposing of excrements] and cradles [wooden beds that were suspended from chains, or over-sized infant cradles] if necessary for their use.
>
> Article 17: All ships furnished with fishing tackle, being in such places where fish is to be had, the Captain is to employ some of the company in fishing, the fish to be distributed daily to such persons as are sick, or upon recovery, if the surgeons recommend it.

At that time, Surgeons' pay was set at $21 ⅓ a month, and Surgeon's Mates' pay at $13 ⅓. Only Captains earned more ($32 per month), whereas Able Seamen's pay was $6 ⅔. New wage scales adopted on 15 November 1776 were far more generous to Captains, at $60 per month, and Lieutenants, at $30, but the Surgeons' raise was much smaller, to $25 if their ships were rated at more than 20 guns, $21 ⅔ if fewer; they also received $4 per week for subsistence on shore when their ships were in domestic ports. However, in July 1777 all Surgeons' pay was increased to $30. Moreover, Surgeons' cabins were, by custom, adjacent to those of First Lieutenants, while Surgeon's Mates bunked with the Midshipmen. Thus, Surgeons were among the most privileged class on men-of-war.

Governments have generally recognized that the effectiveness of their fighting ships depended, at least in part, on satisfying their crews' nutritional needs. Accordingly, the Continental Congress specified the daily diet to be provided for its seamen (officers were responsible for their own food). The diet, adopted from British navy usage, included a pound of bread a day, as hardtack, in addition to:

Sunday:	one lb. beef and one lb. potatoes or turnips
Monday:	one lb. pork, ½ pint peas, and four oz. cheese
Tuesday:	one lb. beef, one lb. potatoes or turnips, and pudding
Wednesday:	½ pint rice, two oz. butter, and four oz. cheese
Thursday:	one lb. pork, and ½ pint peas
Friday:	one lb. beef, one lb. potatoes or turnips, and pudding
Saturday:	one lb. pork, ½ pint peas, and four oz. cheese

The day's allotment of meat and vegetables was served as a sort of stew, while butter, cheese, and pudding were served as side dishes. In addition, each man was entitled to a daily half-pint of rum, diluted with water, but captains were permitted to make a "discretionary allowance [for] extra duty and in time of engagement."

In the first years of the war, the large Marine Committee of the Continental Congress included one physician, Josiah Bartlett of New Hampshire, although it seems likely that other members of the Committee may have been equally conversant with good health practices, especially merchant princes such as John Hancock of Boston. For instance, on 26 April 1776, the Committee wrote to the captain of *Randolph*, then at Charleston, South Carolina:

> We observe with infinite concern that your people have been and remain sickly; this has happened in so many of our ships that we cannot help attributing it to some cause that may with proper care & attention be removed. You should therefore insist that your officers do frequently see the ship thoroughly and perfectly cleansed, aloft

and below from stem to stern, burn powder and wash with vinigar betwixt decks, order hammocks, all bedding and bed cloths and body cloaths daily into the quarters or to be aired on deck, make the people keep their persons cleanly and use exercise, give them as frequent changes of wholesome food as you can, fish when you can get it and fresh food in port. Ventilate the hold and between decks constantly. In short, cleanliness, exercise, fresh air and wholesome food will restore or preserve health more than medicine and it is deserving the utmost attention of any or every officer to preserve the health & spirits of the men.

Three days later, the Marine Committee sent a similar directive to all its commanders, as would its successor, the Board of Admiralty, and, eventually, several secretaries of the U.S. Navy.

It was probably easier to enforce cleanliness than to provide wholesome food. That required considerable cooperation—and honesty—from victuallers, pursers, and cooks, since there was always room for graft in the dealings of on-shore suppliers and those charged with making purchases for the use of ships being readied for duty at sea. Reasonably well ventilated fresh air could usually be supplied by using various mechanical devices, even if their effectiveness was often at the mercy of the weather. Getting the men to exercise their bodies was another matter altogether. Captain Charles Biddle told the Marine Committee how he did it on his ship, on which seasickness was the most prevalent complaint:

> Knowing that exercise is an excellent remedy for sea sickness, and wishing to make the young men on board learn to go aloft whenever the weather was fair I had the hand pump taken up to the head of the main top-mast and there lashed and every one of them that wanted a drink of water was obliged to go up, bring the pump down, and after they had taken a drink carry it up again. For the first five or six days many of them would come up on deck, look wistfully at the pump, but rather than go aloft would go down again. However they were soon reconciled to it and I believe it was a great service to them.

Deane was not ready to leave Boston Harbor again until early in 1780, when she, along with *Confederacy*, *Saratoga*, *Trumbull*, and *Alliance*, which made up the entire Continental Navy at the time, took several prizes along the mid-Atlantic coast; St. Medard seems to have benefited financially from his presence at two of these prize captures. Cruises into the South Atlantic in August and September 1780 netted only one prize, and it was lost soon afterward en route to Philadelphia.

In the fall of 1780, the Navy Board at Boston ordered Dr. St. Medard to be examined as to his professional competence, in order to comply with the Congressional mandate for all naval surgeons. He successfully answered questions put to him by two leading surgeons of the town, Dr. Joseph Gardner and Dr. John Warren; the latter was at that time director of the Continental Army's one remaining hospital facility at Boston, which cared for a little over 30 men near today's Massachusetts General Hospital. Accordingly, on 24 October 1780 the Marine Committee of Congress sent St. Medard his warrant as Chief Surgeon on *Deane*; as he noted later, Surgeons were not yet commissioned officers in the U.S. Navy.

Deane cruised the West Indies in February 1781, along with *Confederacy* and *Saratoga*, an American privateer, and a French brig. St. Medard revisited Cap Français about 2 February, and in the last week of the month the little squadron took a rich prize. In March they were doing convoy duty off the Delaware Capes, where *Confederacy* was taken by British frigates. The remaining Continental ships were back in Boston soon afterward.

Fragments of two medical documents from *Deane* have survived among Dr. St. Medard's papers. Because he was not on board the frigate during the times these documents were written, he must have taken them along with his own papers when he left the Continental Navy, even if they were written by one or more of his predecessors on the same ship. Still, they provide insights into the everyday medical practices of eighteenth-century naval surgeons that will be explored in more detail in later chapters.

The first document records remedies prepared by a surgeon on *Deane*, probably Dr. Silas Barnard, between 16 December 1777 and 25 April 1779. Each day's entry includes from one to nine medications, although none is recorded for from one or two days up to a month throughout the document. Moreover, the entries cannot be correlated with the ship's known itineraries or her stays at Boston or Philadelphia. Regrettably, the list gives no indication of the patients for whom the medicines were compounded, much less their diagnoses, or even clues to who wrote them. The only certainty is that they represent an apparently standardized record of conventional therapeutic practice at the time.

The second fragmentary medical document from *Deane* is a daily log of patients treated aboard her from 9 June through about 31 July 1779, while she was cruising off the Virginia and Delaware Capes, but not during the months covered by the prescription book. The diagnoses of the 24 men treated in the ship's sick bay (out of a crew that ordinarily numbered 210) during those seven weeks were: syphilis (1), gonorrhea (1), shortness of breath with oppression in the chest (1), diarrhea (2), dysentery (2), fever with eruption (1), fever with ague (2), which could have been malaria, although the treatment chosen by the doctor suggests that it was not, and fever with, in most cases, nausea and pain (12); two diagnoses were not recorded. All the treatments recorded for these men were conventional remedies for the time, including bleeding for six of the sickest patients. All 24 men were discharged back to duty after being on the sick list for from four to fifty days; the average was 14 days.

Curiously, included among these pages are seven others that appear to be in St. Medard's hand. They are dated only 9 March through 30 April; the year was probably 1780. Most of the entries on this pages are prescriptions, but an epidemic of small pox is evident among the recorded deaths:

> March 9th. Dempsey Loring [?] a boy died of the confluent small pox in the sixth day of eruption.
>
> March 11th. Ephraim Hanson a sailor died of the same pox in the 8th day of the eruption.
>
> March 12th. Wm. Ode[?] Masters Mate died also of the same disorder in the 9th day.
>
> March 17th. Leonard Mall Gunners Mate died in the 11th day of the eruption. [T]welve hours before death his pulse sensibly decreased with evident symptoms of a fatal & most speedy determination to his breast in consequence of which a suffocation ensued.
>
> March 29th. John Shaw Quartermaster died in the last stage of the confluent small pox: the effects of his disorder were evidently converted into a slow fever partaking much of the putrid and nervous kind to which I consider he fell a prey.
>
> April 7th. _____ Case a Sailor died of a slow typhus [fever] the consequence of an inveterate sort of confluent small pox.

All of these men must have been infected at the same time, since their pocks first erupted on 4 March, although where they contracted the virus is not known; all could have been exposed on shore during a break in their current cruise, or one of them could have brought the infection on board. Because this epidemic was characterized by confluent pustules, rather than the discrete variety usually observed in mild cases, it seems to have run a quicker course than usual in *Deane*. Of course, any outbreak of small pox within the close confines of a ship must have frightened St. Medard as much as Captain Nicholson and the rest of his crew. The doctor used terms such as "nervous," "slow," "putrid," and "typhus" to describe fevers of varying severity; these adjectives provide no good clues to the specific microbial causes of the fevers. While most febrile illnesses were "putrid" to various degrees, the Quartermaster's case must have seemed especially so to *Deane*'s surgeon.

The British surrender at Yorktown in October 1781 threatened to end Peter St. Medard's service to his new country. The Board of Admiralty, created on 26 October 1779 to replace the larger and more cumbersome Marine Committee, had been dissolved. Its work was placed in the financial hands of Robert Morris, in his capacity as Superintendent of Finance. Formerly a member of both the Committee and the Board, in his new capacity Morris acted as Agent of Marine. The naval forces at his disposal now amounted to only two ships, *Alliance* and *Deane*. He sent a new Navy Agent to Boston, charging him to see that both vessels put to sea immediately, but that was not possible, for the usual logistical reasons. At any rate, the new nation was now awaiting the signing of a final peace treaty.

Captain Nicholson had re-engaged Dr. St. Medard on 1 May 1781, while their ship was again at Boston. On the 30th, the young surgeon married Susanna (Pope) Farrington of Boston. Eleven years older than Peter, she was the widow of Joseph Farrington, a merchant marine captain, who had been lost at sea.

St. Medard would have found many compatriots in Boston during his months on shore. Perhaps the earliest prominent Frenchman to settle in the Bay Town was the state's new colonel of artillery and inspector general of foundries, Marie Louis Ansart de Maresquelle, an experienced foundryman who arrived in 1776. After the war he married a Bostonian and became Lewis Ansart.

Two months before Dr. St. Medard was handed over by the British in October 1778, Admiral d'Estaing had arrived at Boston in command of about fifteen ships of the line and frigates. Because his officers and crews numbered over 5,000, they were highly visible throughout the town, whose population was still less than it had been before the war. Visits from these and other French ships, and from French diplomats, provided occasions for well publicized celebratory dinners. However, despite the French alliance and its contribution to the victory at Yorktown, some Bostonians were highly suspicious of "frog eaters."

French military visits became more frequent after Yorktown; like Washington, who was keeping his army intact at Newburgh, New York, until the final peace treaty was signed, the French were unwilling to run the risk of loosening the maritime grip their ships had imposed on the British forces in North America. St. Medard seems to have known the French commander, Count Rochambeau, who took his troops to Boston in December 1782, where the count presented a snuff box to Mrs. St. Medard. She and her husband may also have met the Marquis de Lafayette on his trips to Boston in April 1780, December 1781, and October 1784, on the last occasion to celebrate the anniversary of the victory that the French had made possible at Yorktown.

Several visiting French naval surgeons were well known to the Boston profession during the Revolutionary War. Not only did the visitors present anatomical preparations and the latest French books on anatomy and chemistry to some Boston practitioners, they were also invited to participate in meetings of the newly formed Massachusetts Medical Society. The most influential among them was Sieur Jean Baptiste Feron. Between 6 October 1781 and 12 April 1784 he established, in a Boston brewery, a hospital for about 80 wounded French seamen (another 70 could be accommodated on the second floor if necessary), and placed some 20 sick or wounded officers in homes throughout the town. Feron presented a paper at a meeting of the medical society in 1784, and sent reports of three cases of his attempts to treat depressed skull fractures caused by musket and cannon balls to be read at another meeting. (All three patients seemed to be recovering at first, but eventually high fever and pus appeared, signalling imminent death.) He was among the first men to be made honorary members of the state society, a distinction of which he and his superiors were quite proud. St. Medard was not yet a member, but he knew his celebrated countryman because the expatriate French surgeon sometimes attended patients at Feron's hospital.

No treaty had yet been signed when, in March 1782, Nicholson took *Deane* to the West Indies. While there he captured four British vessels, three of which were armed, and was back in Boston two months later with many prisoners and several cases of fever. Upon his return he was relieved of his command for unknown reasons. Although a court of inquiry found Nicholson chargeable with neglect of duty, wasting public property, and dishonorable conduct, he was cleared of all accusations by the subsequent court-martial in September 1783. Nevertheless, command of *Deane* was given to Captain John Manley on 11 September. At about the same time, the ship was re-named *Hague*, in honor of America's new Dutch allies, because Silas Deane had been dismissed from his diplomatic duties at Paris in late 1778 after arguing in favor of reunion with Britain.

With Dr. St. Medard on board, *Hague* left Boston on 25 September. She was sailing in company with two French warships and a Massachusetts privateer in mid-October. One man was lost overboard and five were badly injured a month later when they fell from the fore-top mast during heavy swells while all hands were employed in repairing damage suffered during heavy gales two days earlier. Several ships were boarded along the way, but none turned out to be a legal prize now that the new United States had a number of ocean-going allies. However, on 28 December, off St. Kitts, *Hague* did capture a richly loaded British merchantman, *Baillie*, 20 guns, bound for St. Lucia, along with 35 prisoners. She was the last major prize taken during the Revolutionary War.

Early in January 1783, *Hague* narrowly missed fights with several British warships, and ended a 36-hour escape from the 44-gun H.M.S. *Dolphin* by running aground on a reef near Guadeloupe. She remained there, under enemy fire, for two days, until Manley got her off, somewhat damaged in her hull and rigging, but with only one slightly wounded man. St. Medard had increasing numbers of very sick patients on his hands during the month. Five men were sick on the 17th, but the number was varying between eight and fourteen by the 27th. Seamen Edmond Blood and Zacheus Blanchard broke out with small pox on the 25th. Three days later they and twelve others had to be left in the hospital at Pointe-a-Pître, a friendly French port on Guadeloupe, where *Hague* had gone for repairs, and where the prisoners from *Baillie* were discharged. Manley sailed for Martinique on the 27th, where more of his men were hospitalized.

Hague continued to shuttle around the Caribbean, largely under the protection of the more than a hundred French warships based at Port Royal in Guadeloupe, until she was recalled by Congress in the wake of the news that a final peace treaty had been signed on 3 February 1783. As he came ashore at Boston in May, Manley was arrested, but as in the case of his predecessor, the specific charges against him, brought by one of his former officers, are not known, nor is it known if he was court-martialled.

The fate of his ship is better documented. After *Hague* was sold off into merchant service on 2 October 1783, the only ship remaining in the Continental service was *Alliance*; when she was sold off two years later America's first navy came to an end.

Dr. St. Medard's first service to his new country also ended on 29 August, at about the time *Hague* was decommissioned. For the rest of his life he would regard his role in helping establish the new country as his proudest accomplishment, one that later generations of federal bureaucrats should remember and reward. In the meantime, now that the United States had no armed force afloat, he could only resume his medical practice in Boston. And start a family.

* * *

Susanna Farrington's two daughters, Sally (1768–1846) and Susanna (1774–1824) Farrington, came to live with the St. Medards, who had three children of their own. The two youngest sons died in childhood: George, born 23 April 1784, died on 12 August 1788 after falling from a window, and Samuel, born 18 September 1785, died of burns on 13 August 1787. The oldest, Peter, born 21 May 1782, went on to study medicine and surgery under Drs. William Ingalls and Charles Jarvis of Boston, and practiced briefly with his father at the Boston Almshouse, probably about 1804. In that year Peter, Sr., unsuccessfully solicited the Secretary of the Navy to appoint his son a Surgeon's Mate. Five years later, the proud father tried to persuade the colonel commanding the army artillery, and then the Secretary of War, to give young Peter a similar appointment in the army, but still to no avail. Finally, as the army was being built up in preparation for possible hostilities with Britain in April 1812, Peter, Jr., was commissioned a lieutenant in the First Artillery Regiment, stationed in Boston. But he was furloughed home from New York in May 1813 because of illness, and died of consumption (probably tuberculosis) on 24 December 1813.

The growing family lived in the North End of Boston, near North Square, a block from the busy waterfront. It was a built-up area of artisans' shops and houses with easy access to goods for sale, or at auction on the town's wharves a few hundred feet away; Paul Revere lived in the next block. A town pump for common use, a public market, and a guardhouse were in the square itself. Although the British troops that occupied Boston in 1775–76 had pulled down about 100 of the town's 4,000 buildings to make firewood during the winter, North Square had been little changed by the war.

Governor Thomas Hutchinson's elegantly appointed four-story brick mansion on Garden Court, near North Square, built near the turn of the century, had been completely looted during the Stamp Act riots on 26 August 1765. The royal governor had the shell repaired that same winter, but he left the house unoccupied when he departed for England in 1774. In April 1779 it was confiscated by the revolutionary Massachusetts government, and had changed hands six times by 16 September 1791, when it was bought by Thomas Farrington, Collector of the Port of Boston (he does not appear to have been related to Susanna St. Medard's first husband). Farrington leased the Hutchinson Mansion, as it came to be known, to Peter and Susanna. Although Farrington sold the house on 4 February 1792, the St. Medards lived in it for at least four more years.

On 1 January 1795 Peter bought a more modest brick house with eleven rooms at 11½ Back Street, near North Square, from a glazier. By this time the 40-year-old doctor seems to have been doing well financially, in part because of the general economic recovery that began about 1787; perhaps his income from the West Indies and France had resumed, although the French Revolution did have some negative impact on it. It is not possible to determine how much his profession contributed to his income; it may have been minimal, since the number of practitioners in Boston had grown from 24 in 1789 to 26 in 1796, and to 31 in 1798. However, even if non-Bostonians like St. Medard were not prominent among the Bay Town's medical community, there was only one other doctor in the North End, so competition for patients' dollars may not have been as intense in that part of town as it was elsewhere. In any event, St. Medard was able to pay off his mortgage in just over two years, and he and his family continued to live on Back Street until they died.

NOTES

PSM's Revolutionary War service record has been reconstructed, while allowing for some imperfectly remembered or recorded exact dates, from his letter of 29 May 1820 to Smith Thompson, Secretary of the Navy (Officers Letters, Microcopy 148, roll 24, National Archives), and from *Massachusetts Soldiers and Sailors of the Revolutionary War*, 17 vols. (Boston, 1896–1908), *15* (1907), p. 39 (although it contains several errors). The operational history of *Providence* while PSM was aboard her was collated from Gardner W. Allen, *A Naval History of the American Revolution*, 2 vols. (1913; rprt. ed. Williamstown, Mass.: Corner House, 1970), I:26, 336; II:382–5, 403; and William M. Fowler, Jr., *Rebels Under Sail: The American Navy during the Revolution* (New York: Charles Scribner's Sons, 1976), pp. 83, 100–101, 103, 130.

The cruises of *Deane/Hague* on which PSM served were extracted with difficulty, because each source selected different facts to report; see Allen, *Naval History*, I:285, 336; II:371–372, 379–381, 398–403, 506–511, 556–559, 582–583, 608–609, 615; William James Morgan, *Captains to the Northward: The New England Captains in the Continental Navy* (Barre, Mass.: Barre Gazette, 1959), pp. 165, 178, 189, 210–15; Howard H. Peckham, ed., *The Toll of Independence: Engagements & Battle Casualties of the American Revolution* (Chicago: University of Chicago Press, 1974), entries for September 1779, 13 September 1780, 12 April and May 1783, and early January 1783; Philip Chadwick Foster Smith, *Captain Samuel Tucker (1747–1833), Continental Navy* (Salem: Essex Institute, 1976), pp. 60–62; and from the expert transcription by E. Gordon Bowen-Hassell of the incomplete "Journal Kept on board Continental Navy Frigate *Hague*, commanded by Capt. John Manley" for 25 September 1782 to 1 February 1783 (Record Group 45, entry 393, no. 5, National Archives), kindly furnished by William S. Dudley, of the Navy Historical Center at Washington Navy Yard. Robert Morris's instructions concerning *Hague* and *Alliance* to his new navy agent are contained in a 19 September 1781 letter from the Office of Finance at Philadelphia to John Brown, Esq., Philadelphia, at the Historical Society of Pennsylvania (Dreer Box). The fragmentary drug lists and patient records on *Deane*, as well as drafts of two letters from Philadelphia, dated 7 and 12 October, to an illegible addressee, that concern PSM's profits in recent prize takings, are in the EBA collection.

William M. Fowler described "The business of war: Boston as a navy base, 1776–1783," in *The American Nepture 42* (1982): 25–35. Congressional rules for the Continental Navy are in Allen, *Naval History*, I:216–218, and II:689,

694–695. Other information about the Continental Navy is collated in Maurice Bear Gordon, *Naval and Maritime Medicine during the American Revolution* (Ventnor, N.J.: Ventnor Publishers, 1978). Charles Biddle's letter about how to insure exercise among his men is in Fowler, *Rebels Under Sail*, p. 254.

The few surviving first-hand accounts by American naval surgeons during the Revolution are Geo. Henry Preble and Walter C. Green, eds., *Diary of Ezra Green, M.D., Surgeon on Board the Continental Ship-of-War "Ranger," under John Paul Jones, from November 1, 1777, to September 27, 1778* (Boston: privately printed, 1875); Solomon Drowne, *Journal of a Cruise in the Fall of 1780 in the Private-Sloop of War, Hope* (New York: Charles L. Moreau, 1872); and the unpublished manuscript of Dr. Zuriel Waterman's *Journal of an Intended Cruize against the Enemies of the United States of America in the Privateer Sloop Providence*, in the Rhode Island Historical Society. Several Continental Navy drug and surgical equipment lists are reproduced in Gordon, *Naval and Maritime Medicine*. A contemporary British naval surgeon's journal is published, in part, in R. R. James, "A naval surgeon's log, 1781–1783," *Journal of the Royal Naval Medical Service 19* (1933): 221–240.

The French presence in Boston is attested in Fitz-Henry Smith, Jr., "The French at Boston during the Revolution," *The Bostonian Society Publications 10* (1913): 9–75; Philip Cash, "The professionalization of Boston medicine, 1760–1803," in Philip Cash, Eric H. Christianson, and J. Worth Estes, eds., *Medicine in Colonial Massachusetts, 1620–1820* (Boston: Colonial Society of Massachusetts, 1980), pp. 69–100, esp. p. 82. Dr. St. Medard's application for membership in the state medical society is in *Massachusetts Medical Society Miscellaneous Papers*, 3 vols., I, f. 180, and Dr. Feron's three skull fracture cases are in vol. II (Boston Medical Library, call no. BMS b75.1/MMS f. 180). Professor Kerneis kindly sent me transcripts of several letters concerning Dr. Feron and his hospital at Boston; from the Archive Nationale Paris Marine [A. N. Paris Marine C6 576, C6 496, C6 568, C7 105], they include: Mémoire, Feron, Boston, 6 September 1782; de Lethombe, Consul Général de France, Boston, 17 September 1782; memorandum, Mr. [Marquis] de Vaudreuil, Boston, 1782; Mr. Delaporte to Mr. Marquis de Castries, Boston, n.d.; [Mémoire], Feron to Monseigneur le Maréchal, Boston, 1784, with attachments by de Lethombe, Boston, dated 30 March 1784 and 13 April 1784.

Information about Boston and the North End comes from Justin Winsor, ed., *The Memorial History of Boston, 1630–1880*, 4 vols. (Boston: Ticknor and Co., 1881), II:525–527; III:168 (some of Lafayette's visits are noted on p. 173); Esther Forbes, *Paul Revere and the World He Lived In* (Boston: Houghton Mifflin Co., 1942), pp. 170–173, 456; and Cash, "Professionalization." The increased number of physicians in Massachusetts is tabulated in Michael B. Brodin, "Why are doctors afield?", *New England Journal of Medicine 304* (1981): 1048–1049. For a detailed example of medical competition in a New England town, see J. Worth Estes and David M. Goodman, *The Changing Humors of Portsmouth: The Medical Biography of an American Town, 1623–1983* (Boston: Francis A. Countway Library of Medicine, 1986), chapters 1–3.

PSM's housing can be followed in Cash, "Professionalization," p. 100; Abbott Lowell Cummings, "The Foster-Hutchinson house," *Old-Time New England 54* (1964): 59–76; and the remarkable typescript by Annie Haven Thwing, of *Suffolk Deeds 1630–1830*, vol. 8 (see entry for Garden Court Street), in the Massachusetts Historical Society. Elizabeth B. Andrews furnished her carefully researched genealogical notes on the St. Medard, Farrington, and Andrews families. In 1793 Sally Farrington, PSM's stepdaughter, married Mammy Masson. In 1816 their daughter Susan married John Andrews; PSM's journals, letters, and other documents passed through the next three generations of their family to Miss Andrews.

The lives of the three St. Medard children are documented in the EBA collection, including PSM's appeals in behalf of an appointment for his son (to Navy Secretary Robert Smith, 20 October 1804; to Secretary of War William Eustis, 20 March 1809, 16 October 1810, and to Henry Burbeck, Colonel of Artillery, Washington, 15 April 1808; the latter outlines young Peter's medical training). Lt. St. Medard's furlough is granted in a letter from John Fenwick, Adjutant General, 3d Military District, New York, 26 May 1813, also in the EBA collection.

In 1789 PSM paid £2/0/11 for a pair of gravestones that were installed in the family crypt at Christ Church ("Old North Church") in the North End, for his two youngest sons, on which were engraved the following lines, typical of mourning sentiments of the time:

In morns fair light the opening blossoms warmed.
Their beauty smiled, their growing fragrance charmed.
Fearce [sic] roared the untimely blast around their heads.
Their beauty vanished and their fragrance fled.
Soon sunk their graces in this wintry tomb
And weeping parents mourned their hapless doom.

When the crypt was opened on 28 February 1878, it contained the coffins of the two young brothers, Peter and Susanna St. Medard, Lt. Peter St. Medard, Susanna Farrington, Susan Masson, and four other children.

Chapter Three

Prologue on
U.S.S. Constitution

$\mathcal{P}$ETER ST. MEDARD was probably relieved, in 1798, that he had begun a new life in America twenty years earlier. In his youth, life in a major French seaport might have been comfortable for the provincial bourgeoisie under the more-or-less predictable government of the Bourbons, but the uncertainties of the French Revolution, culminating in the Terror and the execution of Louis XVI, followed by the five-member Directory which came to power in 1795, would have seemed less attractive to the 43-year-old surgeon, now prospering in one of his new nation's busiest ports.

Both surgery and what we would call internal medicine were practiced simultaneously by American physicians, whereas they had been separated along class lines in pre-Revolutionary France. St. Medard provided both services at sea and in his adopted city, whose dependence on maritime trade would have reminded him of La Rochelle. Little is known of his life during the fifteen years after the Treaty of Paris, but he kept in touch with his commander on *Deane*: when Samuel Nicholson called upon his services as hostilities against France approached a boiling point, Dr. St. Medard again took his medical skills to sea, against the country he had left behind.

The Quasi-War with France began to take shape early in 1798. Although neither government formally declared war against the other, hostilities were almost guaranteed to happen, as much an exercise in confrontational diplomacy between France and the United States as a *casus belli* between the two major American political parties. Twenty years after France and the United States had signed the Treaty of Amity and Commerce which had insured the achievement of American independence—and which led almost immediately to St. Medard's arrival in Boston—the French Directory felt that their country deserved better from the United States than the simple commercial parity guaranteed by the treaty that John Jay had negotiated with Britain in April 1794.

The Directory hoped to shift the Anglophile majority in the Federalist cabinet of President John Adams, inaugurated in 1797, toward the Francophile position favored by Vice-President Thomas Jefferson and his Democratic-Republican party, and encouraged the seizure and confiscation of American shipping in the Caribbean. Adams and his cabinet believed the problem could be solved by re-creating an American naval force, but the country was split on the issue. That is, while Adams's Federalists favored the creation of a navy, Jefferson and the Democratic-Republicans decried it. By 1797 Adams had come to support a negotiated end to the French threat to American merchantmen, but his cabinet did not.

American shipping, upon which the new nation's economic survival would have to depend, had increased in value and tonnage in the early 1790s. As neutrals under the terms of Jay's Treaty, American merchants had felt free to trade with both sides in the Wars of the French Revolution. This freedom was particularly important to both British and French possessions in the Caribbean, including St. Domingue, although the French colony was now under the revolutionary leadership of the former slave Toussaint de l'Ouverture. Indeed, virtually all the West Indies depended on supplies from the new republic on the North American mainland.

Beginning in March 1797, the increasingly belligerent French government defied international custom by promulgating its own definitions of what was contraband and, therefore, could be seized at sea legally. Ten months later, the Directory authorized the seizure of all ships carrying British goods under any flag whatsoever, a direct diplomatic attack on the United States. By then, American merchants, including many in Boston, had lost about 300 ships to French captors. This meant that American shipowners' profits were declining, especially as their insurance premiums were skyrocketing. Congress began to retaliate by placing an embargo on all trade with the French loyalists remaining on St. Domingue, who depended on the United States for food (although so did the rebels).

American anger was further aroused by the public exposure, in April 1798, of the Directory's reception of the American commission that had been sent to Paris six months earlier to negotiate a resolution of their difficulties: in violation of all rules of diplomacy, the commissioners were asked to pay bribes, through the unofficial French diplomats code-named X, Y, and Z, in order to gain an audience with the Directors. Representative Robert Goodloe Harper summarized the national response to that clumsy attempt at bribery in his famous toast at a Congressional dinner on 8 June: "Millions for defense but not a cent for tribute." On 30 April, Congress established the Navy Department, and the Marine Corps was re-established in July.

Back in 1794, during Washington's administration, Congress had authorized the construction of six frigates to counteract the Algerian pirates who were threatening American shipping in the Mediterranean, inasmuch as the last ships of the Continental Navy had been sold. However, by the time peace with Algeria had been concluded in November 1795, only three new warships were under construction. When, in July 1797, full-scale war with France seemed imminent, Congress finally authorized completion of *United States*, *Constellation*, and *Constitution*, as well as the acquisition of other frigates and sloops of war that could be used to convoy American merchantmen, especially in the West Indies. The first warship of the new navy to go to sea (even if she was not the first to be launched) was *Constitution*. Launched from Hartt's shipyard at Boston on 21 October 1797, under the command of Samuel Nicholson, she had been fully manned and fitted out by the following July. Peter St. Medard could have seen her masts and rigging being put in place from his home.

Stephen Higginson, the Navy Agent in Boston, complained to his fellow Federalist, Secretary of State Timothy Pickering, that Nicholson lacked many requisites for the command, as did several of his junior officers, including the surgeon, 26-year-old William Read, who "is the opposite of what he ought to be in morals, in politics and in his profession. There is not a man in this town who would trust the life of a dog in his hands." Higginson went on to criticize the appointment of 24-year-old Charles Blake as Surgeon's Mate, because he was "of the same cast of character as Read, but not so highly finished. I believe that 19 or 20 of our steady citizens [i.e., Bostonians], who know them would say that these characters are correct." However, Nicholson alone had the power of appointing his ship's surgeons.

Although an official inquiry had prompted Nicholson's court martial in 1782, he had been cleared of all charges, and no evidence of the professional competence of either Read or Blake has surfaced; Blake, at least, had satisfactory educational credentials. Thus, the Federalist Navy Agent's polemic was probably motivated chiefly by political factionalism—Nicholson was known to favor Democratic-Republican policies, as the two doctors probably did. Moreover, Nicholson had been credited with taking three British sloops of war while in command of *Deane*, and by 1798 he was the second most senior officer in the U. S. Navy. In the end, Secretary Stoddert withdrew neither Nicholson's appointment nor the two doctors' nominations to berths on *Constitution*.

Midshipman John Roche, Jr., who had never been to sea before, seems to have been surprised by conditions on the ship when he went aboard at Boston. He wrote to his father in Concord, New Hampshire, the first of several letters that provide clues to the health of the men on *Constitution*. Indeed, the 17-year-old Roche seems to have been somewhat preoccupied with the subject:

> We continue to live in the most agreeable manner. The utmost good humor prevails among all the officers, & nothing is wanting. . . . We live on the best provisions the market can afford, fresh beef & veal with corn'd pork occasionally, out of which the steward selects us the best pieces such as the heads & legs, & are stinted to no allowance. This nourishing diet agrees mightily with me, insomuch that it is observed I am already more fleshy; but my two messmates Knox & Johnson who are naturally of a plethoric habit do not bear it so well, both of them, poor fellows, have been very near dying, from an eruption inwardly, occasioned by their veins being overcharged.

The officers and midshipmen, of course, fared much better than "the people," as the enlisted crew were known collectively. Their daily rations, codified as the ship was being prepared for war, were still what Congress had decreed during the early months of the Revolution (see page 18).

FRIGATE CONSTITUTION.

TO all *able-bodied* and *patriotic* Seamen, who are willing to ferve their Country, and
Support its Caufe :

The Prefident of the United States,
having ordered the Captain and Comma der of the good
Frigate CONSTITUTION, of 44 guns, now riding in the
harbor of *Bofton*, to employ the moſt *vigorous exertions* to
put ſaid ſhip, as ſpeedily as poſſible, in a ſituation to ſail at
the ſhorteſt command.

Notice is hereby given, That a HOUSE
OF RENDEZVOUS is opened at the ſign of the
Federal Eagle, kept by Mrs. BROADERS, in
Fore-ſtreet ;—where ONE HUNDRED and
FIFTY able Seamen, and NINETY-FIVE ordi-
nary Seamen, will have an opportunity of entering
into the ſervice of their country for One Year, un-
leſs ſooner diſcharged by the Preſident of the United
States.—To all able bodied Seamen, the ſum of
SEVENTEEN DOLLARS ; and to all ORDI-
NARY SEAMEN the ſum of TEN DOLLARS
per month, will be given ; and two months advance
will be paid by the Recruiting Officer, if neceſſary.

None will be allowed to enter this honorable ſervice, but ſuch as are well organized, healthy and ro-
buſt ; and free from ſcorbutic and conſumptive affections.

A glorious opportunity now preſents to the brave
and hardy Seamen of New-England, to enter the ſervice of their country—to avenge its wrongs—and to
protect its rights on the ocean. Thoſe brave Lads,
are now invited to repair to the FLAGG of the
CONSTITUTION now flying at the above rendezvous ; where they ſhall be kindly received, hand-
ſomely entertained, and may enter into immediate pay.

SAMUEL NICHOLSON,
Commander, United States Frigate Conſtitution.

At the above rendezvous Lt. CLARK of the Marines, will enliſt three Sargeants, three Corporals, one
Armourer, one Drummer, one Fifer, and fifty pri-
vates to compoſe a company for the Ship CONSTI-
TUTION. None can be inliſted who are not five
feet, ſix inches high.

Boſton, *Maſſachuſetts*, May 12

Captain Samuel Nicholson's 1798 broadside for recruiting seamen for *Constitution*. Note that the 245 enlisted sailors and 59 marines had to be certified to be "healthy and robust" and free from scurvy and consumption (i.e., tuberculosis). (Courtesy of the Library of Congress)

On 22 July 1798, *Constitution* left Boston on her first mission, which was to defend American merchant ships against possible capture by French privateers or warships. Seeing no action as she cruised between Boston and Norfolk, she sailed into southern waters, from North Carolina to Florida. Midshipman Roche gained his sea legs rather quickly. As he wrote home from Newport on 21 August:

> Since [early August] I have enjoyd good health & have had the finest time imaginable. I by this time begin to find mself at home on board the ship, being a tolerable sailor, & am delighted with the sea. It is laughable to reflect on the terrible ideas that are entertained of it by those who have never experienc'd it.

Nicholson captured the French privateer *Le Niger* off Cape Hatteras on 9 September and took her into Hampton Roads to be sold as a prize, while sending 75 unruly prisoners to Norfolk on a revenue cutter. However, the capture turned out to be illegal, and the United States was forced to release the ship and to compensate her owners for damages. This incident would fuel future charges against Nicholson's professional competency.

Three days after the capture, John Roche wrote home that "I have enjoyed an unusual degree of health since we left [Newport], which has been the case with all the ship's company. It is now sickly in Norfolk, but we keep clear of the[re]." Nevertheless, soon afterward *Constitution*'s crew, including her captain, suffered the effects of a typical summer epidemic of fever. Both Roche and Seaman William Bryant noted that "many" of their ship's crew of about 400 were afflicted with the disorder while they were at Norfolk; some were sent to an on-shore hospital facility which was probably more a nursing home than a true hospital. The epidemic may have been yellow fever, at least among the population of Norfolk, but the fact that only two deaths on the ship (and possibly a third, a marine private) were attributed to it suggests that that may not have been the infection that actually afflicted the crew.

The ship's surgeon, William Read, came down with the fever on 21 September, followed soon afterward by Midshipman Samuel Nicholson, Jr., the captain's 16-year-old son. Theirs were the first two deaths recorded in *Constitution*'s logs. Three days later Dr. John M. Galt of Williamsburg, Virginia, temporarily took up the duties of Dr. Read, who had died at the on-shore "hospital" on 26 September, a day after young Nicholson died.

The epidemic, whatever its microbial cause, ended almost as quickly as it had arrived. By 29 September Roche could report that "a fortunate wind from the [northwest] has prevented it's being destructive. Had it not been for this, no one can tell the consequence. For my own part, I have not experienc'd any ill effects from the climate & thank God, health is restored to the ship." Dr. Galt probably agreed to remain on the frigate only until Nicholson could enlist a new surgeon. *Constitution* sailed back into southern waters during the first week of October, to convoy American merchantmen to Havana, but off the coast of Georgia her bowsprit split, and she had to return to Boston for extensive repairs to masts and rigging, arriving there on 10 November. Her first full cruise had not been successful.

By that time, Nicholson had no Surgeon for his ship, so, while she was laid up at Boston, he ordered Peter St. Medard, who had served on *Deane* with him, to report on board *Constitution*. When he arrived five weeks later, on 17 December 1798, he became the first surgeon to fill out a full tour of duty on what would become America's most celebrated ship. Indeed, he remained in her through three cruises to the Caribbean theater of operations. On 14 July of the following year, President John Adams confirmed his commission, which he retained for the rest of his life.

It is not known just why St. Medard went back to sea. He does not seem to have been particularly enthusiastic about adventure for its own sake. Nicholson may have pressured him, perhaps because the Captain thought it advisable to have on board an officer who could speak the enemy's language. It is also possible that his Boston practice had not attracted enough patients to pay all his bills. His wages in the new U.S. Navy would be $50.00 a month, almost twice his salary on *Deane/Hague*. It was steady income, and there was always the chance, even the likelihood, that he could become rich by sharing in profits when a prize ship was sold off, since prize-taking was an undeclared goal of the undeclared war with France. On the other hand, financial gain may not have been his chief motive if he had invested wisely the prize money in which he shared while in the Continental Navy; although his offshore business interests were potentially profitable, the new war would impair his access to those rewards. St. Medard's chief motivation was probably financial, although he may simply have wanted to return to the work he knew best, which happened to be at sea.

Indeed, he had been trying to do just that for some years. On 6 September 1789, he wrote to Henry Knox, Secretary of War (the navy had not yet been revived under an independent cabinet department), to seek a Surgeon's berth at sea, and sent the same request, accompanied by testimonials from his Boston colleagues, to Knox's successors. He based his claim to such a position on a republic's "characteristic" appreciation of those who helped establish it. On 3 December 1798, just before he was ordered to *Constitution*, he wrote to Benjamin Stoddert, the new Secretary of the Navy, seeking an appointment to the frigate *Boston*, then under construction in his home town: "although a foreigner by birth, still I flater myself that a residence in the United States as an American citizen since the year 1777 [actually, 1778], a connection with an American lady since 1781, having a family to maintain and holding what property I possess under the laws of the United States," were adequate proof of his concern for the interest of the country.

Charles Blake remained on board *Constitution* as Surgeon's Mate under St. Medard for another seven months. After Blake left in June 1799, Jonas Fay and William Dunn filled out the full roster of two Surgeon's Mates allowed for 44-gun frigates until the following December. Both had been trained as physicians, but Dunn was serving as a midshipman at the time of his appointment as acting Surgeon's Mate. They were replaced by Zephaniah Jenning and Henry Gardner until 27 April 1801, when hostilities ended.

It is not known how or where these four doctors were recruited. Although in 1776 Congress had required that those aspiring to appointment as Surgeons or Mates had to be examined by "gentlemen in their respective States skilful in physic and surgery," that law seems to have been in abeyance in 1798, when someone who wished to practice on a U.S. Navy ship had only to be accepted by its captain; formal appointment by the President was virtually assured once that was accomplished, sometimes as the result of only one visit to a ship by an applicant. Altogether, 42 Surgeons were commissioned in the navy in 1798–1800 (including ten promotions from Surgeon's Mate), as well as 42 Mates. Most men in both ranks had learned their profession as apprentices; four had college degrees, one had earned an M.D., and one had attended the medical school in Philadelphia but had not obtained a degree there. Three Surgeons were transferred from the army.

The basic duties of Surgeons and their Mates were to attend to the injured as well as to men who were sick enough to be relieved from duty; to hold sick call daily before breakfast for those with minor ailments; and to advise the Captain and First Lieutenant of measures that were necessary to preserving the crew's health. Surgeons, who retained their traditional place near the top of the shipboard hierarchy, were quartered in cubicles ranged along the sides of the wardroom, along with the lieutenants, marine officers, sailing master, purser, and chaplain, as they had been during the Revolution. Surgeon's Mates had cubicles in the cockpit, the portion of the ship on a lower deck that was reserved largely for treating men wounded during battle. Dr. St. Medard's cubicle on *Constitution* can still be seen alongside those of his fellow officers. Twentieth-century visitors to her cockpit must stoop at an uncomfortable angle; probably fortunately, it is usually off limits today. Although early American seamen were four to five inches shorter that the average adult American male today, they still averaged five feet six inches, and ranged up to six feet one inch, so even they would not have found it easy to move around the lower decks of their ships.

Soon after St. Medard went on board *Constitution* in late December 1798, she was ordered to rendezvous with other American ships at Prince Rupert Bay in the British island of Dominica, and from there to seize French ships operating around Guadaloupe, the French island directly to the north in the Leeward chain. En route, Nicholson suffered two major professional indignities. Not only was he accused of cowardice for apparently not pursuing the French ship *L'Insurgente*, which was later taken near Bermuda in a famous capture by *Constellation*, he took a ship that he had assumed to be French, but had to give it up when it turned out to be a British merchantman, *Spencer*, which was actually a prize to *L'Insurgente*—a mistake much like the one he had made on his last cruise. *Constitution* reached Dominica on 17 January. From there Nicholson recaptured an American sloop and seized a perfectly legal French prize. But once again, Captain Nicholson narrowly avoided making an illegal capture.

The rest of the voyage was punctuated by repeated damage to his frigate's masts and rigging, and by illness and death. The range of illnesses that Peter St. Medard encountered on this assignment is not known, since no records of his day-to-day work load survive. However, the captain's log reveals the causes of death as well as other problems that were part of the surgeon's work at sea.

The first death to occur among St. Medard's new patients was that of Oliver Nester, a seaman afflicted with a serious "nervous fever," on 20 January, nine days before the ship left Nantasket Roads, just east of Boston Harbor. Cornelius Howard, an Ordinary Seaman who was the only known black man among the original crew of the ship, died of a "putrid and nervous fever" four days later. On 1 February, James Meader was the first of four seamen to die of a "bilious fever" during the month. Typical naval accidents claimed three more lives: Henry Kirk died when he fell overboard from the main topgallant yard on 4 February, Philip Paine when he fell overboard from the mizzen topsail yard 23 days later, and the boatswain, John Hancock, of an accidental pistol shot on 2 March. As was customary, three days later the effects of those who had died so far during the cruise were sold to the rest of the crew while the ship was patrolling off St. Dominque. The proceeds were to eventually be transmitted to the families of the deceased.

On 16 March, John Roche wrote home about the death of young Hancock:

> With regard to my health, I find myself very well, & have not found any disagreable effects from the climate, altho' we are frequently in port. . . .
>
> Our ship's Company are generally healthy, very few have died of sickness, but have lost several by accident, among the rest our Boatswain, a very deserving young man about 21 years of age, . . . [who] was shot thro' the head with a pistol one night when we were coming along side the [British frigate] *Santa Margarita* which we suppos'd to be a Frenchman as she did not understand our signals.

Roche seems to have overlooked that it was one of *Constitution*'s boatswain's mates who had fired the shot that killed Hancock while preparing to board *Santa Margarita* in the dead of night. But Seaman William Bryant remembered it 58 years later, when he recounted everything he could about his days on *Constitution* while justifying his application for a federal land grant in recognition of his naval service.

One of a naval surgeon's customary tasks in the British navy—and presumably in that of the United States, although until now, as will be seen, there has been no documentation of it on American ships—was to certify the fitness of crew members sentenced to be flogged with the cat o' nine tails, a knotted rope, the usual summary punishment that did not require a formal court-martial. He also had to stand by during the flogging, to make sure that the prisoner was still able to take the punishment; even if no report of stopping a flogging on an American naval surgeon's order seems to have surfaced, it almost certainly happened many times.

Dr. St. Medard had at least eight flogging patients while serving in Nicholson's *Constitution*. On 29 January, James Carey was given 12 lashes for striking a superior officer, and two days later another seaman received 12 for fighting and five more for being absent without leave. Two more floggings were administered four days later. Nicholson's reputation for such heavy-handed discipline—he is said to have ordered as many as six floggings on one day alone during this cruise— may have been raising further alarms about his professional behavior, if his fondness for drink had not already excerbated his reputation for precipitous illegal captures with the Secretary of the Navy. However, he could not be faulted for a punishment that was inflicted at the initiative of the crew on their fellows, usually for relatively minor thefts: on 30 January six men who had been caught stealing were condemned by their shipmates to "run the gauntlet" of thrashings, with plaited and knotted lanyards, administered by the crew. The culprit's pace was kept down to a slow walk by the cutlass held at his chest by the master-at-arms, walking slowly backward between the ranks, and another kept close behind the offender by a marine corporal.

William Felt, the ship's sailmaker, died of unrecorded causes on 4 April, and on 16 May Thomas Wood "expired in a fit of the gout" (true gout is unlikely to have been the direct cause of his death; it is most likely that what Dr. St. Medard reported as gout was really something else in modern terms). Two days later another man died "in a fit of gout," but by now the ship was near Boston Harbor, so he was buried on Hospital Island in the harbor instead of at sea. Sickness seems to have been increasing among the crew as the ship neared her home port, because their usual ration of beef and pork was reduced by a third on 25 April. Without a full diet to sustain the nutritional requirements of a hard-working ship's crew, it is not surprising that ten of them were sick enough to be sent to sick quarters as soon as *Constitution* came to rest at Boston.

Nicholson soon learned that Navy Secretary Stoddert had dismissed him from command of *Constitution*, chiefly because of his errors of judgment in taking ships of friendly powers. Captain Silas Talbot, another veteran of the Continental Navy, was assigned to take over the ship. During the next seven weeks Talbot supervised the extensive repairs the frigate needed, recruited 400 new crew members because the first crew's one-year enlistments had expired, and took on supplies, including 18 tons each of salt beef and pork, 5,880 pounds of flour, 3,000 gallons each of rum and vinegar, 250 gallons of molasses, more than 37,500 gallons of water, and, for the cook's stove in the galley, 20 tons of coal. At the same time, St. Medard was replenishing his medical stores; he had to have the local Navy Agent replace two boxes of "sundry Articles of medicine . . . deemed to be unfit for use." On 24 July 1799, Talbot sailed *Constitution* out of Boston Harbor.

Dr. St. Medard probably had time on his hands during the 22-day voyage from Boston to Norfolk and for some weeks afterward. On 17 August John Roche wrote that:

> The crew of the Constitu^n are now remarkably healthy altho' we have melancholy accounts from some ships on the Havannah station. We have not lost a single man since leaving Boston, and a greater degree of satisfaction prevails than I have ever witness'd on board the ship.

Roche's optimism may have been premature. He did not mention that, a few days earlier, 155 pounds of bread and 50 pounds each of cheese and rice had to be tossed overboard because they had rotted. Two seamen drowned when they fell overboard on 3 September and 12 October, and a marine died of scurvy just as the flagship rendezvoused with the rest of the squadron three days later.

However, Dr. St. Medard must have been busy examining men before flogging and treating their wounds afterward. Two men received 12 lashes for theft (25 July and 20 September), two received six lashes for riotous behavior (6 August and 12 October), while two others received 12 for the same offence (6 and 8 October), and another got 12 for using seditious language (8 October). Two men received 12 lashes for desertion (22 August), and a marine received 12 for sleeping while on sentry duty (4 September). This record was, of course, no more benign than Nicholson's on the same score. During the first six months of 1800, eight men were flogged for the usual variety of offenses: on 9 January, a seaman received 12 lashes for neglect of duty and insolence to an officer; on 30 March and 31 May, two men received 12 for neglect of duty and drunkenness; on 7–8 June, three men were punished for theft and associated offences such as insolence and fighting; on 12 June a marine private received 12 lashes for neglect of duty; and on the seventeenth a seaman received 12 for quarreling with a superior officer.

The level of morale on ships of the time can often be gauged by the frequency of punishment—the greater the crew's sense of well-being and morale, the fewer infractions of rules and, therefore, the fewer punishments. The evidence, such as John Roche's, suggests that *Constitution*'s crew felt easier than those on other ships of the time, and historians point out that her punishment record—by the standards of the time—bears out this assessment. One major factor that may have bolstered the crew's morale was the seizure of several French ships during the spring months: the men could expect to share in the proceeds when the prizes were condemned and sold by admiralty courts. Talbot's orders directed him to proceed from Boston to Cap Français, where Peter St. Medard had stayed for several months during his days in the French slave trade. More importantly, *Constitution* was charged to capture and blockade French vessels wherever encountered. On 15 October Talbot took up his appointment as Commodore of the American fleet in the Caribbean when he joined the frigates *Boston* and *General Greene*, and the brig *Norfolk*, at St. Domingue; *Herald* eventually completed the squadron.

Over the next seven weeks *Constitution* tried to fulfill her mission by engaging in an average of a chase a day, but all her quarries turned out to be friendly and not subject to capture. By late November her water supply was dangerously low, and she had to put in at St. Nicholas Mole on St. Domingue, where it took three days to take on 191 tons of water. While there Roche wrote home that the crew were still "remarkably healthy," although a few days later he reported that for the last four days he had been "somewhat indispos'd, but am now fortunately recover'd."

Deaths—and, presumably, sickness—became more frequent from then on. Marine Lieutenant William Amory was put on shore at Cap Français because he had been confined to his cabin for some time with "a dangerous illness." A marine private died on 19 October of a "cramp in the stomack;" two sailors died on 22 October and 16 November, both of "a complication of disorders;" a master's mate died on 25 October of consumption; and on 30 November a man who had recently deserted from *General Greene* and been sent on board *Constitution* by the American consul at Cap Français died of an unrecorded cause. In addition, seaman John Robinson died on 18 October when he fell overboard from the mainsail yard, and on 14 November two men had to be treated after receiving 12 lashes for theft. St. Medard undoubtedly had other men under his care, those with ordinary non-fatal diseases, but no records of their illnesses have survived.

Deaths began to mount among his patients during the new year. On 3 January the sailmaker died of a "bilious complaint," and a week later a marine died of lung disease. On 12 March, Lieutenant Amory returned from sick quarters at Cap Français after 135 days there. A seaman taken aboard from the U.S. schooner *Experiment* died of unrecorded causes on 2 April, and on 6–7 June two marines died of fevers, as did a seaman three days later. The last death recorded on this voyage of *Constitution* was that of Charles Leonard, who died of a fever on 15 August as the ship neared Boston on her return home, although another man drowned after the ship anchored in Nantasket Roads.

The crew was kept busy repairing the mainmast in December, even while the ship was on active patrol. Three seamen were punished with six lashes each for neglect of duty on the 27th, but the arrival of the schooner *Elizabeth* on the 30th, bringing new supplies of bread, beef, pork, Indian meal, flour, potatoes, cheese, rice, peas, and butter, probably facilitated the crew's continuing good health and high morale. This, the U.S. Navy's first exercise in underway replenishment, would be repeated in February 1800. When *Constitution* returned to St. Nicholas Mole to take on more water in mid-March, she had been at sea for 195 of the past 201 days, without having to ration food.

Commodore Talbot had also tried to keep *Constitution* well supplied with limes and oranges from St. Domingue; presumably he knew that some maritime authorities, and perhaps Dr. St. Medard, recommended them for, among other things, preventing or treating scurvy. Nevertheless, as early as 6 June, ten months after leaving Norfolk, Talbot had recognized that scurvy was a growing problem on his ship. Ten days later, the captain's log notes that nearly 30 men were on the sick list; "their chief diseases are the fever and scurvey, the latter of which daily increases." This seems to have been St. Medard's first major experience with what was at that time regarded as an "epidemic" of scurvy. Had Talbot not received orders to return home on 24 July, he might have been forced to do so if the sick list had grown further. Not only that, most of his crew's enlistments would soon expire. Besides, by the time he returned to Boston, he had been at sea for 347 out of 366 days, a remarkable logistical achievement for the time.

On 24 August 1800, *Constitution* reached Boston Light, where town health officials came on board and ordered her quarantined until she could be certified as free of disease, although some of the men were allowed to wash themselves and their clothes on a small island nearby in the harbor. Two sailors had to be sent to sick quarters on Castle Island, but at noon on 27 August the quarantine flag was lowered. Over the next several days the crew was paid off, and the ship began refitting. Peter St. Medard paid the purser $206 to settle his bill for gin, brandy, and other personal wardroom expenses over the past year. He remained in charge of the medical needs of the skeleton crew kept aboard during refitting, and of newly recruited seamen, although these tasks may have been delegated to the two new Surgeon's Mates, Drs. Jenning and Gardner, who went on board on 7 December.

While sails, rigging, and masts were being restored to fighting order, and new supplies of powder and food were being stowed, John Roche wrote home about the new recruits coming on board:

> Our crew is perhaps the finest for [its] numbers that ever were on [board] a ship. [No] one who possesses any bodily infirmities is [allowed?] on board & their places fill'd up with [illegible] expert young seamen. . . . [My] health which for some time past was rather [fit]ful is not perfectly restor'd & only wish [at present] to be at sea as soon as possible.

Roche, a Federalist at heart, was anxious to get to sea again before the incoming Democratic-Republican administration could have a chance, after Jefferson's inauguration in March, to complete the peace negotiations then underway at Paris—even though it had been President Adams who had initiated them. On 17 December, two days after Adams sent the draft treaty to the Senate for ratification, Talbot took his ship back to St. Domingue, where she joined five other American warships twelve days later, to pursue the familiar routine of seizing French shipping. Few official records of this fourth assignment of *Constitution* have survived, but Roche continued to comment on her crew's health and his own. On 30 January he wrote from Cap Français:

An uncommon degree of health has prevail'd in the ship & we have not lost a single person by sickness since we left Boston. For my own part I have enjoyd very good health and have found it constantly improving since I have been at sea. This climate has become natural to my constitution & I prefer it to any other.

The eager young midshipman finally became a patient of Dr. St. Medard: on 24 February he wrote home that "I have perfectly recover'd my health & . . . it prevails in an unusual degree thro'out the ship." It is tempting to ascribe the relatively constant good health of *Constitution*'s crew on this cruise to St. Medard's professional skills, at least when the men were not completely exhausted, as they must have been on their previous return to Boston, when the lack of citrus fruits exacerbated their overall condition.

By this time Roche was preparing himself to accept the inevitable peace that was soon to come, but he was also beginning to look forward to revenge on the British who were increasing their impressments of American seamen, a condition he thought was "worse than Algarine slavery." He would never visit Algeria, but St. Medard would, within two years.

On 23 March 1801 Navy Secretary Stoddert recalled all U.S. warships, three weeks after the Senate had ratified the Convention of Môrtefontaine which ended the Quasi-War. Final ratification of the amendments sought by the Senate and by Napoleon Bonaparte, now First Consul of the new French administration, did not occur until 19 December. Part of the new treaty abrogated the 1778 treaty—the one that had led to Peter St. Medard's first disembarkation at Boston—because both sides had come to regard it as "an entangling alliance." That is, Napoleon realized that continued French opposition to the neutral rights guaranteed by Jay's Treaty would only force the Americans further into his British enemy's camp. Moreover, the United States agreed not to seek compensation for American ships taken by the French, although those that had not yet been condemned as prizes were to be returned.

As James Fenimore Cooper, the first major historian of the U.S. Navy, observed, "On the whole, the country was satisfied with the results of the exertions it had made during this irregular and informal contest." Naval crews were undoubtedly less happy, inasmuch as prizes—and compensations for them—were relatively few. One reason the Americans took so few prizes was that there were few merchantmen to be captured, the Directory having commissioned many of them as heavily armed privateers charged with harrying the enemy's shipping routes. Still, the 40 ships in the U.S. Navy had taken nearly 80 French ships, virtually all of which were privateers. And, even though American shippers had lost about 2,300 vessels to French captors since 1798, their own Caribbean trade had not been interrupted significantly; indeed, American exports, and revenues on imports, had increased during most of the Quasi-War, so most American merchants were content.

Talbot received his recall orders on 4 April, with instructions to take *Constitution* back to Boston. He left Cap Français on 2 June, and arrived home two weeks later. Following several months of official indecision over whether he would be retained in the navy, Talbot resigned. His ship was overhauled under the direction of the first Commandant of the Boston Navy Yard, her former captain, Samuel Nicholson. John Roche had already left *Constitution* while she was en route to Boston, to assume the position of a lieutenant who had been broken for flogging a midshipman on the schooner *Scammel*. After resigning from the navy in July, Roche entered the merchant marine, but he was not as robust as his letters from *Constitution* might lead one to believe, and he died in 1807 after a long wasting illness.

The Peace Establishment Act of 3 March 1801 provided for the retention of only 13 frigates, six to remain on active duty while the rest were to be "laid up in ordinary," that is, mothballed as a reserve force. The number of officers of all ranks was reduced to nine Captains, 36 Lieutenants, and 150 Midshipmen, although the numbers of specialized officers, such as Surgeons and Surgeon's Mates, was left to the discretion of the administration and the constraints of its budget. Dr. St. Medard was among the surgeons who were discharged under the Act. Feeling this was an unjust reward for one who had been serving his new country faithfully since the Revolutionary War, he asked Secretary of the Navy Robert Smith to reinstate him. At the same time, St. Medard wrote to Silas Talbot, his former commander, who was held in high esteem in Washington, asking him to intercede with Smith on his behalf. Within three weeks the Secretary had, indeed, restored the surgeon to his former rank, although at the customary half pay for officers not on active duty. He probably also resumed his civilian practice, but remained attached to *Constitution*, until early 1802.

Notes

The story of the hostilities with France has been oversimplified, but is based on the detailed exegeses in Alexander DeConde's *The Quasi-War: The Politics and Diplomacy of the Undeclared War with France 1797–1801* (New York: Charles Scribner's Sons, 1966), and Michael A. Palmer's *Stoddert's War: Naval Operations during the Quasi-War with France, 1798–1801* (Columbia: University of South Carolia Press, 1987).

The operational history of *Constitution* is collated from Tyrone G. Martin, *A Most Fortunate Ship: A Narrative History of "Old Ironsides"* (Chester, Conn.: Globe Pequot Press, 1980); Commander Martin was her Captain from 1974 to 1978. Further details are in his "Underway replenishment, 1799–1800," *American Neptune 46* (1986): 159–164, and in a typescript that he furnished me, titled "An Appeal to Heaven," which includes the testimony of William Bryant. The deaths and punishments at sea are taken from a typescript (dated January 2, 1976) of entries "Taken from the Log of the U.S.S. Constitution, December 6, 1798–October 20, 1800," in the U.S.S. *Constitution* Museum Foundation Library, Boston, supplemented by the typescript of "Notes Taken from the Journal of [Midshipman] James Pity of the United States Firgate [sic] Constitution, July 23, 1798 to May 11, 1799," in the same library.

Roche's letters were edited by Christopher McKee in *"Constitution* in the Quasi-War with France: the letters of John Roche, Jr., 1798–1801," *American Neptune 27* (1967): 135–149. Part of Stephen Higginson's letter criticizing the first officers and doctors appointed to *Constitution* is in McKee's splendid *Edward Preble: A Naval Biography, 1761–1807* (Annapolis: Naval Institute Press, 1972), pp. 55–56; the rest, along with other information about the first generation of U.S. Naval surgeons, comes from Harold D. Langley, "Medical men of the old navy: A study in the development of a profession," in Department of History, U.S. Naval Academy, eds., *New Aspects of Naval History* (Baltimore: Nautical and Aviation Publishing Co. of America, 1985), pp. 69–79. PSM's appointments are in U.S. Office of Naval Records and Library, comp., *Naval Documents Related to the Quasi-War between the United States and France*, 7 vols. (Washington, D.C., 1935–38), II:445; VI:283; and VII:135–136, 348. Professor McKee also provided biographical data for *Constitution*'s other surgeons and their mates.

Prize taking and its adjudication in U.S. courts, focussing on a case brought by Silas Talbot in which PSM was called as a witness, is described by Frederick C. Leiner in "Anatomy of a prize case: Dollars, side-deals, and *Les Deux Anges*," in *American Journal of Legal History 39* (1995): 214–232. Discipline and punishment in the U.S. Navy are described by James E. Valle in *Rocks and Shoals: Order and Discipline in the Old Navy, 1800–1861* (Annapolis: Naval Institute Press, 1980), and by Christopher McKee in his magisterial *A Gentlemanly and Honorable Profession: The Creation of the U.S. Naval Officer Corps, 1794–1815* (Annapolis: Naval Institute Press, 1991), pp. 233–267. However, the description of the gauntlet of necessity comes from Dudley Pope, *Life in Nelson's Navy* (Annapolis: Naval Institute Press, 1981), p. 214. Seamen's heights are documented by Ira Dye in "Early American merchant seafarers," *Proceedings of the American Philosophical Society 120* (1976): 331–360.

James Fenimore Cooper's assessment of the results of the Quasi-War is in his *History of the Navy of the United States of America Continued to 1853*, 3 vols. in 1 (New York: G. P. Putnm & Co., 1854), pp. 195–96. Important background information is in Leonard F. Guttridge and Jay D. Smith, *The Commodores: The U.S. Navy in the Days of Sail* (New York: Harper & Row, 1969), chapters 3 and 4.

PSM's dismissal from the navy and his reinstatement are outlined in the following letters in the Silas Talbot Collection at the G. W. Blunt White Library at Mystic Seaport, Conn.: PSM to Talbot, 7 November 1801; PSM to Robert Smith, 7 November 1801; and PSM to Talbot, 28 November 1801; purser's receipts dated 19 and 27 January and 7 December 1800, as well as the Navy Agent's receipt for spoiled medicines, are in the same collection. PSM's drafts of his letters concerning his dismissal, dated 1 November 1801 and 28 June 1802, are in the EBA collection, as are Smith's letters to PSM of 23 October, 1 November, and 17 November 1801. The same collection also contains drafts of PSM's letters of 6 September 1789 to Henry Knox, 16 March 1795 to Timothy Pickering, 22 April 1797 to James McHenry, and 3 December 1798 to Benjamin Stoddert. The surgeon's work at the Boston Navy Yard after March 1801 is documented among the following Samuel Brown Papers (Brown became Naval Agent at Boston in early 1801) at the Massachusetts Historical Society: in box 1, list of drugs requested by Silas Talbot, 25 August 1801, and "Appraisement of Medicines taken from the Medicine Chest of the corvette Berceau, December 1801; in box 2, list of drugs delivered to Peter St. Medard Surgeon of U.S. Frigate Constitution from October 1801 to February 28th 1802, and St. Medard's receipt for $38 for board from 19 October 1801 to 28 February 1802.

The Cruise of the
U.S.F. *New-York*
2 September 1802–9 December 1803

Chapter Four

New York Merchants Build a Warship

*T*HE NATIONWIDE Francophobia that launched *Constitution* prompted one of the most unusual outpourings of patriotic fervor in American history: the building of nine warships funded by public subscriptions in eleven maritime communities from Newburyport and Salem, Massachusetts, to Charleston and Beaufort, South Carolina. Only South Carolina's vessel was an outright gift—subscribers to the other eight vessels received "loan-certificates" of so-called "Navy Stock," a sort of bond issue to be repaid at 6 percent. The subscribers collectively raised at least $654,400; the total amount of Navy Stock issued was $711,700, about 9 percent of the total federal budget for 1798. The rest of the ships' cost, up to about 50 percent, was borne by the federal government because it alone could provide some of the necessary hardware, especially cannons.

Most of those who initiated or contributed to the appeals mounted in the eleven seaports appear to have been merchants; not all have been identified. Their intentions were complex, and not easily discerned. Patriotism was surely one motive, especially as American merchants were dominated by Federalists, as was the administration of President John Adams. Shipowners clearly had an interest in having their vessels protected by armed convoys, especially in the West Indies, where the hostile French naval presence was most prominent, and some subscribers believed (erroneously) that the warships built in their cities would be assigned to protect their own harbors. Nevertheless, because the 6 percent return on Navy Stock was less than the 8 percent return on regular government bonds, and because merchants' usual expenses, such as insurance, could outweigh the meager return on their wartime "loans" to the central government, the subscribers' principal motive cannot realistically be assumed to have been profit.

But economic interests were not the only factors involved. The most astonishing feature of the subscription drives for the warships was that they were spontaneously generated grassroots efforts that were completely independent of the federal government. Newburyport began the movement at a meeting of local merchants on 23 May 1798. Newspaper accounts of that meeting spread rapidly southward, reaching Charleston, South Carolina, within two weeks. Indeed, Philadelphia, New York, and Baltimore (which promised two ships), had set their own fund drives in motion before Congress, which was still sitting at Philadelphia, had passed the necessary enabling legislation. As amended, it authorized acceptance of up to twelve warships from the subscription program (although any number could be accepted as gifts); set the 6 percent interest rate; and, despite the original intention of accepting only ships that could mount at least 20 guns, allowed some of the new warships to have fewer. President Adams signed the act on 30 June 1798.

The sloop *Merrimack*, Newburyport's contribution, was the only subscription warship actually launched by the end of 1798. Peter St. Medard, at home between his cruises in *Constitution*, could have witnessed the launching of the second, the 32-gun frigate *Boston*, when it left the ways in the North End in May 1799. The 36-gun frigate *New-York* was launched at its home city on 24 April 1800.

Its origin was a report of the Newburyport committee's meeting that appeared in the New York *Spectator* on 2 June 1798. The subscription effort that began two weeks later aimed to purchase "some stout ships" that would guard New York's harbor, but pledges were painfully slow to materialize—indeed, embarrassingly slow, when compared with those of Baltimore and Philadelphia. One newspaper attributed the glacial rate of fund-raising to the characteristically "slow but sure pace" of the careful Dutchmen who dominated the local business community. On the nineteenth, a committee of local merchants and bankers began a more energetic campaign. The $66,000 it raised in nine days turned out to be 41 percent of the ship's final cost.

Probably designed by Joshua Humphreys of Philadelphia, *New-York*'s keel was laid by Peck and Carpenter at the latter's yard two months later. When completed under the supervision of Captain Thomas Robinson, whose task was to ensure that she was built according to navy specifications, the gun deck between perpendiculars was 144 feet 2 inches in length, and the beam was 37 feet, while the mainmast was 87 feet 4 inches in height. Designed to carry 36 guns, the ship was rated a 38, but actually carried 26 18-pounders, two 9-pound chase guns, and 12 18-pound carronades.

Although Navy Secretary Benjamin Stoddert recognized that it was desirable to appoint as captains of the subscription warships men nominated by the merchants who had underwritten their construction, in this case he could not, because Robinson was too junior in the service. Consequently, the secretary appointed a more senior captain, Richard Valentine Morris of New York, to the command of the new frigate once she was put into service. As Stoddert explained to the New York committee, "Captain Morris has been so long in service without having been to sea that I am sure it would be very mortifying to him to be longer employed in the superintendence of the building of ships." However, Stoddert was unsure whether Morris, who was at the time commanding the frigate *Adams*, then cruising off the English colony of St. Kitts in the West Indies, would return in time to take over *New-York* before she went out on her first cruise.

On 24 April 1800 the new frigate was launched from her ways. A New York newspaper reported:

> Another auxiliary to our infant Navy was added this morning by the launch of the beautiful frigate New York, pierced for thirty-eight guns. She moved from the lower shipyard into her destined element a few minutes past ten o'clock, amidst the loud proclamations of thousands of citizens. On her entering the water, Federal salutes were fired from the Aspacia Indiaman, and the Governor Jay cutter, which lay in the stream brilliantly decorated with the colors of different nations. . . .
>
> The ship is highly praised for her form and workmanship. Mr. [Stephen] Carpenter was the builder. . .
>
> Our little Navy grows apace. May it soon be fully competent to the protection of our commerce against all insults and depredations.

A crew was recruited during the months occupied by the construction and fitting out of *New-York*. She was authorized 100 able seamen at $17 a month, and 137 ordinary seamen and boys at $5 to $14 a month, "according to merit." Stoddert specified that they were to be enlisted for one year "from the ship's first weighing anchor on a cruise—You may allow two months advance [pay]; but previously take care to obtain responsible security to resort to in the event of desertion." The secretary was obviously well aware that once a recruit had his enlistment bonus in hand he might never be seen again by the recruiting officer. Dr. St. Medard would later become the unwitting victim of just such a desertion.

Captain Morris returned in mid-July, but he failed to notify Stoddert, who was probably more concerned with the impending courts-martial of two men under Morris's command. Neither had Morris reported that his squadron had captured 38 vessels. Finally, on 18 August, the secretary ordered him to *New-York*, and Thomas Robinson to the command of *Adams*. In a hint of troubles to come, President Adams wrote Stoddert about the court-martial, adding, "I pray you to impress upon all our commanders, without alluding to this case in particular, the necessity of keeping at sea as much as possible." That is, the President, one of the country's ablest lawyers, had concluded that Morris's prolonged inactivity at St. Kitts had provided ample opportunity for the infractions that culminated in two trials. Morris's disregard for orders, and for custom, would soon bring about his own disgrace.

New York's frigate was ready for sea by 10 October, nearly six months after launching, but the commander assigned to her was still in the Caribbean. Morris sailed from St. Kitts twelve days later, to convoy a naval store-ship, the brig *Amazon*, to Martinique. On 6 December he arrived at Basseterre Roads, off St. Kitts, to receive further orders from Commodore Thomas Truxtun, in *President*. While there a seaman, John Van Ort, who had deserted from *New-York* after receiving his two months' enlistment pay, made the mistake of shipping aboard her again, which resulted in his being put in irons on Truxtun's flagship. He was later returned to Morris's ship.

The little American squadron was on patrol duty around Guadeloupe until the end of the month, when the men in *New-York* were afflicted by an epidemic of what was probably yellow fever. When 40 men of his crew had to be hospitalized at Basseterre, Morris recruited replacements locally in order to continue his assignment to protect

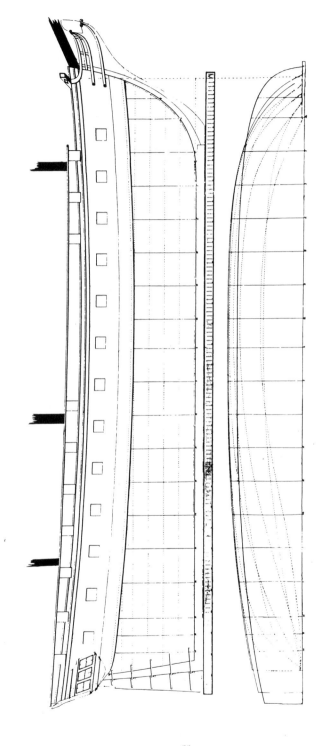

Hull plan of *New-York*. (From Dudley W. Knox, ed., *Register of Officer Personnel, United States Navy and Marine Corps, and Ships Data, 1801–1807* (Washington: Government Printing Office, 1945)

navy ships and merchantmen against French privateers. On 15 January Truxtun sent Morris to cruise around Guadeloupe, and ordered him to return to the Commodore's station off Martinique every 15 days in case new orders should arrive from Stoddert. During these weeks *New-York* won an enviable reputation as a fast sailor.

She was still in the Windward Islands when word arrived in late January 1801 that a peace agreement had been reached in Paris on 30 September. *New-York* remained on the West Indian station until April, when she headed home carrying Captain James Barron of *Warren* because he had become "violently" ill with yellow fever. Morris, too, was ill upon his arrival at New York on 29 April, so Navy Secretary Samuel Smith, recently appointed by the new president, Thomas Jefferson, instructed him to have his First Lieutenant bring his ship to Washington Navy Yard.

One of the frigates retained under the Peace Establishment Act, *New-York* was among those laid up in ordinary in the Eastern Branch of the Potomac River (now called the Anacostia River). Each was kept in condition for possible future service by a skeleton crew of Able Seamen who, every so often, turned the mothballed warships around so that they would weather evenly—as is still done each year for *Constitution*, the last ship of their generation afloat. A year later *New-York* would be back in service, with Peter St. Medard as her Surgeon.

Notes

The origins of *New York* and her sister ships are described by Frederick C. Leiner in "The subscription warships of 1798," *American Neptune 46* (1986): 141–158. Data pertaining to her entire history are given in the remarkably detailed database from his own research generously furnished to me by the late William M. P. Dunne, his *Resource Data File: Operational History United States Frigate New-York, 1799–1830* (Hampton Bays, N.Y.: The Naval Scribe, 1988), pp. 1–20; many entries therein are collated from Dudley W. Knox, ed., *Naval Documents Related to the Quasi-War between the United States and France*, 7 vols. (Washington: Government Printing Office, 1934). They are briefly summarized in *Dictionary of American Fighting Ships*, vol. 5 (Washington: Government Printing Office, 1970), p. 69, and Dudley W. Knox, ed., *Register of Officer Personnel, United States Navy and Marine Corps, and Ships Data, 1801–1807*

(Washington: Government Printing Office, 1945), pp. 75–76. The ship's construction is described by Howard I. Chapelle, *The History of the American Sailing Navy: The Ships and their Development* (New York: W. W. Norton & Co., 1949), pp. 164–5, 547. Chapelle, unlike other sources, attributes the design of *New-York* to Joshua Humphreys's son Samuel; a putative draft of the ship faces p. 169, and details of her masts and yards are on p. 490. The structural details given by Chapelle and Dunne differ to an insignificant extent.

Diplomatic aspects of the Quasi-War are described in Alexander DeConde, *The Quasi-War: The Politics and Diplomacy of the Undeclared War with France, 1797–1801* (New York: Charles Scribner's Sons, 1966), while the naval side is outlined in Michael A. Palmer, *Stoddert's War: Naval Operations during the Quasi-War with France, 1798–1801* (Columbia: University of South Carolina Press, 1987), and Eugene S. Ferguson, *Truxtun of the Constellation* (1956; rprt. ed.: Annapolis, Md., 1982). *New-York* is not mentioned in any of the three books.

Chapter Five

Sick Bays and Cockpits, Humors and Tones

$\mathcal{A}$ NAVAL SURGEON'S workplaces were his ship's sick bay and cockpit. Because no detailed plans or descriptions of *New-York* have survived, other than her hull plan, it is not known where her sick bay was located. However, if she did have a purpose-built sick bay, it was probably designed, according to a British custom that had been widely adopted in American ships, to fill the roughly triangular space in the starboard side of the forward part of the berth deck (just below the gun deck, which was below the main, or spar, deck).

Patients were confined in the sick bay chiefly if they had to be kept at rest or required frequent observation. Sick quarters might have four or more hanging wooden platform beds with raised sides, to prevent their occupants from rolling out in heavy seas, or, perhaps, conventional hammocks, and occasionally an adult-sized crib on side-to-side rockers, for men with the most serious illnesses and wounds. The surgeon's medicines, instruments, and desk completed the area's furnishings. However, it seems unlikely that the sick bay on any wooden warship could accommodate her entire sick list on a day when it was as large as 50, as it sometimes was on *New-York*, a fairly small warship. Some of those 50 men were undoubtedly ambulatory, but, if necessary, additional areas for the sick, adjacent to the sick bay, could be separated, by wooden or movable canvas partitions, from the rest of the berth deck, where all enlisted men slung their hammocks.

The medical day aboard American warships mirrored traditional British practice; it was not codified by formal naval regulations until the War of 1812, and even they merely ratified custom. The Surgeon's Mate visited the sick bay before breakfast, to attend to whatever patients' needs had developed overnight. At eight o'clock, the end of the morning watch and after the gun deck had been cleansed, the loblolly boy rang a bell on the main, gun, and berth decks to summon to sick call those who were slightly indisposed, or under treatment for venereal disease, or who had superficial ulcers; men who were injured or who fell seriously ill during the day could report to the Surgeon at any time. He took morning sick call at the mainmast or in the sick bay, where he and his Mate examined those who presented themselves, and then made their daily rounds of men already confined to quarters or the sick bay, while the loblolly boy washed, shaved, and fed the bedridden patients (loblolly was a thick gruel that was often fed to patients on land and sea). In addition, the Purser or his steward sometimes dispensed drugs to those who had continuing prescriptions for them, or to men who simply thought they needed a little something to make them feel better.

The Mate spent the rest of his day preparing and administering medicines in the sick bay, dressing wounds and skin ulcers, or bleeding men who needed it. He was also responsible for maintaining the ship's surgical instruments, for keeping accurate records of medicines and expenditures, and for inspecting the cook's pots and pans, as well as for supervising the loblolly boy. The Surgeon's duties, to be outlined in detail in the next chapter, included overall responsibility for his Mates and boys, as well as personally visiting every patient at least twice a day, but especially for keeping accurate records on each patient admitted to his care. Unfortunately, Dr. St. Medard's records do not permit differentiating his ambulatory patients from those confined to the sick bay, but it seems likely that the former included many of those he treated for syphilis, ulcers, and mild colds; even so, all had to be formally discharged back to duty before the Surgeon removed them from his rolls.

Although naval surgeons were trained, in the first instance, to take care of men wounded in battle, they also had to use their surgical skills to correct everyday occupational traumas, as well as to treat non-surgical conditions. That is, they were expected to treat hernias, hemorrhoids,

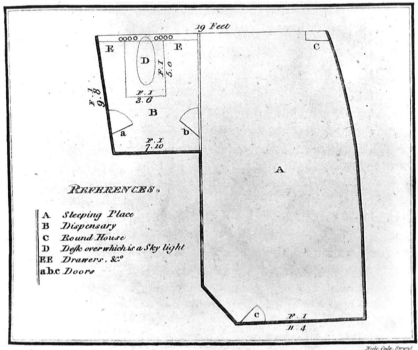

Published March 11 1806, by Rich.ᵈ Phillips New Bridge Street.

Plan of the sick bay devised by Admiral Markham, when captain of H.M.S. *Centaur* in 1801, in which he set apart a space 19 feet long to accommodate 22 swinging cradles for the sick. It included a dispensary, where drugs were prepared and dispensed to sick patients, or where men came to have their wounds dressed. The area, designed for maximum efficiency, was situated between two forward guns; it had access to the heads, but also had its own privy (the "Round House"). Walled off from the rest of its deck by white-washed canvas walls which excluded the smoke from the nearby galley stove, it was illuminated by a skylight, to facilitate examining patients. This arrangement was copied in few other ships in the British fleet, despite recommendations for its universal adoption by several prominent Royal Navy surgeons and admirals. From William Turnbull, *The Naval Surgeon* (London, 1806). (Courtesy Boston Medical Library)

anal fistulas, inflammations and strictures of the bladder and urethra, and fluid in the scrotum, as well as to reduce simple fractures of the jaw, nose, ribs, clavicle, and the bones of the arm and leg, and dislocations of all joints. Other potentially treatable wounds included cuts, contusions (i.e., bad bruises), punctures, stab wounds (fights were frequent on some ships), burns and scalds, frostbite, superficial ulcers, excoriations by a cat o'nine tails, and abscesses. Because of the high risk of sepsis and gangrene, compound fractures and crushed limbs were usually treated by amputation. Deep injuries of the thorax and abdomen could not be treated definitively; although surgeons did try to keep such injuries clean, realistically they could only hope for the best.

The basic procedures for treating wounds, whether they were suffered during the course of an ordinary work day or during battle, included removal of foreign materials; cleaning the wound site (even though the microbiological causes of wound infections had not yet been discovered); the use of a tourniquet and ligatures to control bleeding; and the application of appropriate dressings. Although many of these operations, from the most minor to the most serious—the latter were called "capital" operations, because death was always a possibility— could be successful and even life-saving, it should be noted that the benefits of general anesthesia were not demonstrated until 1846.

Before then, surgeons learned how to complete their operations quickly enough to spare their patients as much pain as possible, and they could tighten tourniquets sufficiently to cause a primitive form of local anesthesia. In 1784 a young British surgeon, James Carrick Moore, promoted his invention of a device for compressing the major arm or leg nerves so as to minimize the pain of amputation. However, it does not appear to have been adopted by any surgical writers, and it certainly would not have been suitable for use by naval surgeons because it took 15 to 30 minutes to be effective. Fainting produced sufficient protection from pain in a large number of capital cases, while, as Moore and others acknowledged, many patients simply accepted pain as a necessary accompaniment of life.

Men about to undergo major operations were usually gagged, to keep them from screaming, and held down with straps, leather-covered chains, or by other sailors. Opium-based drugs like laudanum could provide some modest pain relief, but they were used for that purpose primarily in the post-operative period, and because they induced sleep while the patient was recovering from what can only be regarded as the horror of a major operation. Hard liquors such as undiluted rum may have been administered as well, but many physicians considered alcohol to be a vasodilator, a property which would have been undesirable when bleeding was a risk.

The cockpit was usually a rather large area surrounded by the cubicles where the Midshipmen and Surgeon's Mates bunked, and by a few storerooms. But as a ship prepared for an impending battle, the

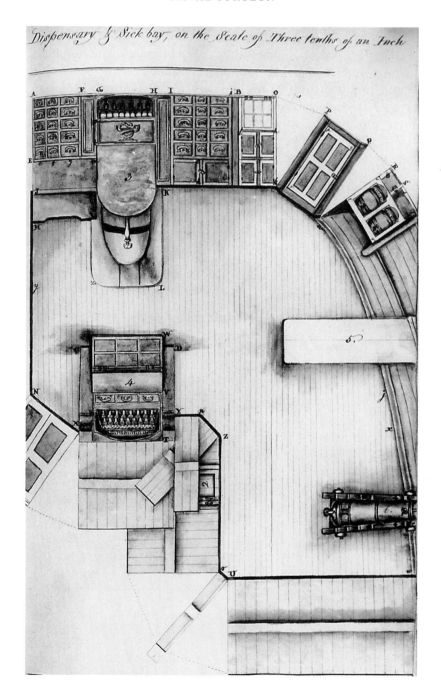

Dispensary & Sick bay, on the Scale of Three tenths of an Inch

area was cleared to receive the wounded. *New-York*'s cockpit was probably on the orlop deck (below the berth deck), just forward of the gunner's storeroom. Although its placement was usually designed to provide the shortest route over which wounded men had to be carried to the surgeon during a battle, its location might have drawbacks, as is evident in the 1755 report of an English naval surgeon whose cockpit was just below his ship's gun deck:

> At the very instant when I was amputating the limb of one of our wounded seamen, I met with an almost continual interruption from the rest of his companions, who were in the like distressed circumstances; some pouring forth the most piercing cries to be taken care of, while others seized my arm in their earnestness of being relieved, even at the time when I was passing the needle for securing the divided blood vessels by a ligature. Surely, at the time when such operations are in contemplation, the operator's mind as well as body ought to be as little agitated as possible; and the very shaking of the lower gun deck, owing to the recoil of the large cannon which are placed just over his head, is of itself sufficient to incommode a surgeon.

In the cockpit, the Surgeon was assisted by his Mates, the Purser, and a seaman or a loblolly boy; on the largest ships the Chaplain and other nonmilitary personnel were expected to report there as part of their duties. While the rest of a warship's crew prepared cannon and other guns for fighting, the Surgeon and his Mates prepared the cockpit by laying out their instruments and filling buckets with sand to catch

(*Opposite*) The only known picture of an actual early nineteenth-century sick bay, from the watch and quarter bill of Captain S.J.B. Pechell on H.M.S. *San Domingo*, 1814. The entire area measures 24 by 23 feet, but was only 5 feet 9½ inches in height. This sick bay was screened from the rest of the deck by wooden panels. As Markham had recommended, the dispensary area is at the top, fitted over the bowsprit, and decorated with the staff of Aesculapius; the door to the heads is to its immediate right, followed by a door to the "round house" and a locker containing two large jars containing water and vinegar. A table or bed is fixed over the upper gun (5). The mate's desk is just below the drug dispensary. (Courtesy National Maritime Museum, London)

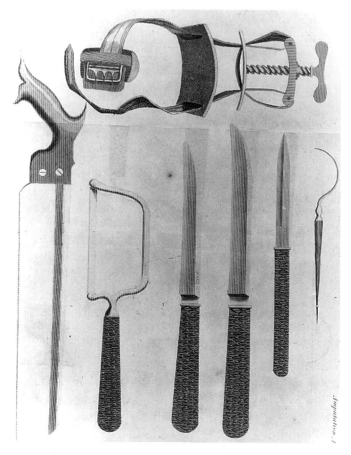

Amputation knives, saws, and screw tourniquet, from William Turnbull, *The Naval Surgeon* (London, 1806). (Courtesy Boston Medical Library)

the blood from amputation stumps, and by covering the deck with sand to prevent slipping in whatever blood did spill. They set up tables, or laid boards across unused cannons, on which maimed seamen could be stretched out while the Surgeon removed bullets, shrapnel, or large flying fragments of splintered wood or sailcloth, or where he amputated arms or legs, or drilled through the skull to relieve pressure on the brain caused by depressed skull fragments.

Most first-hand accounts of cockpits in action portray scenes dominated by blood and screams. One of the few by an enlisted man to survive among early nineteenth–century descriptions is by a seaman on H.M.S. *Macedonian* when she was defeated by the American frigate *United States* on 25 October 1812:

> The first object I met was a man bearing a limb, which had just been detached from some suffering wretch. . . The surgeon and his mate were smeared with blood from head to foot: they looked more like butchers than doctors. Having so many patients [36 were killed and 68 wounded], they had once shifted their quarters from the cockpit to the steerage; they now removed to the wardroom [in the officers' quarters], and the long table, round which the officers had sat over so many a feast, was soon covered with the bleeding forms of maimed and mutilated seamen. . .
>
> Our carpenter . . . had his leg cut off. I helped to carry him to the after wardroom, but he soon breathed out his life there, and then I assisted in throwing his mangled remains overboard. . . It was with exceeding difficulty I moved through the steerage, it was so covered with mangled men and so slippery with blood.
>
> We found two of our mess wounded. We held [one man] while the surgeon cut off his leg above the knee. The task was most painful to behold, the surgeon using his knife and saw on human flesh and bones as freely as the butcher at the shambles.

Ironically for Peter St. Medard, although this was the professional milieu for which he had prepared himself for nearly 30 years, never once did he have a chance to exploit his skills under enemy fire.

The Pathological Basis of Medical Thinking

The pathophysiologic theories upon which Dr. St. Medard and other physicians trained in the eighteenth century relied were unlike our own ideas of specific diseases with specific causes and specific treatments. Instead, several kinds of factors were said to result in easily identifiable symptoms:

1. The "predisposing causes" included the seasons, the weather, and the patient's constitution—body build, gender, age, inherited

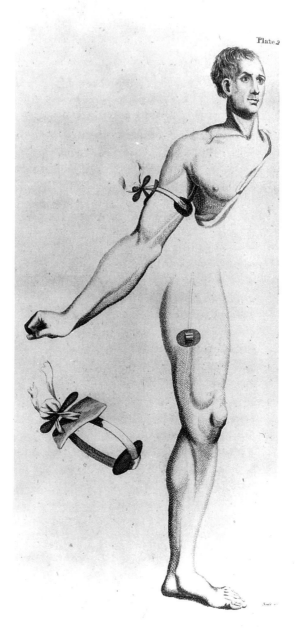

Sites for applying single tourniquets, tightened by twisting, to occlude the major arteries in the arm and leg before amputating them, from William Turnbull, *The Naval Surgeon* (London, 1806). (Courtesy Boston Medical Library)

traits, and way of life. For instance, in the case of seamen, according to Dr. Charles Turner Thackrah, sailors

> are generally very healthy and robust, hardy and enterprising. Living well, and enjoying good air and exercise, their diseases are few, and commonly of an inflammatory kind, as . . . Pneumonia &c. . . the most prevalent complaints, as the cause of death, are the sequelae of [such] diseases. . . next to these I may mention disorders of the bowels, as Colic, Diarrhea, and Dysentery.

2. The "antecedent causes" of the patient's symptoms included two kinds of air-borne factors: "miasmas," invisible disease-producing particles that emanated from decaying animal and vegetable matter—for example, from rotting carcasses, privies, and swamps—and "contagions" or "effluvia," equally invisible particles given off from patients afflicted with any of a number of fevers. The overwhelming sepsis that often killed men wounded in battle, even after successful amputation, was among the naval surgeon's most serious encounters with contagions.

3. Disturbances in the "six non-naturals" would result in illness when they were deficient or excessive in amount or quality. Abnormalities or mere changes in one or more of these factors—air, kinds of food and drink, amount of diet, sleep, exercise, and mental state—could produce illness, by, for instance, obstructing natural routes of elimination or by increasing or suppressing normal physiological actions, such as the heart beat.

4. One or more of these three factors were seen to eventuate in the "immediate causes" of illness, the disturbances in body function which produced the symptoms on which physicians based their diagnoses. Diseases were not then diagnosed or classified according to their etiologies, as they are today; instead, their symptoms *were* their diagnoses, and were described clinically in terms of imbalances.

Physicians' interpretations of their patient's symptoms—their physiological imbalances—arose, in the first instance, from a theory of disease causation that originally had been elaborated in ancient Greece. It assumed that the maintenance of health required stabilizing the equilibria among the four "humors" of the body: blood, associated with heat and moisture; phlegm, with moisture and cold; black bile, with cold and dryness; and yellow bile, with dryness and heat. When

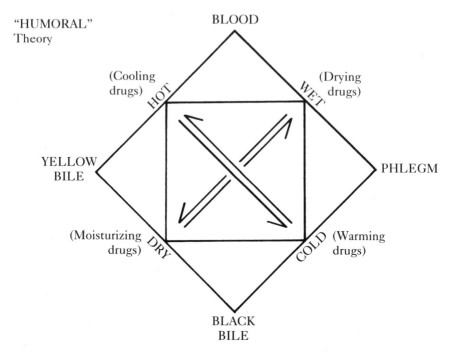

FIGURE I. Diagrammatic representation of the basic principles of humoral therapy, showing the associations of the four humors with correlative symptoms expressing the body's relative heat and fluid content, and the balances among them that drug therapy was assumed to achieve.

any of the humors increased or decreased, from whatever cause, the resulting destabilization produced symptoms characterized by excess or deficient body heat or moisture. Not only did this explanation of their patients' symptoms provide satisfactory explanations of doctors' observations at the bedside, it permitted the conclusion that unbalanced humors could be restabilized by remedies with appropriately opposite properties. For instance, because bilious fevers were associated with dryness and increased body heat, they could be neutralized with cool, moist drugs, to rebalance the blood and yellow bile, the humors that were most seriously disturbed in such patients.

The next major medical theory of the "immediate causes" followed from hypotheses that had become widely accepted by 1700. They were built on the premise that illness, or, more accurately, a given symptom, represents disturbed, or unbalanced, irritability of the solid fibrous components of nervous and cardiovascular tissues, as expressed by their tone—their innate strength and elasticity, disturbances of which could secondarily disturb the four humors. The new theory further expanded older humoral concepts of the significance of the secretions and excretions of the body as clues to unbalanced physiological processes. That is, physicians now conceived of both vessels and nerves as hollow tubes—like the gastrointestinal tract—that propel their contents through the body with forces proportional to the tones of their constituent fibers, as well as pathways for removing the humors associated with the organs that manufacture them.

For instance, Hermann Boerhaave of Leiden, one of the most influential physicians of the early eighteenth century, argued that disease occurs when a patient's fibers are too weak or too stiff, and that such unstable fibers, in conjunction with possible irregularities in diet, can secondarily alter any of his humors. That is, the body is healthy when blood or the "nerve fluids" can circulate freely, or when sweat, urine, and feces can be expelled freely, and so forth. Historians have since labeled this concept as the "solidist theory," to distinguish it from the older humoral theory, built around putative fluids.

The newer theory prompted the development of two major formulaic approaches to the treatment of disease, especially fevers. If a patient's symptoms indicated that they were caused by hyperirritability of his "system," manifested by a rapid heart rate, the physician's first goal was to reduce the pulse, to indicate that he had corrected the excessive irritability. Thus, the first step in conventional fever treatment consisted of the so-called "depletive," "evacuant," or "antiphlogistic" (the word indicates its specifically antifebrile character) regimen, using drugs thought to be directly antispasmodic or indirectly sedative, to remove or neutralize the symptoms produced by increased tones. Such drugs included emetics, cathartics, diuretics, narcotics, and refrigerants. Conventional depletive treatment also required avoiding whatever might "feed" the internal fires of the inflammation, such as meat and exercise and, in the early stages of a fever, doctors relied on bleeding to reduce tension and tone in the arteries, as well as to remove foul humors from the blood. Thus, a decreased heart rate was the principal criterion of drug efficacy in fevers. Other therapies designed to reduce the force of the fevered circulation included diaphoretics, to stimulate sweating, and externally applied heat; both measures were thought to dilate and relax blood vessels on the surface of the fevered body, to facilitate the loss of pathological heat along with the sweat.

The second major goal, or step, in the usual therapeutic sequence for fevers, was to strengthen the body after the acute stage had weakened it during the characteristic "crisis." This step relied on stimulating measures, such as the remedies classified as tonics, to increase the tone of the weakened heart and arteries, so that they could contract more forcefully and speed the removal of whatever pathogenic factors had debilitated the patient. It was assumed that stimulating the nerves with tonics secondarily increased activity in cardiovascular tissues as well as in the brain, but direct nerve stimulation, with cold water or static electricity stored in a Leyden jar, was also used to strengthen paralyzed limbs or failing kidneys. In addition, some of the drugs used as evacuants could simultaneously be interpreted as stimulants of specific tissues. Emetics, for instance, were said to stimulate the stomach, just as diaphoretics were assumed to stimulate the arteries that supply the sweat glands.

As Hippocrates had taught more than two thousand years earlier, physicians trained in the eighteenth century used their remedies to assist nature's own attempts to respond to disease, by attempting to restore the appropriate physiological imbalances and remove or neutral-

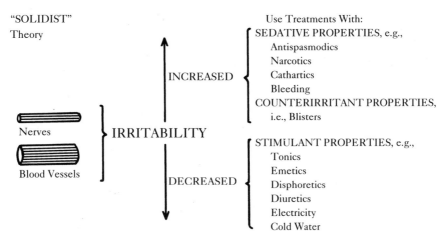

FIGURE 2.   The basic principles of solidist therapy, based on physical signs of increased or decreased irritability of the body, especially of the nerves and blood vessels.

ize the underlying causes, whatever they were. That is, the doctor's principal tasks were, first, to determine what was producing his patient's symptoms, and then to help nature remove or at least neutralize their immediate causes.

Few of the remedies used in either evacuant or stimulant therapeutic regimens were new to medical practice in the eighteenth century. For instance, ancient humoralism had encouraged the use of emetics to remove pathogenic materials or foul humors—especially yellow bile—via the stomach, while solidism permitted the additional conclusion that emetics diverted pathogenic irritations from deep within the body to the gastrointestinal arteries, whence the excess heat generated by the feverish pulse would be freely dissipated into the stomach cavity and from there continue on out into the outside air. At the same time, the act of vomiting was evidence that an emetic had strengthened the stomach's fibers, giving them added therapeutic tone that would then be transmitted to the rest of the body via the vagus nerves that connect the stomach with the central nervous system.

A third pathophysiological concept, based on chemical reactions, had entered medical thinking in the mid-sixteenth century, but physicians could not fully exploit the concept until the last decades of the eighteenth century, in the wake of Antoine Lavoisier's discovery that the body utilizes food as fuel, by combining it with oxygen ("vital air") to form carbon dioxide ("fixed air"), which was then released from the body with each exhalation. For centuries the physical signs on which doctors had relied most when diagnosing fevers were the pulse and respiratory rates. The discovery of the chemistry of respiration, beginning in the 1770s, facilitated the clinical interpretation of rapid breathing. That is, physicians readily added Lavoisier's chemical concepts to their humoral and solidist medical thinking, partly because the new information made it easier to interpret a fast respiratory rate as one more manifestation of increased combustion within the fevered body: they thought rapid breathing was necessary for replacing the excess oxygen that was being burned up in their febrile patients.

The new medical chemistry also expanded older notions about acidic and alkaline remedies, by noting, for instance, that when carbon dioxide dissolves in water, it forms carbonic acid, which then forms neutral salts when it combines with certain bases. The most important aspect of pathological acid-base imbalance was that physicians associated fevers and inflammations—including those associated with serious trauma—with an excess of alkali at the site of inflammation. Thus, sepsis of whatever origin should be curable with acid remedies. By the end of the eighteenth century, then, chemical notions of therapeutics had found new applications in the balance between acids and alkalis.

The tabular records that Francis Clifton promoted in 1731—a form of record-keeping that St. Medard may have known—took account of all these notions of disease causation and assessment simultaneously. His recommended record form included spaces for recording, on a daily basis, each patient's:

— name, disease, and history of the attack;
— age, temperament, and constitutional peculiarities;
— habits of life;
— contingencies and occasional causes;
— climate and season;
— epidemics [now in progress];
— time since onset of the disease;
— the seat and degree of localized symptoms;
— countenance, pulse, respiration, skin, tongue;
— gastric symptoms, intestinal habits, and appearance of the feces;
— urine;
— sleep and degree of intellectual activity;
— regimen, or usual diet;
— miscellaneous observations; and
— medicines taken so far.

Clifton concluded his argument by pointing out that, "if this *Plan* be fol-low'd, the consequence will be, that Disease will be better known, and easier cur'd; even supposing the *Materia Medica* shou'd stand as it does." That is, as a French physician observed 70 years later, the drugs remained the same—it was only the theories about disease that changed.

Despite the superficial differences among them, humoral, solidist, and chemical theories were not competitive explanations of patients' symptoms—that is, of the "immediate causes" of their symptoms. Instead, doctors relied on all three simultaneously to explain their clinical observations at the bedside. As will become evident, Peter St. Medard had been trained in, and relied chiefly on, humoral and solidist concepts, as well as on the conventional manipulative techniques of general surgery. However, his clinical notes suggest that it is less certain that he relied on the chemical discoveries of Lavoisier to the same extent. He had, of course, left France before his countryman's ideas had fully permeated medical thinking, and by 1802 chemical notions had not yet filtered down from academic medicine to the average American practitioner. That is, St. Medard may have been conservative in his acceptance of new ideas, or, like other physicians with no academic pretensions, he may simply have been unfamiliar with current academic textbook hypotheses. On the other hand, as will also become evident, the extent of his knowledge would have made little difference to either his choices of remedies or to the outcome of his patients' illnesses.

DRUGS, BLISTERS, AND BLEEDING

The most prevalent of all illnesses, whether on land or sea, were fevers, diagnosed at the bedside not with thermometers but by a fast pulse and rapid breathing. A general approach to their treatment had evolved over the centuries, but it took its final form only in the eighteenth century, in the form of the two-step depletive-stimulating regimen. Most medical authorities agreed that an effective depletive regimen should avoid:

1. external heat, exercise, thirst, excessive mental activity, and excessive food, especially red meat;
2. corruption of humors in the stomach, by administering emetics or acids;
3. fecal retention, by administering cathartics and enemas; and
4. bitterness—i.e., alkalinity—in the body's fluids, by administering diaphoretics and antiseptics (not in the modern sense of antiseptics, but acidic drugs that were assumed to neutralize putrefactive processes).

The use of auxiliary techniques, such as blistering or bleeding, was dictated by the species of fever to be treated, especially by its severity. Like his contemporaries, Peter St. Medard began treating his febrile patients with depletive remedies, such as bleeding, emetics, and cathartics, during the first few days of treatment, then followed them with strengthening tonics.

The medicines, surgical instruments, and other supplies he ordered through the Washington navy agent for use in *New-York* are listed in Appendix I. Medicine chests for warships contained up to 100 of the approximately 1,300 remedies then being prescribed by doctors on land and sea. Civilian doctors ashore relied on their own favorite lists of about 125 different drugs, but space limitations forced a surgeon at sea to limit his choices to no more than about 100, based on his personal experience with each, and on the size of his ship's crew. But the kinds of drugs, in terms of drug classes, used by naval surgeons were the same as those used by their counterparts on land.

For instance, tonics, remedies thought to strengthen the body when it had become weakened by disease, especially during convalescence from a fever, were among those prescribed most frequently at sea or on land. For this purpose the universally favored drug was Peruvian bark, or cinchona. Because it had first entered medical practice in the mid-seventeenth century as an effective remedy for the intermittent fevers, now known as malaria (today we know it contains quinine, which is still used in antimalarial therapy), physicians soon came to use the bitter-tasting drug in the treatment of virtually all other fevers.

The next most frequently prescribed drugs were cathartics, drugs assumed to flush out unbalanced humors with the feces as well as to relax abnormal tensions that constricted their patients' intestinal fibers, thereby inhibiting normal evacuations by patients with constipation, a frequent accompaniment of febrile illnesses. Typical of this class of drugs were the chemical agents calomel (mercurous chloride) and cremor tartar (sodium potassium tartrate), and the ancient botanicals jalap, rhubarb, and castor oil.

Drugs that stimulated bowel movements were prescribed even more often by civilian doctors ashore, where it would have been easier to dispose of their end product, a task that was, at best, difficult at sea. Chamber pots were available in all homes of the time, in sick bays, and in the officers' cubicles around the wardroom, but healthy sailors did not have that luxury. They had to relieve themselves at the "head," four to eight latrine seats ranged along the bowsprit, forward of the forecastle; some are said to have mastered the art of sitting on the side rails of the main deck. Because the head emptied over the leading edge of the ship, the hull below was kept partially clean simply as the ship nosed into and out of waves, but swabbing the head was also assigned as a daily punitive chore. It is also said—although it cannot be documented—that the difficulties inherent in relieving the bowels led many sailors to become constipated as a result of their reluctance to climb out onto the head or elsewhere. Thus, cathartics may have been among the minor remedies they might ask for at morning sick call when the intra-abdominal pressure became unbearable. In frigates as large as *New-York*, the captain had two latrine seats in the quarter galleries on either side of his cabin. (Examples of all these facilities can be seen in *Constitution* at Boston.)

Doctors gave emetics, drugs that made patients vomit, to remove foul humors from the stomach, as well as to strengthen what they took to be weak stomach muscle fibers. Tartar emetic (antimony potassium tartrate) was administered for that purpose, as was ipecac, still used in hospital emergency rooms to remove unabsorbed poisons from the stomach. Diaphoretics were given in order to make patients "sweat out" their unbalanced humors; at the same time, these drugs, especially those made with antimony, were assumed to strengthen the blood vessels that supplied the sweat glands in the skin.

Opium, as well as opium preparations such as laudanum (also known as paregoric or Thebaic tincture, it was an alcohol solution of opium), were correctly regarded as sedative and antidiarrheal, and as analgesic. Although it was well known that patients who required treatment with opium for a prolonged period could require increasingly large doses of it to produce the same degree of pain-killing effect (the phenomenon now known as tolerance), addiction to it was not yet the social problem that would develop in the late nineteenth century.

Because syphilis was considered to be almost an occupational hazard of sailors, navy surgeons stocked their favorite mercury salts with which to treat them. Most victims required prolonged therapy with oral mercury preparations, such as calomel or corrosive sublimate (mercuric chloride), and with unguents made with the latter or even with metallic, liquid, mercury. All mercurials were cathartic and diaphoretic, providing routes for eliminating the contagious factor responsible for venereal afflictions through the stool and sweat. These drugs also produced a metallic taste in the mouth, and stimulated salivation, effects which were taken as proof that they were producing their desired effect, removal of the syphilitic "poison." Although the two latter effects were unpleasant, they were considered among the penalties that patients had to pay for having contracted a socially unacceptable disease in the first place. Worse, treatment for venereal diseases was prolonged and sometimes debilitating in itself, which made it far more expensive than treatment for other illnesses. Moreover, the pay of afflicted soldiers and sailors was docked, ostensibly to compensate the government for both the treatment itself and the loss of work time, but also as punishment. To add further to the guilt heaped on syphilitic patients, military surgeons received extra pay for treating them.

Blisters and bleeding were reserved for the sickest patients, those with the most serious fevers or injuries. Blisters, also called epispastics, were administered as an alcohol solution of powdered cantharides beetles (*Lytta* [formerly *Cantharis*] *vesicatoria*—sometimes called "Spanish flies," although they were not flies and came not from Spain but from the eastern Mediterranean). When placed on the skin, usually in the form of a plaster which was left in place for several days, cantharides does raise a large, painful blister. Originally thought to facilitate the removal of foul humors into the blister fluid, by the eighteenth century it was also thought that the artificially induced inflammation produced when the skin blistered would neutralize the naturally occurring inflammation that had caused the patient's symptoms in the first place, by the process called "counter-irritation."

The rationale for bleeding, too, had changed over the centuries. When introduced in the ancient world, it was assumed that it removed the pathologically unbalanced humors, especially blood, that were producing the patient's symptoms; St. Medard's contemporaries also thought it relaxed tension on the hyperactive fibers of the fevered cardiovascular system. Cullen noted that "bloodletting is one of the most powerful means of diminishing the activity of the whole body, especially of the sanguiferous system; and it must therefore be the most effectual means of moderating the violence of reaction in fevers," especially those fevers that were accompanied by a fast pulse. In short, pulling the plug to release some of the patient's blood was thought to reduce the excessive motion of the corpuscles in the blood, or perhaps the friction, between the blood and the walls of the arteries, that was producing the febrile patient's increased body heat.

Bleeding was most often accomplished, after tightening a tourniquet around the upper arm, by cutting one of the veins just below the skin on the inner surface of the elbow and allowing the blood to flow freely into a bowl, sometimes graduated so that the physician could determine exactly how many ounces he was removing. Dr. St. Medard appears to have used just such a bleeding bowl. Most doctors removed an average of twelve ounces at a time, but up to twice as much from their sickest patients.

Thus, St. Medard's remedies were not designed to counteract well-defined disease processes, as modern drugs do. Instead, he used drugs to adjust, to fine-tune, each patient's own special internal equilibria, his physiological balances, regardless of what might have disrupted them in the first place. The occurrence of catharsis, vomiting, sweating, or blisters after the administration of a corresponding drug indicated to both doctor and patient that the remedy had indeed altered the humors, tones, and acid-base balance of the body in the way that had been intended. Thus, within the theoretical frameworks of his day, medical treatments were entirely rational, and followed logically from the basic premises of humoralism, solidism, and chemistry.

NOTES

The outline of late eighteenth- and early nineteenth-century medical and surgical thinking given here has been synthesized from the following works of leading naval surgeons of the time (although they are entirely consistent with those of academic and other civilian practitioners): Gilbert Blane, *Observations on the Diseases Incident to Seamen* (London: Joseph Cooper, John Murray and William Creech, 1785); Edward Cutbush, *Observations on the Means of Preserving the Health of Soldiers and Sailors* (Philadelphia: Thomas Dobson, 1808); James Lind, *An Essay on the Most Effectual Means of Preserving the Health of Seamen*, 3d ed. (London: J. Murray, 1778); William Northcote, *The Marine Practice of Physic and Surgery*, 2 vols. (London: T. Becket and P. A. De Hondt, 1770); Usher Parsons, *Sailor's Physician* (Cambridge, Mass.: Hilliard and Metcalf, 1820); Robert Robertson, *An Essay on Fevers* (London: G. G. J. & J. Robinson, 1790); Thomas Trotter, *Medicina Nautica: An Essay on the Diseases of Seamen*, 3 vols. (London: T. Cadell, Jun., and W. Davies, 1797–1803); William Turnbull, *The Naval Surgeon* (London: Richard Phillips, 1806); and the anonymous *Medical Advice to Masters of Ships* (Lancaster, England: 1799). For details of sick bays and cockpits, see Christopher Lloyd and Jack L. S. Coulter, *Medicine and the Navy,*

1200–1900, 4 vols. Vol. 3: *1714–1815*. (Edinburgh: E. & S. Livingstone Ltd., 1961), pp. 57–69; the two accounts of cockpits in action are on pp. 58 and 61. For American correlates, see Louis H. Roddis, "A short history of nautical medicine," *Annals of Medical History*, 3d ser., *3* (1941): 203–247. James Moore described his nerve "compressor" in *A Method of Preventing or Diminishing Pain in Several Operations of Surgery* (London: T. Cadell, 1784).

Charles Turner Thackrah's observation on the health of seamen is in his *The Effects of Arts, Trades, and Professions on Health and Longevity*, 2nd ed. (1832; rprt. ed. Canton, Mass.: Science History Publications, 1985), p. 71. Francis Clifton's plan for medical record-keeping may have been more influential than he has been given credit for. He outlined it in *Tabular Observations Recommended, as the Plainest and Surest Way of Practising and Improving Physick* (London: J. Brindley, 1731); his sample table pages are on pp. xl–xli, and his conclusion is on p. 30.

Definitions of the drugs and other therapies employed by PSM and his contemporaries, within the framework outlined above, are given in J. Worth Estes, *Dictionary of Protopharmacology: Therapeutic Practices, 1700–1850* (Canton, Mass.: Science History Publications, 1990). For data comparing the practices of four near contemporary physicians, see J. Worth Estes, "Therapeutic practice in colonial New England," in Philip Cash, Eric H. Christianson, and J. Worth Estes, eds., *Medicine in Colonial Massachusetts, 1620–1820* (Boston: Colonial Society of Massachusetts, 1980), 289–383; also see J. Worth Estes, "Drug usage at the infirmary: The example of Dr. Andrew Duncan, Sr.," Appendix D to Guenter B. Risse, *Hospital Life in Enlightenment Scotland: Care and Teaching at the Royal Infirmary of Edinburgh* (New York: Cambridge University Press, 1986), pp. 351–384; J. Worth Estes, "Quantitative observations of fever and its treatment before the advent of short clinical thermometers," *Medical History 35* (1991): 189–216; and J. Worth Estes, "The medical properties of food in the eighteenth century," *Journal of the History of Medicine & Allied Sciences 51* (1996): 127–154. For the diagnosis and treatment of yellow fever, which PSM seldom if ever encountered, but which was a major hazard of many cruises, especially in the Caribbean, see J. Worth Estes, "The yellow fever syndrome and its treatment in Philadelphia, 1793," in J. W. Estes and Billy G. Smith, eds., *"A Melancholy Scene of Devastation": The Public Response to the 1793 Philadelphia Yellow Fever Epidemic* (Canton, Mass.: Science History Publications, 1997). The most celebrated case of iatrogenic exsanguination is outlined in J. Worth Estes, "George Washington and the doctors: Treating America's first superhero," *Medical History 1* (1985): 44–47. For medical care on a near contemporary American warship, see J. Worth Estes and Ira Dye, "Death on the *Argus*:

American medical malpractice vs. British chauvinism in the War of 1812," *Journal of the History of Medicine & Allied Sciences 44* (1989): 179–195. An important recent study of the introduction of Lavoisier's chemical discoveries into contemporary medical thinking is Frederic L. Holmes's "The chemical revolution and the art of healing," *Caduceus 11* (1995): 103–126.

By the President of the United States of America

SUFFER the *Schooner Jack*
Isaac Allen master or commander, of the burthen of
One Hundred & Five tons or thereabouts, mounted with
no guns, navigated with *Seven* men,

TO PASS with her Company, Passengers, —
Goods and Merchandize, without any hindrance, seizure or molestation; the said *Vessel* — appearing, by good testimony, to belong to
one or more of the Citizens of the United States, and to him or them,
only.

Number Sixteen

Given under my Hand and the Seal of the
United States of America, the *First*
day of *April* — in the year of our Lord one
thousand seven hundred and *Ninety seven*

John Adams

By the President.

Timothy Pickering Secretary of State.

State of *Massachusetts*
District of *Gloucester*

Countersigned by *William Tuck* Coll

To all Persons whom
these may concern.

Chapter Six

Diarrhea and Dysentery in the Potomac

2 September–10 December 1802

I N THE 1790s George Washington's administration had signed treaties of peace and friendship with Algiers, Tunis, and Tripoli. All three agreements required substantial cash payments by the United States to guarantee protection from attacks on American shipping by those Barbary Coast states that depended on piracy for a large part of their incomes. That is, the North African rulers were extorting cash or goods, or both, from America, as well as several European countries, to insure they would not attack ships of the new mercantile republic that ventured into the Mediterranean. However, in October 1800, when Yusuf Qaramanli, the Pacha, or ruler, of Tripoli (often called the Bashaw by con-

(*Opposite*) Passport, signed by President John Adams and Secretary of State Timothy Pickering, requesting free passage for the schooner *Jack*, her passengers, and her cargo; the piece cut from the scalloped edge at the top was sent to Algiers, so that the validity of the passport could be verified when needed. Presumably the passport might have prevented seizure or other molestation by ships of other powers, but that could not be guaranteed. (Courtesy of the Peabody Essex Museum, Salem, Massachusetts)

81

temporary Americans), learned that his counterpart the Dey of Algiers was receiving several times more than he was, he demanded a larger annual payment through the American consul there, James Leander Cathcart. By the time his diplomatic dispatch reached Washington the following March, Thomas Jefferson had just been inaugurated. Because Qaramanli had received no reply to his demand by 14 May 1801, Tripoli became the first country to declare war on the United States.

Jefferson opposed paying off the Barbary rulers, unlike his Federalist predecessors (though John Adams had been unwilling to pay bribes to the French officials in the XYZ affair). Even before Tripoli declared war, the new president ordered the navy to confront the piratical North African states with military force. His administration decided to send two squadrons made up of ships retained under the Peace Establishment Act, in rotation, to protect American shipping in the Mediterranean. The first squadron, under the command of Commodore Richard Dale, included the frigates *Philadelphia*, *Essex*, and *President*, and the schooner *Enterprise*.

Because neither side had yet formally declared war, the squadron was charged only to use the appearance of force to persuade the North African states to adhere to their earlier treaties. Unless, of course, any of them should declare war, in which case the American floating fortresses were to punish hostile states by blockading their ports. However, when Dale reached Gibraltar on 1 July 1801, he finally learned that Tripoli had declared war on the United States six weeks earlier. The *Enterprise* soon captured a Tripolitan boat and destroyed her rigging and armaments before sending her home, but Dale did not think his orders permitted him to bombard the port of Tripoli. He asked for specific orders to attack the city, and recommended that enough warships be sent to insure an adequate blockade.

When Robert Smith became Secretary of the Navy in May 1801, he prepared orders for assembling the second squadron. Under the command of 35-year-old Commodore Richard Valentine Morris, it was to include the frigates *Chesapeake*, *Adams* (Morris's first ship in the Quasi-War), and *Constellation*; *Enterprise* was to be reassigned to the new squadron. It was reinforced in February 1802 with Congressional authority for the navy to use "such of the armed vessels of the United States as may be judged requisite . . . for protecting effectually the commerce and seamen thereof on the Atlantic Ocean, the Mediterranean and adjoining seas." Additional orders authorized naval commanders to take

Tripolitan ships and to carry out whatever other hostile acts were necessary, although the Jefferson administration realized that effective bombardment of an enemy port was more expensive than maintaining a simple blockade, which required fewer ships on station.

Smith instructed Morris to provide convoys for American merchant ships, if detaching ships for such duty did not impair the squadron's blockading effort, but the secretary also gave the Commodore considerable freedom of action in choosing among alternative courses. Because Tripoli had shown signs of being willing to sign a new treaty, Morris was further instructed to display America's military might before Qaramanli's fortified seawalls, to impress upon him the great likelihood of blockade, or even destruction, if renewed negotiations failed.

By the time Morris reached Gibraltar in May 1802, Maulay Sulaiman, the Sultan of Morocco, had decided to support the Pacha of Tripoli. On 22 June, the Sultan declared war on the United States. Because he had ports on his Atlantic coast, war with Morocco was potentially more threatening to American shipping than war with the other Barbary states, whose only ports were on the Mediterranean. Moreover, there were hints that Tunis and Algiers might soon declare war. Two more frigates, *New-York* and *John Adams*, were added to Commodore Morris's fleet. James Fenimore Cooper regarded the new squadron as, "In some respects, . . . the best appointed force that had ever sailed from America."

New-York had been laid up in the Potomac for just over six months when she was recommissioned on 13 August 1802, under the command of 34-year-old Captain James Barron. In addition to reinforcing Commodore Morris's squadron, the ship's mission included delivering naval supplies to the squadron, a payment of $30,000 to the Dey of Algiers, and 100 gun carriages as an inducement for the Sultan of Morocco to renew peace with the United States. However, at the last moment the government decided against sending the latter gift, which meant that the ship could carry an extra month's provisions, for a new total of five months' worth. Captain Barron was given a substantial sum in cash with which to replenish his ship's supplies in the Mediterranean, and authorized to draw on funds or credit from naval agents at Gibraltar and at Leghorn on the northwest coast of Italy.

Soon after reporting on board *New-York*, Midshipman William Lewis of Virginia echoed, in a letter home, what seems to have been the prevailing opinion of his new commanding officer:

Capt. Barron is a man of warm passions, but good natured withall. In the line of his Profession, I am told he is extremely clever, and from what I can judge, I believe it to be true; in other respects, his education has not been very liberal. He possesses a strong understanding notwithstanding. The greatest allowance ought to be made for his hasty temper, for the difficulties and disappointments which he (as well as every other man in his line) has to encounter, are enough to provoke the temper of the most patient.

In early September Barron took his ship into Washington Navy Yard to be readied for sea duty. Secretary Smith authorized him to recruit the standard complement of about 350 men for a 38-gun frigate:

Commissioned
Officers: Captain
    Lieutenants (4)
    Surgeon
    Surgeon's Mate

Warrant Officers: [Sailing] Master
    Boatswain
    Chaplain
    Purser
    Gunner
    Sailmaker
    Carpenter
    Captain's Clerk

Midshipmen (12)

Petty Officers: Master's Mates (2)
    Boatswain's Mates (2)
    Gunner's Mates (2)
    Sailmaker's Mate
    Carpenter's Mates (2)
    Cockswain
    Yeoman of Gunroom

Quarter Gunners (10)
Quartermasters (10)
Armorer
Steward
Cooper
Master-at-Arms
Cook

Marines: Lieutenant
    Sergeant
    Corporal
    Drummer
    Fifer
    Privates (ca. 50)

Other Ranks: Able Seamen (100)
    Ordinary Seamen (110)
    Boys (ca. 30)

Although seamen were to be recruited at Norfolk, their one-year enlistments were to date only from the time their ship actually left for the Mediterranean station. Ordinary Seamen and Boys were to be paid five to eight dollars a month, depending on their skills, while Able Seamen were to receive a maximum of twelve dollars. Captains were paid $1,200 per year; Lieutenants $480; Surgeons $600; Surgeon's Mates $360; and Midshipmen $228. All officers except midshipmen received additional cash in lieu of rations, which added substantially to their total incomes. The annual base pay of officers enabled bachelors to make ends meet, but was insufficient for maintaining a wife and children on shore for those below the rank of Captain. It has been estimated that married officers with children could maintain a "comfortable middle-class existence" at $1,300 to $1,700 a year. An optimistic officer might expect to strike it rich by participating in the capture of enemy prizes, but the more realistic probably recognized that they could not count on such windfalls.

* * *

In July 1802 Secretary Smith had ordered Peter St. Medard to *General Greene*, another of the laid-up frigates, but a month later he reassigned all her officers to *New-York*. St. Medard reported to his new ship on 1 September 1802, while she was still at Washington, along with Dr. Nathaniel T. Weems, his Surgeon's Mate. A native of Maryland, Weems was appointed from Virginia, but virtually nothing else is known about his life before that date, not even his age.

The *Naval Regulations* issued in January 1802, as the nation once more prepared for war, covered many aspects of life at sea on her warships, again following British custom. The expectations for a naval surgeon covered his professional skills as well as his administrative tasks:

1. To inspect and take care of the necessaries sent on board for the use of the sick men; if not good, he must acquaint the captain, and he must see that they are duly served out for the relief of the sick.
2. To visit the men under his care twice a day, or oftener, if circumstances require it; he must see that his mates do their duty, so that none want due attendance and relief.
3. In cases that are difficult he is to advise with the surgeons of the squadron.

4. To inform the captain daily of the state of his patients.

5. When the sick are ordered to the hospitals, he is to send with them to the surgeon [on shore], an account of the time and manner of their being taken ill, and how they have been treated.

6. But none are to be sent to sick quarters [on shore], unless their distempers, or the number of sick on board, are such that they cannot be taken due care of; and this the surgeon is to certify under his hand, before removal. If the surgeon of the hospital finds they might have been cured in a little time on board, the surgeon on the ship is to have charged against his wages for every man so sent, ten dollars.

7. To be ready with his mates and assistants in an engagement, having all things at hand necessary for stopping of blood and dressing of wounds.

8. *To keep a day-book of his practice, containing the names of his patients, their hurts, distempers, when taken ill, when recovered, removal, death, prescriptions, and method of treatment, while under cure.*

9. *From the last book he is to form two journals, one containing his physical, and the other his chirurgical practice, which are to be sent to the navy-office, at the end of every voyage.* [Italics added]

10. Stores for the medical department are to be furnished upon his requisition, and he will be held responsible for the expenditure thereof.

11. He will keep a regular account of his receipts and expenditures of such stores, and transmit an account thereof to the accountant of the navy, at the end of every cruise.

Peter St. Medard's implementation of Regulations 8 and 9 above provides us a rare view of the everyday work of a physician trained in the eighteenth century. As required, he wrote down, from 1 September 1802 through 9 December 1802, in the large folio leatherbound manuscript of his *Physical and Chirugical Transactions* now in the U.S.S. *Constitution* Museum in Boston, the name, rank, and age of every patient he admitted to the sick list each day for those 16 months, along with each patient's diagnosis, brief comments about his progress, his treatments, and whether he was returned to duty, discharged for medical reasons, or died. Only one other similar American naval document has surfaced, and it is dated 1813.

As noted earlier, St. Medard had had experience in keeping such records earlier in his career at sea. Civilian physicians on shore kept day-books or other journals that included notes about the treatments they prescribed, chiefly in order to compute their patients' fees, but seldom did they include the diagnoses they made. Because St. Medard's *Transactions* lists virtually all the patients he treated, and why he treated them, it provides a valuable window into the professional minds of eighteenth-century physicians on both land and sea.

Fortunately for the historian of medicine—but not, as it turned out, for the commanding officer of *New-York*'s squadron—the ship never engaged in battle. In addition, most of her crew, except for the officers, were confined to the ship even when visiting ports, which limited opportunities for introducing new infectious diseases to the crew. In short, Dr. St. Medard's clinical notes reveal not only clues to his diagnostic and therapeutic reasoning, but also to the epidemiology of shipboard illness undisturbed by bloody fighting. The one partial gap in the record, toward its end, provides another kind of clue to the stresses of medical life at sea in the age of sail.

* * *

Just as a surgeon was responsible for stocking his sick bay, Captain Barron's first tasks included enlisting a crew as well as provisioning his ship. Throughout September and into October she took on supplies of beef and pork brought from New London and Newport; rice, butter, and flour from Baltimore; and beans from New York, while shipwrights were readying her for sea after several months of inactivity in the Potomac. After only a few days on board *New-York*, at St. Mary's, on the north shore of the mouth of the Potomac, her captain was becoming increasingly dismayed at her defects. Ordered to survey them, the First Lieutenant, Sailing Master, Boatswain, and Carpenter found her topmasts "dry and unfit for sea service," from "having been expos'd to the sun." Similar problems would recur during the next sixteen months.

Dr. St. Medard's first days on his new ship kept him fully occupied. A week after he reported for duty, a seaman fell from the main topgallant yard and "struck in the main chains," presumably killing him, although the surgeon did not record this event himself. A day before the ship sailed for the Mediterranean, he wrote to the Secretary of the Navy about the most prevalent illnesses he had treated while his ship was in home waters, and outlined appropriate preventive measures that should be standard on all ships:

Presuming that informations in the line of my profession will be agreable especially comming out of the United States Frigate Newyork as being the first ship of the government [illegible] out of the Eastern Branch and under your directions, being desirous of promotting the good of the service in making you acquainted with incidents and causes which originate diseases in order when in our power to have them removed; I shall in this instence *of the Newyork* make it my duty to inform you that since we have left Washington Navy Yard I have had no less [than] from 15 to 30 sick [actually, he had as many as 33] on my [sick] list, chiefly with diarrhea & dysentery, & the most of them of a very obstinate a nature. Hardly one of the men has escaped it and many of the officers have been ill with it. I think it then highly necessary to acquaint you of that disaster and to inform you it is my opinion that it does not proceed from any other cause than that of the river water, which the officers & men were forced to drink in aboundance while suffering with intence of heat in the river, and no other water or but very little could be provided for them.

Therefore precautions ought to be taken when vessells of the government are either fitting out or lay in fresh water rivers, to correct the quality of such waters and to prevint the men from drinking it from a long[side] of the vessell in order to avoid as much as possible its dreadful effect, which, when epidemical, carey[s] its calamity through a whole ship's company, debilitated them to such a degree that near half of them are kept in a state of invalidity and consequently unfit for any hard duty during one twelve month cruise.

Zeal and anxiety of our captains, I presume in obidence to your orders (and their duty of course) in fitting out their vessells for service, I suppose prevint them from attending to any precaution & prevint those ill consequences, but they are of a too serious nature not to be attended to; therefore proper men ought to be spared, stationed, or appointed to attend and correct the water in cleaning and burning the casks insid[e], and about [a] half pint of lime put in to an hundred gallons of water which will be sufficient to correct its quality, keep it swe[e]t & wholesum. Two have died of the dysentery, one of them having been removed from the Navy Yard Hospital to the Newyork very ill.

> Since our arrival in this river I have had [a] number of cases of bilious fevers of a most malignant nature, likewise of intermitting and or ague fevers in aboundance, diseases peculiar to this season and climat, of the former two have unfurnately fellen victim to its rage.

Other navy surgeons had noticed the association between diarrheal disease and drinking foul river water. Edward Cutbush, for instance, had made the same observation in July 1799 while his ship was anchored in the Delaware River near Wilmington.

St. Medard caused eleven men to be discharged from the navy, because of ill health, while *New-York* was being prepared for her Mediterranean assignment. Midshipman Winlock Clark, 24 years old, complained of summer diarrhea (called "cholera morbus," although it was not true cholera) on 3 September, but by the end of the month Dr. St. Medard certified his medical discharge because he now suffered from chronic obstruction of the liver "which keep[s] him in a state of invalidity and renders him unfit for his duty." William Dawling, a 21-year-old landsman, was discharged with a similar diagnosis. Jacob Abbert, the Marines' drummer, was discharged because he had an inguinal hernia that could not be kept in place even with a steel truss, and a landsman, Reuben Allen, was paralyzed on his left side, probably from a stroke. Seven other seamen were discharged because of intractable intermittent fever, catarrhal fever, diarrhea, dysentery, or bilious fever; two of them were sent to the naval hospital facility in Norfolk.

Although Dr. St. Medard was kept busy by the large number of patients under his care, he seems to have enjoyed the work he felt he had been cut out for. It was probably shortly after his ship finally left Chesapeake Bay that he prepared another report for the Secretary of the Navy:

> While the new york remained near Norfolk to compleat her for sea, which was about 28 days, an increase of alarming diseases infected without regard the ships company, particularly that of bilious fevers which assumed a most destructive character. High intermitting or ague fevers of the most obstinate [kind] spared none or but few of the officers & men; two died of the dysentery & three with a malignant bilious fever, one of them complicated with an inflamation of the bladder & the other with a rheumatic gout [illegible] to the stomach; five in number was our list of men with this . . . caracter of diseases.

Here is a short abstract of the most prevalent diseases on board from the 1st of Sept. to the 8th of October, the day of our sailing for the Mediterranean station:

Dysentery & Diarrhea	50	
Bilious fevers	12	93 [sic] men
Intermitting [fevers]	29	
Catarrhal cough [and fever]	11	

The microbial causes of most of these illnesses cannot be identified today, chiefly because eighteenth-century diagnoses were called by the patient's dominant symptoms. Thus, dysentery was the term used for severe bloody diarrhea accompanied by violent abdominal pain. Bilious fever may have been acute hepatitis, but the term usually indicated only that the patient had both fever and diarrhea, and perhaps jaundice. The intermittent fevers were the various forms of malaria, each characterized by the length of the interval between bouts of shaking chills and fever, while catarrhal fevers were what we might call bad colds or perhaps influenza (although the latter diagnosis was used on its own).

Three cases in particular interested Dr. St. Medard more than the others, prompting him to append detailed reports of each to his report to the navy secretary. Few such detailed case descriptions, typical of the most severe illnesses and treatments of the time, have survived:

Case of Shubel Cross, Sergt. Marines

On the 20th of Sept. 1802, Cross, aged 24 years, complained of burning with fever, the pulse light & full, thirst, anguish, & a retching to vomit, a violent headache, pains in the loins & back. All those symptoms indicating to blood letting, I thought it proper to cause to be taken from his arm about twelve ounces of blood, by which & with the assistance of the chammomil infusion produced in about half an hour an easy perspiration [which] abated in part the pains at the head, loins, and back; on the 21st the pains being easier, the fever some less, with distinct remission, the tongue foul with nausea, and rather a dryness of the skin, I then administered small doses of ant[imonial] wine & 15 gr[ains] of pulv[is] ipecac, which operated as a mild diaphoretic & vomit in producing at three different times large discharges of bile, in the course of the afternoon. [One ounce] crem[or] tartar, 3 gr[ains] calomel, & 15 gr[ains] of sal nitri was given him every 2 hours; assisted with the chammomil infusion which likewise operating downwards procured an aboundan[t] discharge of the bile, he appeared easy after the operations of both; on the 22nd being with very little fever, the pulse easy but small, partly free from pains, but very weak & debilitated with nausea & at times vomiting, I prescribed from 10 to 15 drops of [spirits of dulcified niter] Every 2 hours, continuing the chammomil infusion acidulated with . . . elixir vitriol. Likewise the calomel by small doses was often repeated, on the 23th nausea continuing altho the vomiting less the pulse small & very little fever. The skin dry & the pains light but a general great debility, 20 grains of [powdered Peruvian bark] in 2 oz. of Madeira wine was administered every [?] hours & in the evening 20 drops of tincture Thebaic[.] He rested some in the night, but in the morning of the 24th appeared delirious at time[s] and complained of a pain & operation [i.e., nausea] at the stomach, & an ophthalmia arising. I immediately applied the epispastics [i.e., cantharides blisters] at the sternum & legs, the wine & bark & the ether vitriol as above were continued during the day. At 5 pm the blisters had no effect, the extremities [were] cold & at nine o clock in the evening [he] died.

Case of Oratio Cooper, Master's Mate

On the 24th Sept. [H]oratio Cooper, aged 25 years, complained of a violent rheumatic pain which appeared seated on the thigh & at the same time made itself felt in the back & loins as a s[c]iatic & rheumatic gout. I applied a large epispastic plaister on the thigh which removed the pain from all parts; on the 28th Mr. Cooper went to his duty and worked in the spirit room, threw himself in[to] a violent perspiration, & came up upon the dacke in that situation and in his shirt sleeves; the next day on the 29th he complained of the same pains in the back & loins with considerable of fever, having been costive [constipated] a few days before. A cathartic of calomel & jalap was given him which operated severally & advantageously. On the 30th the fever remitted, & the pains continuing, some æther vitriolic [i.e., ether] drops from 15 to 18 was administered occasionally, the pains were [? reduced] with the same and the patient received temporary relief. On the 1st of October the pains repercuted towards the stomach and was thrown in a state of spasm & irritability, vomiting everything. The fever increased, the pulse tight & small with a violent head ache, the dry skin tempering & diaphoret[ic] powders which acted together as laxatives was given him every 2 hours such as 8 gr[ains] crem[or] tarter, 4 gr[ains] sal nitri, 1 gr[ain] calomel, & ½ gr[ain] camphor . . . which produced the intended effects in discharging downwards a quantity of bile & promoted an easy perspiration; on the 2nd October the vomiting some less & the fever remitted. The powders as above were continued, with a chammomil infusion, on the 3th the vomiting increasing or more frequent, the pulse small & debilitated, with but very little [force]. Administered ½ dr[achm] sal absinth, ½ dr[achm lemon] juice, 2 drops [Oil of Peppermint, a common proprietary remedy] ½ dr[achm], [white sugar,] 1 oz aq [simple syrup], . . . which was repeated every 3 hours & supressed the vomiting for near 6 hours. The 4th the vomiting having returned as the day before & the sal of absinth & acid praparation proving inefectual & being costive, I prescribed the enemas which he took to the number of 4 on that day, of folia sennae ½ oz, [chamomile flowers,] ½ oz., Glaub[er's] salts [3 oz, oil of limon 2 dr[achms], which produced gentle discharges and checked intirly the vomitting, administering at the same time, spt. laven comp^d [compound spirits of lavender] 1 dr[achm] with loaf sugar every 2 hours. On the 5th he complained of pain near (the bottom of) the stomach. The pulse being small & suppressed and weak, I applied the epispastic at the part & a [illegible] which remained til the 6th without any success and [he] died at 9 o'clock AM.

Case of James Denis, Seaman

On the 2d of Sept. James Denis, aged 24, complained of a headache, pains in [his] joints, loins, and back, considerable fever, the pulse tight & small, the skin dry. I administered the antim^o[nial] wine by small doses as [a] diaphoretic. The perspiration having taken place but the pains still existing, I took from his [arm] about 12 oz of blood & contin^d the anti^m wine as before until towards night 3 different times a large quantity [of] green bile. On the 4th, being much easier [and] the pains having partly subsided, there remained a light operation & couch [??] with a difficulty of urine, ½ oz elixr pareg^o[ric] & 20 drops of [spirits of dulcified niter mixed] as [a] pectoral [i.e., a chest remedy] & [a diuretic] was given every 3 hours, 8 gr[ains] crem[or] tart[ar], 1 gr[ain] calomel, & ½ gr[ain] of opium . . . was administered as above every 2 hours, & continued the 5th & 6th. The pains having subsided, the urine passing freely, & the pulse easy & no fever in the

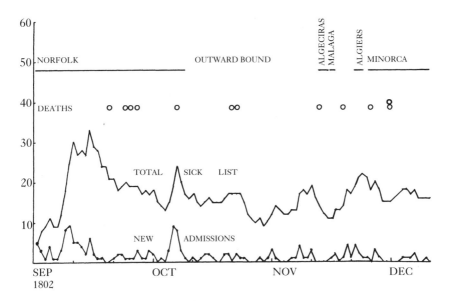

FIGURE 3. Total number of patients Dr. St. Medard treated each day, the new admissions to his sick list, and deaths among the crew of *New-York*, indicated by the circles, from 2 September to 10 December 1802.

night, 20 drops of tinct[ure] Thebaic was prescribed. Rested easy; on the 7th the perspiration being again intersepted, the anti^m wine was again ordered as [a] diaphoret[ic] which, after a few small doses restored in the cours[e] of the day the perspiration. The 8th given a light cathartic, the 9th bark & wine, & the 10th discharged well.

During the 37 days between the time Dr. St. Medard reported for duty and *New-York*'s departure for the Mediterranean, he admitted up to nine men a day to the ship's sick list. On 14 September he had as many as 33 patients under his care. A few had intermittent fever— malaria—but most of the sick suffered from diarrhea and dysentery, and a few from bilious fever. Altogether, four men died while the ship was still being fitted out.

The surgeon did have help in caring for his patients, although we lack documented details of the specific chores performed by his assistants. Few clues to Dr. Weems's work appear in St. Medard's records; all entries in his *Transactions* are in the surgeon's hand. However, the Surgeon's Mate undoubtedly assisted with the treatments prescribed by his superior, by bleeding febrile patients and preparing blisters and drugs for others, and by administering enemas, among other tasks. He also attended patients who were temporarily quartered on shore or in other ships. A 25-year-old seaman, Jesse Denning, provided other assistance, such as cleaning and fumigating the sick bay, and emptying its chamber pots. In addition, one or more loblolly boys performed chores such as bringing food from the galley for sick patients. (Unlike many warships, *New-York*'s sick bay may not have had its own galley.)

William Lewis may have been impressed by his commanding officer when he reported to *New-York*, but he was disgusted with the quarters assigned him and his fellow apprentice officers. He wrote home that "The apartment belonging to us is very confined & hot, very low, for I was obliged to stoop in it, and altogether quite disagreeable." Still, he had been at sea during the Quasi-War with France, memories of which may have encouraged him to think more positively: "I expected it will go pretty hard with me at first, but I think I shall soon get used to it, and like the life extremely well."

Perhaps because Lewis had read medicine for a while after graduating from the College of William and Mary, and perhaps because he had had some earlier service in the navy, Captain Barron's first assignment for him was the care of about 30 men on a schooner used as hospital quarters for Dr. St. Medard's bedridden patients. The makeshift facility, anchored about 200 yards from *New-York*, was probably necessitated by the difficulties inherent when sick men were on a ship being buffetted by carpenters, armorers, sailmakers, riggers, coopers, and all the other workers necessary to make *New-York* seaworthy again. Moreover, as Lewis reported on 16 September, "We have not yet finished recruiting men, and moreover, the ship is almost entirely dismantled of her rigging, all of which, will keep us here ten days longer at least. Some of the Officers think three weeks." Their estimate was correct.

Lewis might have disagreed with Dr. St. Medard about the origins of the bilious fever then plaguing their ship. The doctor attributed it to drinking foul river water, but both the former medical student and Captain Barron were more fearful of simple contagion brought on board by the new recruits who joined the ship at Norfolk, then in the midst of a mild epidemic of the same fever. While shopping for supplies for the hospital schooner, Lewis "took every precaution which was necessary, and kept as much out of the streets where it rages as possible. We have very little communication with the place, and nothing but my being totally unprovided with necesaries, caused the Captain to permit me to go."

The number of sick declined during the second half of September, but a new outbreak of dysentery caused it to peak again, at 24, on 6 October, two days before *New-York* sailed for European waters. Although several men had to be given medical discharges, or were left behind on the hospital schooner, Captain Barron had a full complement when his ship weighed anchor on 8 October.

Sailing east beween the 36th and 40th parallels, she reached the Azores in 20 days. The number of sick was falling again, and seldom did St. Medard have to admit more that two men a day to his sick list, many of them with the same illnesses that had plagued the crew back in Chesapeake Bay. Upon leaving the Azores he reported to his commanding officer:

Having made it a practice every since I have [had] the honor of belonging to the Navy to lay at times before my Commander the different diseases that occur from time to time, & . . . my oppinion of their causes, I therefore think it proper while under your command to continue that line of duty, and now have the honor to insert for your perusal (which I hope will be satisfactory) an abstract list of them taken from my books of those diseases. Which have not ceased to infect the ship's company from the 1st of Sept to this date, and such as have assumed a most malignant & obstinate a charactere, leaving off those of a most mild one, I shall likewise observe that a number of them have been aggravated at the same time with a complication of diseases—viz.

Dysentery & Diarrhea	53	occasioned by an immoderate drinking of the river water [illegible]
Catarrhal fevers, Influenza & Rheumatism	29	[occasioned] by laying exposed to the evening air on a baire deck uncovered
Intermit. fevers or ague	28	[occasioned] by the same causes, & that of the river water
Bil[ious] malignant fevers	17	produced by the season & peculiar to the climat
	127	

NB. A number of other cases which were too simple as to be noticed on my books & which were easely removed by single applications.

It is unfortunate that St. Medard did not think it necessary to record the "simple" cases he treated. They probably did not contribute substantially to the ship's burden of illness, but they were equally probably a good sample of the unsung majority of patients—and their treatments—that were more typical of contemporary medical practice than the serious illnesses of Shubel Cross, Oratio Cooper, and James Denis.

The surgeon's sick list doubled over the next week or so, as *New-York* sailed through a prolonged storm recorded by Midshipman William Lewis:

One or two days after leaving [the Azores], we met with a severe gales of wind which lasted nearly eight days. My troubles just then commenced. I can't describe to you the terrible appearance of the sea. The tremendous waves, the furious wind and rain, lightning & thunder, altogether formed a scene horrid enough to frighten the oldest sailor, much more such a *young hand* as I was. Happily, I did not experience any sea sickness as I had been seasoned a few days after leaving the Capes of Virginia.

We housed the guns the first evening and the Capt., who is one of the most experienced and able seamen in the service, endeavoured as much as possible to put the ship in a state for riding out the gale; but notwithstanding all his precautions & skill, we expected to roll away our masts, and were prepared to clear the wreck in case of such an event. We made the Spanish coast on Friday the 12th inst. & sounded in 42 fathoms water. . . . The next morning we anchored in this Bay [i.e., Algeciras Roads, just south of the Gibraltar promontory], where I now have the pleasure of beholding that famous fortress. . . . It is impossible for me to give you an accurate idea of it, being high and irregular, covered with fortifications and signal towers. . . . I have not been able to gratify my curiosity in going over the rock, as none of us was permitted to leave the Ship.

The reason no one could go on shore even after the 38-day crossing was that, because the Supreme Board of Health at Madrid had heard that yellow fever was then raging in Philadelphia, all American ships had to be quarantined until the Spanish consul at Philadelphia could inform his superiors at home that the epidemic had ceased. Still, *New-York*'s water casks had to be filled, and Captain Barron needed to repair the damage done by the recent storm, so he took her on to Málaga, about 60 miles

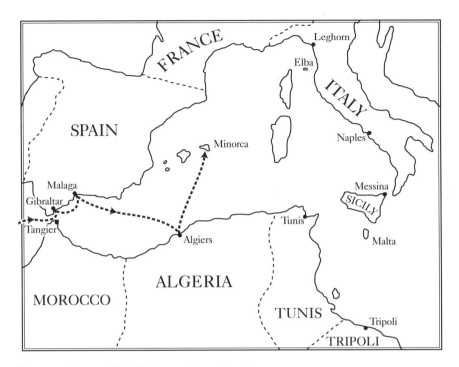

MAP I. Route of *New-York* to 10 December 1802.

northeast of Gibraltar, on 11 November. Even though his crew could not go ashore, the Spanish authorities objected to having the American ship there, so Barron took her another 500 miles to the east, to Algiers, where she arrived on the 21st, after 3,800 miles at sea. While there Barron delivered instructions from Secretary of State James Madison, and the $30,000 payment for the Dey, to the American consul, Richard O'Brien. After sailing north for three more days, *New-York* arrived at British-held Port Mahon on Minorca, the easternmost of the Balearic Islands and the key to the approaches to central Mediterranean shipping lanes.

Its fortified harbor, long and narrow, provided ample protection from both the weather and hostile ships. George Cleghorn, a British regimental surgeon stationed there in the late 1740s, had praised Minorcan air as clearer than that at home, although he added that it was more humid, which probably explains his observation that intermittent fevers were the most prevalent illnesses on the island. His *Observations on the Epidemical Diseases in Minorca* was still being cited by naval surgeons more than 50 years after it was published in 1751. Cleghorn was somewhat astonished that "Although the Natives make three or four plentiful Meals a Day, they are generally costive [constipated]; and many in perfect Health, have no Occasion to ease themselves oftener than twice a week." Today we, in turn, can only be astonished that stool habits—and cathartics—were as prominent as they were in the eighteenth-century mind.

When British naval surgeon John Brigges visited Port Mahon in 1801, he attributed shipboard dysentery, the "first and most inveterate of diseases" he observed in that place, to the poor quality of the water taken aboard British ships there, although Mahon was well known for its supply of good fresh water. He sent his captain a vivid description of the worst cases of the illness he had treated:

> In inflammatory dysentery, the usual symptoms of excruciating pains coming on about the *regio umbilicalis*; frequent inclinations to stool; sometimes vomiting; . . . tension of the abdomen; thirst; a fulness and frequency of the pulse in proportion to the disease; and last of all, a discharge of blood, &c. by stool.

Brigges went on to include ulcerations of otherwise insignificant skin wounds and lesions among the other hazards of duty on the Mediterranean station, as well as the "*ardent and bilious fevers*" he thought were common to all warm climates, and, especially, chronic lung disease. A few years later an American naval surgeon, Usher Parsons, agreed with Brigges about the prevalence of pulmonary afflictions, especially on Minorca, adding that "Catarrhal affections and rheumatisms are frequent in every port in the Mediterranean." However, unlike Brigges, Parsons thought that the shore of North Africa from the Straits of Gibraltar to Tripoli was healthy, perhaps because that region lacked the marshes that usually harbored the mosquitoes that transmit intermittent and bilious fevers.

Barron's first task, after filling his water casks, was to make repairs to his ship. When the First Lieutenant, Sailing Master, and Carpenter again surveyed *New-York*, they reported that the decks were leaky and needed recaulking with oakum, and that the badly sprung foremast required reinforcement. Because the repairs would take about a month to complete, Dr. St. Medard was able to send 15 of his sickest patients to the lazaretto, or contagious disease hospital, at Mahon.

Earlier, on 5 April 1802, Secretary Smith had told Commodore Morris that the lazarettos at most Mediterranean ports, "are, I believe, very justly considered as the graves of all foreigners who are so unfortunate as to be obliged to enter them." Smith went on to urge Morris to establish a U.S. naval hospital somewhere in the Mediterranean, preferably at Syracuse, in Sicily, which was not only a relatively healthy place but also near Tripoli, the navy's probable principal theater of operations in the near future. A few months later Smith directed Captain Edward Preble, on *Constitution*, to establish a hospital on Malta, because "Care must be taken of our seamen & great advantages will result from their being made sensible that we regard them as an useful class of citizens and in all respects deserving of our care and attention." Preble would later look into the feasibility of Smith's proposal, but Morris seems never to have given the Secretary's request to him a second thought. St. Medard continued to use local hospitals ashore throughout *New-York*'s stay in the Mediterranean. Presumably the costs of caring for American sailors sent to such institutions were reimbursed from the captain's cash account or through the local consul. Three Americans died at the Mahon lazaretto (one with bilious fever, the others with dysentery), nine were returned to duty, one deserted the navy from the lazaretto, and another attempted to do so; the remainder returned to their ship just before it left Mahon, still sick.

John Holand (or Holland), one of the men sent to the lazaretto, had recently been flogged. Only two other men on *New-York* are known to have been sentenced to corporal punishment on the entire voyage; on 24 January 1803, while the ship was at Malta, one was saved from more than 25 lashes by Dr. St. Medard's certification that he was too debilitated, from the usual mercurial treatment for syphilis, to withstand any punishment, while another was too sick with diarrhea to withstand more than ten to twelve lashes. Such a minimal record of summary punishment was rare among early U.S. Navy ships, especially among those commanded by James Barron. Moreover, these are the first known instances of punishments restrained by an American naval surgeon.

Although it is not known how Dr. Starling Archer became attached to the ship on 3 December, while at Mahon—presumably it was as another Surgeon's Mate—he was soon detailed to the care of the men St. Medard had sent to the lazaretto. One day Archer left the hospital without permission, causing Barron and St. Medard to require that he return to the ship to explain his disappearance.

Finally, the ship's mast and decks were repaired, the patients in the lazaretto had returned to the ship, and on Christmas Day she sailed for Malta.

NOTES

Almost all the events chronicled in this and the next four chapters can easily be followed in dated entries in PSM's manuscript *Physical and Chirurgical Transactions* and in his manuscript *Copybook*, both of which are in the library of the U.S.S. *Constitution* Museum, Boston, and in Dudley W. Knox, ed., *Naval Documents Related to the United States Wars with the Barbary Powers*, 7 vols. (Washington, D.C.: Government Printing Office, 1939). PSM's manuscript private *Journal*, written during the cruise of *New-York*, is in the EBA collection. I have used W. M. P. Dunne's *Resource Data File* for *New-York* to guide my reconstruction of the chronology of the ship's story from such diverse primary and secondary sources. The precise dates on which many events occurred are sometimes difficult to pinpoint inasmuch as even eyewitnesses appear to differ by a day or two. Fortunately, such discrepancies make no difference to our story, and for the sake of consistency with my primary sources, PSM's own manuscripts, I have arbitrarily chosen to follow the dates he gives.

The clearest account of the complicated diplomatic maneuverings in North Africa is given in McKee's *Edward Preble*, pp. 86 ff. The following have their merits as stories, and even as reasonably accurate histories, but lack scholarly bibliographic citations: J. Fenimore Cooper, *The History of the Navy of the United States of America*, 2 vols. (London: Richard Bentley, 1839) (Cooper's opinion of Morris's squadron is on p. 425); Gardner W. Allen, *Our Navy and the Barbary Corsairs* (Boston: Houghton, Mifflin, 1905); Glenn Tucker, *Dawn Like Thunder: The Barbary Wars and the Birth of the U.S. Navy* (Indianapolis, Ind.: Bobbs-Merrill, 1963); and A. B. C. Whipple, *To the Shores of Tripoli: The Birth of the U.S. Navy and Marines* (New York: William Morrow, 1991). Naval pay scales and other valuable details may be found throughout Christopher McKee, *A Gentlemanly and Honorable Profession: The Creation of the U.S. Naval Officer Corps, 1794–1815* (Annapolis, Md.: Naval Institute Press, 1991); for the adequacy of officers' pay, see pp. 333–337.

Substantial portions of the letters of Midshipman William Lewis were published in Mary Lewis Cooke and Charles Lee Lewis, "An American naval officer in the Mediterranean, 1802–7," *U.S. Naval Institute Proceedings 67* (1941): 1533-1539. I have reconciled them with, and quoted additional portions from, the originals, now in the Earl Gregg Swem Library, College of William and Mary, where they may be found as follows (this includes letters cited in later chapters as well): 29 August 1803 (Conway Whittle Papers, Box III, folder 4); and 16 September 1802, 14 November 1802, 10 January 1803, 31 March 1803 (two items), 10 May 1803, and 13 October 1803 (all in folder 5).

For the diseases prevalent around the Mediterranean littoral, see George Cleghorn, *Observations on the Epidemical Diseases in Minorca for the Years 1744 to 1749* (London: 1751), esp. p. 56; Thomas Trotter, *Medicina Nautica: An Essay on the Diseases of Seamen*, 3 vols. (London: T. Cadell, Jun. and W. Davies, 1797–1803), III:429–440 (the description of dysentery is on p. 431); and Usher Parsons, *Sailor's Physician* (Cambridge, Mass.: Hilliard and Metcalf, 1820), pp. 184–185.

Dr. St. Medard's patient log (properly, his *Transactions*) on *New-York* may well be a unique survivor from the American navy before the War of 1812; see Kenneth F. Bartlett, comp., *Preliminary Inventory of the Records of the Bureau of Medicine and Surgery* (Washington: National Archives, 1948), pp. 9–16. Moreover, only a few first-hand accounts of their work by naval surgeons have been published, although others may languish among unsearched attics and other repositories of family hand-me-downs. Cutbush's observation is in F. L. Pleadwell, "Edward Cutbush, M.D.: The nestor of the medical corps of the navy," *Annals of Medical History 5* (1923): 337–386; it is cited as from his diary, but I have been unable to ascertain its present location.

The published journals of American naval surgeons include, in addition to those cited in the Notes for Chapter Two: Victor Hugo Paltsits, "Cruise of the U. S. Brig *Argus* in 1813: Journal of Surgeon James Inderwick," *Bulletin of the New York Public Library 21* (1917): 383–403; and Usher Parsons, "Surgical account of the naval battle on Lake Erie, on the 10th of September 1813," *The New-England Journal of Medicine and Surgery 7* (1818): 313–316. Abstracts of several near-contemporary British surgeon's logs have been published. They include J. D. Alsop, "Sickness in the British Mediterranean fleet: The *Tiger*'s journal of 1706," *War & Society 11* (1993): 57–76. *The Diary of a Surgeon in the Year in the Year 1751–1752, by John Knyveton*, "edited" by Ernest Alfred Gray (New York: Appleton-Century, 1937, and London: R. Hale, 1942), is, in reality, "a work of imagination," according to the card catalogue of the Wellcome Institute for the History of Medicine in London.

Herman Melville's descriptions of a sick bay and of medical treatments at sea, as portrayed in *White-Jacket, or the World in a Man-of-War* (1850), are perhaps surprisingly accurate, if one segregates them from the dark humor personified by Fleet Surgeon Cadwallader Cuticle, M.D. and his colleagues on the fictional U.S.S. *Neversink*; the story is based on Melville's 1843–1844 voyage on the frigate *United States*, built at the same time as *Constitution*. Medicine had seen no important changes in diagnostic and therapeutic techniques over the 40 years after PSM left *New-York*.

We do not know the sources of PSM's medical knowledge after he joined the U.S. Navy. However, 33 works from the library of Dr. Amos Evans, whose journal covers the famous fight between H.B.M. *Java* and U.S.S. *Constitution* in 1812, are in the library of the U.S.S. *Constitution* Museum in Boston. They include his manuscript notes of medical lectures Evans attended in Boston and Philadelphia, as well as works that are regarded as typical of the best medical and surgical texts of his day, some of which may have been known to PSM.

One of the three New-Yorkers who died in the Port Mahon lazaretto was named Nathaniel Bumpus. I have wondered if James Fenimore Cooper, who was in the navy and certainly knew its history, might have used his name when creating Natty Bumppo as the hero of the *Leatherstocking Tales*. However, according to Kay S. House, editor of Cooper's papers, no documentary evidence that supports my suggestion has surfaced. She writes (14 July 1993) that "he became a midshipman in 1808 and that he read voraciously everything he could find that had anything to do with the history of the U.S. Navy," but no clear evidence indicates that he ever came across PSM's patient, even though "such a name would have stuck in JFC's subconscious." Still, I wonder.

Chapter Seven

Duels and Runny Noses

10 December 1802–20 March 1803

THREE DAYS LATER *New-York* arrived at Valetta, the well-fortified port of Malta that many regarded as the best harbor in the Mediterranean; the rest of the squadron arrived over the next week. The short sail from Port Mahon had been uneventful for Dr. St. Medard, although he had been badly bruised in a fall; he thought it was serious enough to have himself relieved of several ounces of blood. The treatment was successful: he was back to work in a couple of days. Indeed, he would be kept busy during his entire stay at Malta.

Midshipman William Lewis thought it was

> the most wonderful place in the World. At this moment we have all the fruits of the tropical & temperate climates, the Harbour as good as that of Mahon, the fortifications impregnable, and the curiosities innumerable. I have been over the church of St. John of Jerusalem, the floor of which is the most elegant & curious mosaic covering the ashes of those famous Knights of Malta who lived & died a few centuries ago, and filled with statues, paintings & tapestry, the production of the greatest masters of the arts.

Valetta's Grand Harbor is still one of the world's finest, even if it has now lost its military strategic value. Surrounded by imposing sixteenth-century fortifications erected to protect the essentially medieval town behind them, it was important in 1802 chiefly because it commanded the principal east-west sailing routes through the Mediterranean at its narrowest point. Not only were its honey-colored walls almost impregnable, as they were even to German attacks in the 1940s, but its harbor was also so well protected from the winds that the largest warships under sail could anchor there in the stormiest weather, "almost without a cable," according to an English visitor in 1790. Moreover, the island provided excellent ship-building and repair facilities, as it still does, as well as a large hospital.

Known officially as the Holy Trinity Infirmary, it was one of several hospitals on the island that had been established by the Order of St. John of Jerusalem, founded in the Holy Land during the eleventh century to nurse pilgrims who fell sick while visiting Jerusalem. The Hospitallers of St. John went on to establish similar hospices throughout Europe, and to assume a military role in order to protect both their institutions and their wealth. When the Ottoman Empire began to gain control of the eastern Mediterranean, the order moved eastward to Malta, where it settled in 1530. After the Holy Roman Emperor, Charles V, ceded the island to the order, for the price of a falcon each year (none of the prized hunting birds remain on the island), they became known as the Knights of Malta.

The Infirmary, begun in 1574, was their major hospital. Its importance to visiting ships is indicated by the underground passage that led directly from the port to the hospital. By the sixteenth century it was reknowned for its nursing care. For instance, it provided each patient his own bed, whereas from two to four patients had to share a single bed in other European hospitals. Additions over the centuries had expanded the Infirmary's bed capacity to 554 by 1789, and in an emergency it could accommodate as many as 900 patients. Although in 1786 an experienced British observer noted that it had become offensively dirty and understaffed, it still served as many as 4,000 patients a year, all men; their death rate, about eight percent, was about the same as that at one of the most enlightened hospitals in the West, the Royal Infirmary at Edinburgh, but much less than that at the Hôtel Dieu and other large urban hospitals in France.

After Napoleon captured Malta and expelled the Knights in June 1798, while on his way to Egypt, the garrison of 6,000 he left behind attempted to bring order to the chaotic conditions in the Infirmary, now dedicated chiefly to military use. But a revolt by the Maltese, aided by a British blockade, soon reduced its supplies of food and water just as outbreaks of disease were sending more and more patients to the hospital with scurvy, diarrhea, and dysentery. At least two-thirds of the French garrison had been hospitalized with fevers during their 27-month occupation of the island before a British army displaced the sick and demoralized French in September 1800. The Treaty of Amiens, signed nine months before *New-York* reached Malta, required that the island be restored to the Knights, but the British were there to stay, in part at least because they did not trust Napoleon not to go to war again—as he would do in May 1803.

The British garrisoned the island with 5,000 men and installed Rear Admiral Sir Alexander Ball as its Governor-General. They worked to restore the capabilities of the Infirmary, now called the General Hospital. However, because the British successfully reduced the sickness burden of the island, partly by restoring its food supply, the number of hospitalized patients rapidly fell, and much of the building was put to other uses. But, in the tradition of the medieval Hospitallers, the British provided medical services to the crews of ships from friendly nations, including the United States. Later, at the suggestion of Lord Nelson, the British built their own facility at Bighi, near Valletta.

* * *

When *New-York* reached Malta on 28 December, Dr. St. Medard sent nine patients to the General Hospital. Eight were enlisted men with severe cases of biliary colic, dysentery, slow and catarrhal fevers, phthisis (probably tuberculosis), and scurvy. Six returned to duty in 16 to 19 days, but one, Marine Corporal William Thompson, who suffered from both dysentery and phthisis, died after eight days in the hospital. Seaman Benjamin Gardner was still sick with diarrhea and scurvy when his ship left Malta, and did not return to duty until she came back on 2 May.

The ninth case Dr. St. Medard sent to the General Hospital became his most notorious patient of the entire cruise. On 13 January 1802, Third Lieutenant Henry Vandyke of *New-York* got into an argument which resulted in a duel with the ship's Marine Lieutenant, William S. Osborne. Osborne was not wounded, but the 24-year-old Vandyke

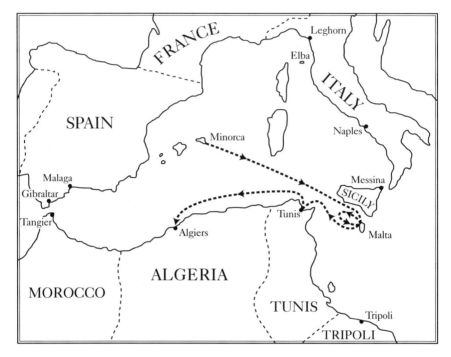

MAP 2.   Route of *New-York* from 10 December 1802 to 20 March 1803.

received a serious wound. St. Medard reported it to Commodore Morris, then on *Chesapeake*, the squadron's flagship:

> Sir / in obedience to your order in the case of Mr. Henry Vandyke, 3th Lieut. of this ship, I have the honor to inform you that after a close examination of the wound which took place yesterday evening, I find that a pistol ball has passed through by the exterieur part of his wright thigh and about 4 inches from the great[er] trochanter [a bony prominence on the upper end of the femur] close and on the anterieur part of the femur, has directed its course through the perinæum [the lowest part of the abdomen, containing the bladder and anus] and left thigh, where it has been extracted skin deep on the exterieur part, having not injured any of the bones, nor in my opinion any material part through which it has directed its course; by its great extent altho not imediatly mortal yet it may be dangerious.

Morris, as the ranking American officer at Malta, might have expected to have to cope with any legal charges brought by the governor.

However, none were, presumably because Governor Ball realized that the affair concerned only Americans. The Maltese themselves probably would not have prosecuted them: a British visitor had noted, in 1790, that Malta was probably the only place in the world where duelling was permitted by law. Indeed, one Knight had recently been jailed for life because he had refused to fight a duel over a disputed billiards game.

Vandyke was sent to the General Hospital almost immediately. St. Medard ordered that he be bled of 20 ounces on each of the first two days. Other than mild cathartics to keep his bowels moving, and daily changes of wound dressings, the lieutenant was given no other medicines. He seems not to have developed the characteristic signs of febrile complications from his wound. However, despite St. Medard's initial optimism, he sought aditional opinions from physicians on other American ships, including Dr. Triplett of *Chesapeake*, and a Dr. Reynolds, who may have been an English naval surgeon.

Captain Barron was disgusted by the duel and its cause, one that seems to have been endemic in Malta. On 28 January he wrote to his brother, Commodore Samuel Barron:

> . . . I cant omit one pease of disagreeable information namely the situation of Mr Vandike who is now laying momently expecting death to his relief from a most horrid wound which he received in a duel from Mr. Osborn, Lieut of Marines. Two days will end his voyage through this life, all for the preferance in a simple game of billiards.

According to his doctor's notes, Vandyke was "livelier" the next day as his symptoms continued to improve, so it surprised St. Medard when the lieutenant died, as Barron had predicted, on the 30th, seventeen days after being wounded. Eighteenth-century physical examinations were not nearly as detailed as they are today, but Vandyke probably succumbed to an infection that spread to the rest of his body after the bullet passed through his anus.

Duelling was not unknown in the early U.S. Navy, despite attempts to make it illegal. It was not prohibited by naval regulations, but naval duellists and seconds could expect to be reprimanded, and suspended from duty for a while; some might even be transferred or given prolonged furloughs, but their punishments were never unsupportable. (Indeed, the only punishments known to have been carried out while Morris's squadron was at Malta were inflicted on three enlisted men from *John Adams* who were whipped through the fleet, the most serious form of punishment short of execution, for desertion, insolence, and drunkeness.) Between 1794 and 1815, at least 18 American naval officers (7.3 percent of all whose causes of death are known), died from wounds incurred in duels, including Vandyke. All were junior officers displaying a deadly form of post-adolescent bravado. Three years later, 27-year-old Dr. Starling Archer, who had come on board *New-York* a month before Vandyke's duel, would become the only American naval surgeon known to have died defending his honor.

Captain Barron had no respect for his new commander, Commodore Morris—or for the Commodore's wife. Secretary Smith had probably been unable to avoid awarding command of a squadron to Morris. Not only was he a member of the prominent New York family of financiers of the Revolution, his brother was the representative from Vermont whose change of vote after 36 ballots had broken the tie that permitted Jefferson to win the presidency from Aaron Burr. Moreover, Morris had achieved an enviable reputation for prize captures during the Quasi-War with France, during which he had won a substantial, although not munificent, amount of prize money. Barron was further aggravated when he learned that he was to be reassigned to the frigate *Chesapeake*, which he regarded as a command inferior to that of *New-York*. On 28 January he confided to his brother:

> I am told we are bound for Tripoli but what to do cant say perhaps to make peace. I wish so sinceorly for in the way the war is carried on disgrace must fall on our flag[.] . . . The Navy is more & more disagreeable. How little consideration have the officers of government for our feelings. Just as I have worked through innumerable troubles and made the New York an object worthy of admiration I am ordered to give her up and take the command of a much neglected & horridly disciplined ship for my pains; I have heard that you were to command the next squadron. If so, my dear brother, let me intreat you to come provided in such a way as not to be ashamed or [afraid] to return the hospitallity you may receive in this or any other port. I have now dined at all the houses of rank & respectability in this place accompanied by our [Commodore] and now we are to sneek . . . of[f] without one return [invitation]. O how detestable is a mean man and how improper to have a woman Comod^{re}. I have said to[o] much, yet I will leave you to guess the remainder for more there is from the bad state

of the Chesapeake she is not to leave this [place] untill the spring, say some time in March.

At the same time, William Lewis was becoming disillusioned by the behavior of his superiors while his ship languished at Malta:

the etiquette which exists on board ships of war . . . prohibits any social intercourse between officers while on duty, and thus has a tendency to deaden it while in their private [berths] and apartments. You can't imagine how different the relations are, which exist between men as officers, and as private individuals. Superior Officers, subject to no control wile on board a ship, & accustomed to command inferior ones, can't help putting on airs of authority, while on shore, as Gentlemen enjoying the same amusements. . . . there is a change taking place on board this ship, which I lament very much. The Com^{re} is coming here [i.e., on board *New-York*], and Capt. Barron & some other of the Officers are to return in the Chesapeake. Capt. B. has been particularly attentive and kind to me, and I have tried (probably with some success) to make a friend in him, who may serve me hereafter. I regret beyond measure that it is not in my power to continue under his command.

Lewis and other midshipmen were as reluctant to give up Barron's tutelage as he was to leave the ship he had worked to convert into an effective war machine. He did not blame Morris, of course, for the change of command, but he, like Barron, was disgusted by Mrs. Morris's influence over her husband. As required by naval regulations, the Commodore had sought and received Secretary Smith's permission to bring his wife and young son, Gerard, as well as the boy's nurse, to the Mediterranean, but already he was rumored to have thought that Mrs. Morris's desire to be seen in polite society and to participate in its entertainments should override the strategic demands that were expected of his squadron. Indeed, the naval rumor mill had already credited the "Commodoress" with detaining Morris at Gibraltar for most of the summer.

Barron knew that the squadron was under orders to blockade Tripoli, in order to force the Pacha to come to terms, and that both Tunis and Algeria were threatening to declare war on the United States. Because Morris appeared to be making no preparations to attack Qaramanli's capital, Barron concluded that Mrs. Morris wished to continue enjoying the social life that Barron was embarrassed to be unable to repay as protocol demanded. *Chesapeake*, which was still Morris's flagship, *New-York*, and *John Adams* finally sailed for Tunis on 31 January, en route for Tripoli, but they failed to reach their destination.

James Leander Cathcart, the American consul at Tripoli, had been on board *Chesapeake* since she left Leghorn for Malta in December. He blamed eleven days of "very boisterous" weather for the squadron's failure. Midshipman Henry Wadsworth, also in *Chesapeake*, described the circumstances more dramatically:

> [since we left Malta] it has been a continual gale: The deck directly over my cot leaks very much, of course my bed & bedding are much wet as the element water is continually in boisterous weather washing over the gun deck: ... we expect much stormy & tempestuous weather during our cruize off Tripoli, wither we are bound—& ye Tripolitans beware, for the *Chesapeake, New York* & *John Adams* are coming towards ye in battle array.

On 3 February, Peter St. Medard and William Lewis finally saw the Barbary Coast they had come to confront, but only from about 30 miles off shore. The little squadron had to return to Malta, where all three frigates had anchored by the 11th. And where two more officers on *New-York* were involved in yet another fatal duel three days later.

This one had international implications. Midshipman Joseph Bainbridge, younger brother of Captain William Bainbridge, seconded by Lieutenant Stephen Decatur, Jr., was challenged by James Cochran, said to be an experienced duellist, during an exchange of insults between British and American officers at the local opera house in which Bainbridge had knocked Cochran down. As Bainbridge's second, Decatur chose pistols at four yards rather than the usual ten. The Englishman was not satisfied after the first shot, so they fired again, and he died instantly of a head wound.

Because Cochran was a civil servant, it is not surprising that the British governor demanded that Bainbridge be tried for murder, because killing an opponent in a duel was defined as murder under British law; the occupying forces did not recognize Maltese law. However, this may have been a *pro forma* demand; nothing came of it. The duel had been a fair one, according to contemporary standards. Henry Wadsworth wrote,

"With pleasure I observe that Mr. Bainbridge was clearly in the right & behav'd honorably throughout the affair." Nevertheless, two months later Morris maneuvered Bainbridge and Decatur out of the governor's reach by sending them home with Captain Barron on *Chesapeake*.

The officers—at least some of the midshipmen—broadened their education by sightseeing around Malta during the week they were forced to spend there while the weather cleared. Lewis visited the major church several times, as well as a cave where St. Paul was said to have taken shelter when he was shipwrecked.

After a week at Malta the squadron set sail once again. While en route to Tunis Captain Barron forwarded to Dr. St. Medard a memorandum outlining Commodore Morris's expectations of a naval surgeon's duties to his squadron. Most were already standard procedures, but some may have been suggested by current British practices, especially the concept of a Fleet Physician (who outranked the Fleet Surgeon) implicit in these orders:

It has been the usage of most navies to make the Surgeon of a temporary or provisional hospital do and perform the duties of a fleet physician, when the general health does not require his services on shore. This, as well to prevent any officers remaining inactive, as to apprize the Commander in Chief of the health of each ship, in order that there may be no delay in procuring sick quarters [on shore], should their number render such a measure expedient, as also, to investigate the causes of epidemics in the fleet, or squadron, so that it may be known if the internal regulations, as it respects *diet, cleanliness,* &c: in the influence of *climate, prevailing winds* &c, or the particular practice of the Surgeon on board, has had any influence, in producing or increasing the same, so that the Commander in Chief may take the speediest measures, not only to check, but prevent the occurrence of a similar evil. His duties may be thus defined—

1st. He is to be considered as the General Consulting Physician, and Surgeon, as well by the request of a particular Surgeon as by the order of the Commodore.

2d. He is to attend all surgical operations, if the situation of the squadron will admit of it.

3d. He is to attend all medical surveys, whether [of] medicine[s], hospital stores, &c:

4th. He is to examine the general watering places of the different ships in order to analyse, and detect any noxious qualities, as also to point out the means of correcting it.

5th. He is to receive the monthly reports of the different Surgeons (in the annexed form) or weekly if the state of the squadron should require it, from all of which he is to form a general report with such remarks as may to him appear proper.

After three days Morris's squadron at last reached Tunis Bay, where the Americans' anchorage, to the delight of Dr. St. Medard and Midshipman Lewis, overlooked the site of ancient Carthage, 18 miles from the town. Lewis was frustrated at not being allowed ashore during the 18 days they spent there. In a letter home he lamented, "I saw at a distance Cape Carthage and the plain on which that famous city once stood. I could'nt help reflecting on the instability and change to which all human institutions & Governments are liable." In another letter he observed that "what was once the seat of Valour, Arts, and Commerce [is now] mere desert, without even a ruin by which to know

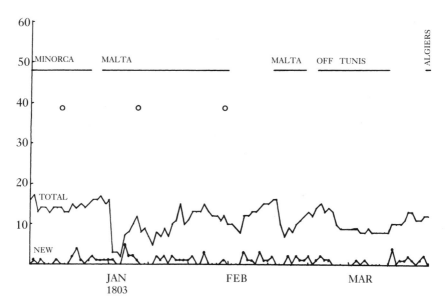

FIGURE 4. Total sick list, new admissions, and deaths (circles) on *New-York* from 10 December to 20 March 1803.

its place. . . . If my sensations are delightful at knowing that I tread upon classick ground, how infinitely more exquisite would they be, if I was intimately accquainted with Antient History."

While at Malta during the week of enforced inactivity, *New-York*'s sick list fell from a high of sixteen patients to a low of seven, but it had increased to fifteen by the time they reached Tunis, where it hovered at nine or ten until it began to rise again when they departed. St. Medard's records show that he was averaging ten to fifteen patients with catarrh—manifested chiefly as runny noses and coughing, indicating a surfeit of phlegm—throughout the winter months, and two to five with diarrhea. Thus, he had fewer patients then than in any other comparable period of the entire cruise—for the most part it was routine work, save for Lieutenant Vandyke's fatal duelling wound. Perhaps prodded by the Commodore's memorandum, or as a way of employing his time while his ship was at rest, at the end of February Dr. St. Medard reported to Morris on his "Method of Treatment":

> The catarhs having been the prevailing complaint on this station [i.e., in the Mediterranean] I shall on this case occupy your attention, and particularly on those of a phlogistic [i.e., febrile] character. In this case I find that blood letting more or less according to the nature and height of the symptoms, diaphoretic mixtures, with [spirits of dulcified nitre] & antimonial wine would in the course of twenty four hours correct the diathesis. After having produced an ease in the system and an indication of a necessity of expediting the excretion of the bile & mucus of the stomach and lungs, I would then administer two grains of [tartar emetic] & about two dragms of antimonial wine . . . sufficient to procure three or four vomitting[s] & one or two downward discharges [i.e., stools]. This together with some mild diluent drinks, a little warmed & sweeten[ed] such as chammomil, balm [i.e., mint], or barly tea would easily promote a gentle perspiration. The patient after this treatment being generally relieved from that phlogistic state would give an opportunity of passing a cathartic commonly of calamel & jalap; I have therefore observed this treatment to be the best adapted in this disease, as in a few days the patient would recover his health and be put to duty.

Rheumatic complaints have been likewise very trublsom to some & very often complicated the catarrh, therefore in this case I shall include them with that disease, except when by themselves, the [tincture of gum] Guayacum internally administered, the embrocations with linim[en]t soap, the flesh brushes, frictions, & when tenatious the applications of blisters would generally after [a] while remove them.

The diarrheas on this station have been of more mild a nature and have often subsided to a vomit, or mild cathartics, if obstinate a few doses of calamel from thirty to fourty grains would make a cure.

The intermitting [fevers] being still less in number have subsided in less than 6 or 8 days after evacuants, & strong doses of bark administered at the first of the paroxism.

It was probably unusual for a naval surgeon to report to his commanding officer on his methods of treatment. Commanders had a legitimate professional interest in the disease burden on ships under their command, because that could affect the manpower available for sailing their ships and for fighting; it is difficult to guess why a commander might wish to know how his surgeons were treating their patients, just as it is difficult to guess what a commander would do with such information. Perhaps Dr. St. Medard was simply being complete.

A few days later, on 1 March, he prepared his regular quarterly report for Captain Barron while *New-York* was riding at anchor off Tunis. It provided the kind of information that commanders were able to use when making their professional decisions:

Since my last communication dated 1st November last on the same subject, . . . the diseases which at that time infected with malignancy our ship's company have since early in December fortunately subsided, and removed that terror of contagion which we had reason to dread;—therefore I have the pleasure of inserting for your satisfaction a statement of those diseases which have prevailed from 1st of December last to this day, vizt.

Month	Dysent & Diarrh	Intermit	Catarrhs & Rheut
in Decbr	2	2	18
in Jan^{ry}	5	3	19
in feb^y	2	1	22
Total	9	6	59

While the doctor was writing reports and attending to his patients, Commodore Morris, Consul Cathcart, and William Eaton, the American consul at Tunis, began negotiating a peace with the Bey of that country. St. Medard recorded the diplomatic events of the next few days in his journal:

> [24 Feb 1803] Mr. Eaton our Consul came off on board of the Commodore [i.e., he boarded *Chesapeake*] and told him that the Bey was making extravagant demand to our government, such as a frigate, 32 guns, 2000 stand of arms & the restoration of damages of a vessell which the Enterprize had taken a month before & which was detained at Malta for adjudication. All those demands were accompanied with [the] threat that if our government or the Commodore should not agree to them he would put the Consule in slavery or perhaps put him to death; the Commodore after being informed of his demand negotiated with him through the said Consul & Mr Cathcart, Consul [at] Tripoly. At last the Bey said he would relinquish his demands [for] all but what property that was in that prize & belonging to the Tunisians, & invited the Commodore to see him.

Eaton had already told Morris that it was crucial for him to visit the Bey, who regarded it as a major affront that no American of such high rank had ever come to his court. When it was discovered that a Tunisian merchant had a legitimate stake in the vessel captured by *Enterprise*, arrangements were made to have it honored. But the Bey held out for other payments and indemnification, as well as other conditions to which the Americans would not agree, whereupon the Bey kept the Commodore from leaving his shores, as surety for honoring the debts incurred by Eaton during his service as consul. The Bey was finally persuaded to accept Captain John Rodgers of *John Adams* as a hostage, in place of Morris. Several more days were spent in the contest of wills between the Bey, the Commodore, and the Consul. St. Medard could finally note, on 8 March, that the Americans had paid the Bey $34,000, and that Morris had removed Eaton from his consulate "on account of his conduct," appointing Dr. George Davis in his place. The Bey released Captain Rodgers the next day. The main body of the squadron sailed for Algiers on 11 March, while *Enterprise* was charged to take Eaton to Leghorn.

Along the way St. Medard was glad when *New-York* hailed a four-masted merchantman en route from London to Constantinople, because it brought the latest newspapers. As they neared Algiers a French frigate was exchanging salutes with the Algerians. The American consul there, Richard O'Brien, came on board to discuss the latest diplomatic exchanges with the Commodore, and, about 24 hours after their arrival, the squadron sailed for Gibraltar.

NOTES

See those for the previous chapter. For more on young officers' proclivity for duelling, see McKee's *Gentlemanly and Honorable Profession*, pp. 403–406. The extracts from Commodore Barron's letter of 28 January 1803 are taken from the original, in the James Barron Papers, Box 1, folder 21, in the Earl Gregg Swem Library of the College of William and Mary, although I have used Christopher McKee's careful transcription of it. The sources of the letters of William Lewis are cited in the Notes for Chapter 6.

Information about Malta and the Infirmary is in Paul Cassar, *Medical History of Malta* (London: Wellcome Historical Medical Library, 1964), esp. Chapter 5; P[atrick] Brydon, *A Tour through Sicily and Malta*, 2 vols. (London: A. Strahan and T. Cadell, 1790), I, 338–363; J. Falconer Hall, "The Royal Naval Hospitals, Malta," *Journal of the Royal Naval Medical Service 13* (1927): 251–255; Edgar Erskine Hume, *Medical Work of the Knights Hospitallers of Saint John of Jerusalem* (Baltimore: Johns Hopkins Press, 1940), pp. 93–96, 101–109, 191–207; and Prosper Jardin, *Les Chevaliers de Malta: une Perpétuelle Croisade* (Paris: Librairie Académique Perrin, 1974), pp. 193–194.

Chapter Eight

Alarums and Excursions

20 March–30 June 1803

AFTER THE 400-MILE passage from Algiers to Gibraltar, Midshipman William Lewis was astonished at the amount of American shipping he saw entering the Mediterranean there:

> While we have been here, I have seen swarms of American vessels arrive with the produce of [our] country for the Mediterranean markets. Every Western Breeze brings in an American Merchantman. You would be astonished to see the number and size of the Yankee schooners that trade to this country. I wonder how they could have weathered the Storms which they must necessarily have passed thro' in getting here. It helps to establish the character of those men, that of being the most enterprizing, industrious set of mortals in the world. Our country is very much respected for its riches and prosperity, and if we had a Navy [of sufficient strength] to protect & support our commerce, we should be thought a great people.

That is, Lewis well understood why he and his squadron had been sent to confront the pirates who ruled the North African coast.

The American fleet assembled at Gibraltar on 22 March. James Barron must have had to control his temper the next day when Commodore Morris came on board *New-York*, preparatory to making it his flagship, while Barron had to begin preparing the sagging *Chesapeake* for the trip home. However, he may have taken some comfort in the letter of appreciation composed by Lewis and signed by all eleven midshipmen in *New-York*. The trainee officers were "well aware that we shall lose the benefits which were derived to us, both from your example and those lessons of instruction which you were so anxious to bestow upon us." When added to the apparent rarity of punishments for enlisted men on the frigate, this spontaneous encomium is one more piece of evidence that its crew may have been as content as, if not happier than, the crew of any warship then afloat.

Chesapeake sailed for home on 6 April, bearing the disgruntled Captain Barron and his clerk as well as Joseph Bainbridge and Stephen Decatur. Midshipman Alexander Contee Harrison was another passenger; Dr. St. Medard had recommended his discharge from the navy for "debility." Although he appears only briefly in the surgeon's daybook of patients, Harrison's discharge certificate states that he had been chronically ill since an attack of bilious fever seven months earlier: his bilious complaints "[together] with Rheumatism which arise[s] from heavy dews & unfavourable weather will often keep him from his duty."

That same day, Morris broke out his commodore's pennant and transferred several of *Chesapeake*'s former officers to *New-York*. Because Commodores did not ordinarily command their flagships, he brought along Lieutenant Isaac Chauncey as her Flag Captain, and David Porter replaced Decatur as First Lieutenant. James Jennison continued as the Captain's Secretary, John Shultz as the Commodore's Secretary, and 17-year-old Henry Wadsworth took the Midshipman's berth vacated by Harrison. Well aware that Morris retained him among his entourage when he went on board *New-York* chiefly because Wadsworth's father was influential among the Federalists who had supported Morris for many years, thanks to the prominence of his family in Maine, the midshipman seems not to have resented his exploitation; indeed, family ties were often regarded as favorable talismans of success in the navy.

The Secretary of the Navy had permitted Morris to take his wife to the Mediterranean; although such permission was required, it was usually granted; petty and warrant officers could be given the same privilege by their squadron commanders. For instance, Boatswain John Newton Cannon's wife was in *New-York*, and accompanied him when he transferred to *Constitution* in October 1803. And, when a baby was born in the boatswain's storeroom to Mrs. James Low, wife of the captain of *Chesapeake*'s forecastle, on 22 February 1803, she was attended by the Gunner's wife, but not by the wives of the Boatswain, Carpenter, or Corporal of Marines, all of whom were also on board. The Lows named their son Melanchton Woolsey Low, in honor of a midshipman who would later be assigned to *New-York*. Because Woolsey was the baby's godfather, he provided "a handsome collection of wine & fruit" when the boy was baptized. Thus, it would appear that even pregnancy was no bar to women who sought to accompany their husbands; indeed, Mrs. Morris was pregnant when the Commodore left for his new assignment. During his months on *Chesapeake*, Wadsworth came to admire both the Commodore and the "Commodoress," of whom he later wrote to a lady friend at home: "All the Virtues which constitute the chief loveliness of your sex are in her conspicuous. Her knowledge of geo[graphy,] history &c are extensive & a passion for reading is predominant; her person is not beautiful, or even handsome, but she looks very well in a veil."

When Wadsworth first joined Morris on *Chesapeake*, he began to keep a journal of his adventures. Indeed, he had persuaded that ship's Carpenter to build him a writing desk because, as he wrote to his sister, "It is a fortunate circumstance that I am so fond of writing & when

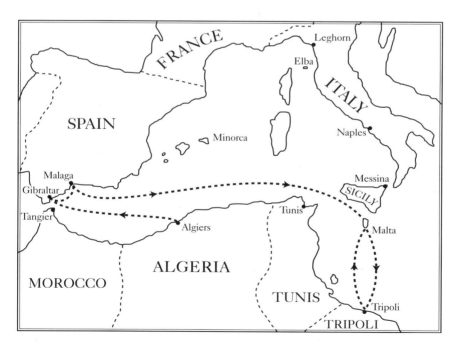

MAP 3.   Route of *New-York* from 20 March to 30 June 1803.

I get to sea I should write a good deal." His letters and journal after 6 April tell us much about life on board *New-York*.

After the American squadron—now consisting only of the frigates *New-York* and *John Adams* (commanded by Captain John Rodgers), and the schooner *Enterprise* (commanded by Lieutenant Isaac Hull)—had been resupplied at Gibraltar, it moved around to the northeast, to spend a day filling water casks at Málaga before sailing back to Malta en route to establishing a blockade at Tripoli. The weather was favorable at first, and once again *New-York* displayed her enviable sailing qualities by continuing to beat her companions whenever they raced. However, the squadron was often either becalmed or buffeted by adverse winds, and it took two weeks to reach Malta.

The second week at sea began with a sailor's nightmare. At 8:30 P.M. on 25 April the watch on *John Adams* saw smoke rising abaft *New-York*'s mainmast, and that she was signalling for immediate assistance. According to Wadsworth's account of the near disaster:

> It appears from the Gunner's account, that early in the morning as usual he had directed John Staines[,] Gunner's Mate, to return the signal lantherns to the store room & that he (the Gunner) going into the storeroom soon after to see every thing in its proper place, found that Staines had left a candle there which he extinguished and came back on deck to reprimand his mate for such carelessness: not yet satisfied that all was safe he returned to the store room to examine it & by removing some sheep skins he observed some sparks of fire which fell out of them into a bucket that contain'd some damaged powder prepar'd for smoking [i.e., disinfecting] the berth deck, from them it communicated to the powder horns hanging up in the store room & by the explosion of them & the damaged powder the bulk head of the Marine store room burst & it communicated to about 37 dozen blank cartridges therein.

Perhaps the most vivid recollection of the event was that of William Lewis. Not only was he literally on top of the explosion, but his own injuries also suggest the range of the surgical problems that faced Dr. St. Medard and his mates:

> I was standing on the grating of the cockpit hatchway [with fellow Midshipman Lewis Alexis], when about one hundred pounds of pow-

der blew up in the gunners store room just below me. I was thrown up with great violence against the beams, but I fortunately caught one of the gun deck stauncheons or else I should have fallen below where a miserable death awaited me. Ten of us were wretchedly burnt & wounded. The Gunner & three others died during the next day & night, but the rest have, or are now, recovering. I have lost all my hair, eye brows, & my face is blistered—but I can't describe the figure I cut. However there is nothing dangerous [to me]. . . This accident happened in consequence of the negligence of one of the gunner's mates in carrying a naked candle into the room, a thing expressly contrary to orders.

Wadsworth's journal picks up the story at the time the ship's company was first alerted by the explosion:

The consternation among the people was great, but soon ranks were form'd & those in the cockpit [all the wounded except the two midshipmen] supplied with water, wet blankets, swabs &c—& the fire was extinguished in one hour & an half: The boats were hoisted out on the first alarm, & the signal of distress made. Found very considerable damage done. The Gunner's stores almost entirely consum'd, Pursers slops [i.e., new clothing for the crew], Marine cloathing & hospital stores reciev'd considerable damage, amount not yet ascertain'd.—But the greatest misfortune is the injury done to those in the cockpit at the moment of the explosion: a number of whom are so shockingly burnt that their lives are despair'd of. . . . We [i.e., the entire ship] were in the utmost danger of blowing up as the door opening to the magazine passage was bursted. In the wardroom there is a scuttle for the purpose of passing up cartridges in time of action; this scuttle was lifted & another passage opened by the explosion, otherwise it is the opinion of all that we should have been lost, for the explosion would have burst the only remaining door into the filling room: here there are always a hundred or two of cartridges already filled: This explosion would momently have been followed by the magazine & then adieu.

When Flag (acting) Captain Chauncey ordered the drummer to beat to quarters, the disciplined crew immediately went into action. However, when the Commodore had the ship's boats hoisted, in what the crew took as the prelude to an order to abandon ship, some of the crew panicked and began to jump overboard.

Presumably Dr. St. Medard complied with the customary General Orders in Case of Fire by examining his stores as soon as the alarm had been raised. His own journal entry was briefer than those of the impressionable young midshipmen; perhaps he had little time for writing after treating those injured in the explosion. Of the nine men wounded seriously enough to require medical attention, four died. David Hamilton, a loblolly boy, and Richard Merrill, the 24-year-old Gunner who had discovered his Mate's error, died within 24 hours. John Shultz, the Commodore's Secretary, died three days after the explosion, while James Jennison, the Captain's Secretary, died at the Malta hospital another nine days later. Midshipman Lewis returned to duty after seven days. Patrick Kennedy, the Purser's Steward, Midshipman Lewis Alexis, and Marine Private William McGee were also hospitalized at Malta, and all three eventually returned to duty.

Surgeon's Mate Nathaniel Weems was hospitalized as well. In his pension application twelve years later he described the wounds he had suffered in the explosion: "I was affected with an umbilical hœrnia (or rupture of the navel) by which my general health became impar'd and has now render'd me incapable of providing for my family. I also lost a part of one of my ears and had my right arm contracted so that I can now make but little use of it." St. Medard dressed the wounds of all the victims of the explosion, mostly with olive oil. He gave pain-killing laudanum only to Shultz and McGee, although several others required a cathartic after three or four days.

New-York was forced to change course for Malta, where she arrived on 1 May. She needed a complete cleaning and repainting, as well as repairs to her structural damage—although Morris was almost certainly looking forward to dallying with his family, who had remained there. St. Medard had between eight and twenty patients under his care each day during the 19 days the ship remained at Valletta.

On 5 May, Midshipmen Christopher Gadsden and Henry Wadsworth went sightseeing in a horse-drawn carriage to Bosquetta, the former palace of the Grand Master of the Knights of Malta, distinguished for its large grove of orange trees, and visited underground catacombs and St. Paul's Cathedral. Two or three days later St. Medard visited the same "curious and antient places," perhaps at the younger men's suggestion. He went shopping almost every day to replace the hospital stores he had lost in the explosion: for eggs (about a penny each), about 30 dozen oranges (18 cents a dozen), 13 dozen lemons (12 cents a dozen), vegetables, mutton, and chickens (40–45 cents each). On the 18th he watched an English squadron comprised of a frigate and nine 74- and 84-gun ships of the line under Admiral Sir Percy Bridgeton leave Malta for Italy, because, as Midshipman Lewis thought, a new war between England and France seemed imminent.

While his flagship was being repaired, the Commodore dispatched *John Adams* to cruise in the Gulf of Sidra, off Tripoli. On 12 May, while sailing about 20 miles east of his target, Captain Rodgers captured *Meshouda*, a ship belonging to the Sultan of Morocco, as she was attempting to run the American blockade (otherwise the capture would not have been legal because the United States was not at war with Morocco). She had begun life as the American brig *Betsey*, but after being taken legally by a Tripolitan ship in 1801, she had been sold to the Sultan, who had equipped her with 28 guns and loaded her hold with small arms for his new ally, the Pacha of Tripoli. Rodgers brought *Meshouda* into Malta a week after taking her.

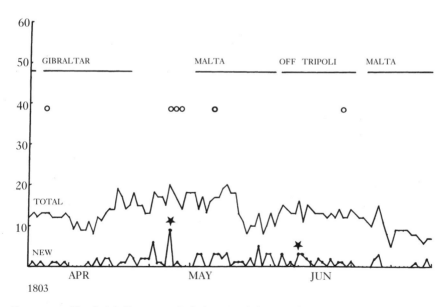

FIGURE 5.   Total sick list, new admissions, and deaths (circles) on *New-York* from 20 March to 30 June 1803. The star on the left indicates the explosion in the storeroom, and the star on the right the small powder explosion.

At 6:00 P.M. two days later, *John Adams, New-York,* and *Enterprise* sailed for Tripoli once again, arriving at 9 P.M. the next day. Henry Wadsworth regretted that it had been twelve months from the time he had first entered the Mediterranean, on *Chesapeake,* until he had finally reached his destination. The American squadron came under hostile fire almost immediately. St. Medard recorded the first skirmishes in his journal:

> Off Tripoly the schooner [*Enterprise*] chased a Tripolitan vessell on shore. The first from the town & about 12 miles to the westward w[h]ere the vessell was [run] on shore fired at the scho[o]ner. We sailed [within] 2 ½ & 4 miles from the shore. Saw a number of men in a body, & a troop of horse comming to the assistance of the vessell & thus prevent our landing, about to the number of 4 or 5 hundred.
>
> The 23th at ½ after 6 p.m., being of[f] Tripoly about 4 miles off, about 8 or 10 gun boats got underways and fired a number [of] shots after us & the John Adams. Their metal [i.e., their shot] being very heavy, of 24 & 32 pounders, [a] number of shots fell near us. We returned the fire—about 8 guns from the Newyork and a broadside from the John Adams.

The next day was quiet in the harbor of Tripoli as the adversaries tried to ascertain each other's strengths and weak points; "No fun," wrote the exasperated Henry Wadsworth. The frigate *Adams,* under Captain Hugh G. Campbell, joined the squadron on the 26th. The next day provided Wadsworth at least a small dose of the "fun" he longed for. At about 5:00 P.M. ten enemy ships were spotted trying to run the American blockade,

> But alas the wind died away, & when within long gun shot the setting sun seemed to destroy at once our shining prospects. . . It was now just dusk & we could no longer discern our enemies but by the flash of their guns: had there been anyone on board, who like Joshua of old could have commanded the sun to stand still, thy gun boats would have been ours[,] Tripoly, and thy people our slaves.
>
> It was a most elegant sight. The frequent flash & heavy report of the gun boats: the still more frequent broad sides of our squadron form'd the most sublime scene you can imagine. The shot from the gun boats whistl'd over us & struck all around—but none hit us.

However, we engag'd to a great disadvantage. The enemy close in under the land which threw a dark shade over them—were not to be seen, whereas we being on their western horizon made an excellent mark for them: We haul'd close to the wind & ceas'd firing.

Wadsworth did not confide even to his private journal that his revered Commodore had sent *John Adams* to do most of the fighting that evening. Lt. Thomas W. Hooper, the senior Marine in *New-York*, later described how Morris held back and fired off only two or three broadsides, while *John Adams* remained in the vanguard all night. It may—or may not—be relevant that Dr. St. Medard was treating the commodore for intermittent fever—malaria—during that entire week.

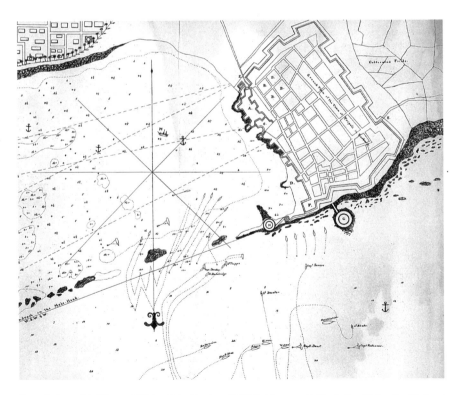

Detail from "A View of Tripoli in Barbary" Midshipman F.C. deKrafft in the United States brig *Siren* off Tripoli on 28 September 1804. Detail from frontispiece to *The Record of the United States Naval Institute* 5 (1879), no. 4.

The Surgeon's account of the fight is consistent with those of others who were there, although much briefer. He also records how several men in *New-York* were injured during, but not because of, the night's gunnery:

> One of our boatswain's mates got hurt by the explosion of his powder horn in priming his gun, which burnt him in the face, eyes, loin, & brest very dangerously, another man at the same gun badly bruised by the pieces of the powder horn at the brest & abdomen, another man at another gun having got his fingers jamd in the [touch hole] of the gun, by which I have emputated the 2 first joints of the index & [middle fingers].

The Boatswain's Mate was 41-year-old Francis Spry, whose concussion and burns required treatment for 21 days. The other injuries were suffered by Ordinary Seaman Peter McGregor, who was back to duty in eight days, and Jesse Denning, the Surgeon's assistant. The surgeon later learned that American fire had killed three and wounded five men on Tripolitan gunboats.

Although desultory skirmishing continued for a day or two, the Pacha was finally coming to think in terms of peace with the Americans. The Commodore feared being held hostage if he went ashore to negotiate with Qaramanli's representative, who was said to be too ill to come to the American flagship, but, as St. Medard noted, Morris gave his own men another explanation for his refusal to meet the Tripolitans on their home ground:

> May 29th. The schooner Enterprise was [showing the American] flag about 2 miles from the fort & harbour of Tripoli. At 2 o clock a boat came of[f] from the town on board of her with 2 of the Bashaw's officers. The schooner beat up to us and the Commodore communicated to the Bashaw through the [neutral] Danish consule on shore. The communication was [carried] to the 2 officers on board the schooner by Capt [Rodgers] of the John Adams, the Commodore wishing not to communicate himself with them for [fear] of being quarantined at our return at Malta;

On 30 May the French commercial agent at Tripoli assumed responsibility for Morris's safety ashore. St. Medard became involved in the negotiations at that point, probably because he could act as an interpreter for the new French negotiator, but any new discussions were delayed for a week when minor skirmishing broke out. The Surgeon continued:

> The 31st the Adams & Enterprise in [chase] to the westward. In shore in the evening fired a number of guns. . .
>
> June 1st. the Adams at anchor about 1 ½ miles from the shore in a bay called at Tripoly, bloking up 10 Boats from 28 to 35 tuns. Loaded with [wheat] from Tunis . . . at noon the Enterprise was dispatched of[f] to us with the above intelligence. We made sail for the said place and anchored ahead of her. We saw a great number of men [on] foot & horsback in every direction on the hills, marching & forming in order of battle to the number in appearance of 2 to 3 thousand beside 3 or 4 hundred secreted behind one old castle built near the water w[h]ere the above vessells run ashore. All returned with guns within about 2 [hours].

According to Wadsworth, Captain Hull of *Enterprise* reported that ten Tunisian ships were trying to unload cargoes of wheat at Tripoli, while about a thousand enemy horsemen were galloping back and forth waving their guns in the air and "cutting Capers" meant to intimidate the Americans. They clearly had no intention of obeying the Commodore's demand that they stop the unloading. Lieutenant Porter proposed a direct attack on the grain ships, but Morris refused his permission, arguing that he could accomplish his goals by negotiation, an argument that a later court of inquiry would agree displayed his "ignorance of the character of those people." Nevertheless, that evening he permitted Porter, Wadsworth, armed with cutlass, musket, and pistols, and three enlisted men, to set off in *New-York*'s jolly boat, to reconnoiter the Tunisian fleet in case negotiations should fail. Joined by a boat from *Enterprise*, they had hoped to surprise the men unloading the grain boats. However, they were spotted and fired upon, so they rowed off to a large rock where they landed. In his enthusiasm Wadsworth "stood on its summit & with my right hand extended towards heav'n (laugh here H.W.) took possession in the name of the United States—thus pleasantly passed the time." More "fun" for the midshipman from Maine.

The next morning the Americans observed that the grain boats had been safely beached after being unloaded, and large numbers of men and cavalry had been positioned to protect them behind the large rocks in the harbor. Six boats with about 50 men from *Adams, Enterprise,* and *New-York* mounted a new attack, under Porter's command. The other officers on the latter's two boats included Marine Lieutenant Enoch Lane, and Midshipmen Higinbothom, Lewis, Downes, and, of course, Wadsworth. This time the "fun" would result in wounds and death. The Tripolitans, who were waiting for an American attack, opened fire from several ships as well as from shore. After taking a few shots, the Americans used up all their ammunition and returned to their ships. They set several enemy grain boats on fire, but the flames were quickly extinguished, and the Tripolitans were still unloading as the Americans rowed back to their respective ships. Dr. St. Medard's account of the adventure was, as usual, less dramatic than Wadsworth's:

> In the evening, one boat from each vessell was sent close in shore to the vessels to watch their mottions, the boats were discovered by the favour of the moon, and were fired at by the Turks [all the Moslem North African states owed nominal fealty to the Ottoman Empire], which was returned by the boats & kept up for near one hour; the next morning the 2^d of June at 7 o clock 2 boats were armed with officers, sailors & marins to attack the shore & to burn the [enemy's] boats, which was executed, the boats being covered by the 2 ships & the schooner's fires. The hills, shore & the old castle were covered with men, a constant fire was kept up on both [sides.] We saw a great number of the Turks fall by there & a number shot on horsback. At half after nine the boats returned firing as they retreated & left the Turk's boats on fire; M^r. David Porter our 1st Lieut—& one of our marins being wounded—Likewise, 2 out of the Adam's boat & one out of the Enterprise's boat, at 11 o clock ceased firing & got under ways; we saw the Turks comming in great numbers to their boats & went to put the fire out.

Twelve to fifteen Americans, from the three ships of the blockading squadron, were killed or wounded by Tripolitans defending the grain boats that were trying to break through the blockade. One of the only two casualties among *New-York*'s crew was 23-year-old Porter, who was shot in both thighs. Dr. St. Medard bled him and then dressed his wounds. The next day the surgeon gave him a cathartic and applied a salve he thought would speed the healing process, and Porter was back to duty in nine days. The other casualty was a 25-year-old Marine private with the improbable name of Direct Winds; he was far more seriously wounded in one thigh. St. Medard treated him in the same way, but Winds lost his kidney function and developed other signs of widespread inflammation and sepsis; he died six days later. Still, Henry Wadsworth judged the fight to have been "good sport," especially because he claimed a victory for the 50 Americans over what he estimated to have been 1,000 Tripolitans (he reports that the Commodore counted several thousand enemy on shore). Although the Danish consul wrote to Cathcart about the "glorious blockade," its high water mark had just passed.

Even during the excitement on 1 June, the surgeon compiled his usual quarterly report to his captain. St. Medard informed Chauncey that, since his last report on 1 March,

> The prevailing diseases which have chiefly affected our ship's company were of a catarrhal kind, & the most of them of a malignant nature, most complicated with rheumatism, a few scurvy, diarrheas, intermiting & 2 typhus, but fortunatly of no contagious a nature, & no death[s]; and [h]ad it not been for the unfortunate accident of the 25th of April, I should have the happiness of informing you that none have died.
>
> The ship is kept clean, sweet, & wholesome in these seas. Particularly on this coast the dews are excessively h[e]avy & hurtful. It is then necessary for the health of the crew & the benefite of the service that the officers [on] watch should keep the men perfectly awake in their night watches & not to suffer them to lay on a bare [deck], as they would be diseased with various complaints generally produced from those h[e]avy dews.

Month	Diarrheas	Intermit.	Catarrh & Rheumat	Typhus	Scurvy	Hurt
March	1	1	15	—	—	2
April	2	—	24	2	—	9
May	—	5	29	—	7	4
Total	3	6	68	2	7	15

Although the numbers above are not entirely consistent with the actual numbers of new cases of catarrhal fevers for the three months tabulated as shown in his patient log, they do reflect a serious increase that peaked in May but fell to a record low in June as the epidemic wore itself out. By the end of May, eight to fifteen men a day were on the sick list.

Dr. St. Medard resumed his narrative of the blockade and its consequences two days later:

June 4th—Joigned the John Adams before Tripoly. At 9 o clock the Enterprise was sent in for communication [i.e., to arrange a truce or cease-fire] but the fort fired at her & she returned to us, & at about 5 o clock pm a boat came of[f] from the town, with the Bashaw's prime minister having dispaches from him for Commodore Morris, whishing to know that if the Commodore was fully impowred from the American government he might come near shore and hoist a white flag as a flag [of] truce. He would then communicate & commence a negotiation. The wind blowing hard prevented the boat from going on shore this night. The boat was hoisted on board, & the next morning at 9 o clock the weather being pleasant and being about 6 miles from the town, the boat was hoisted out & the prime minister went on shore with an answer to the Bashaw's letter. In the afternoon the Turk's boat returned on board with an answer from the Bashaw to the Commodore & returned on shore at about sun set.

June 6th. The Turks boat came of[f] from the shore at about 9 o' clock in the morning with letters from the Bashaw's minister & the Commissioners of the Fransh Republic [Napoleon was still First Consul], the last including an assurance of the Commodore's security & of any of his officers on shore, being himself & his government responsible for his & [the] officer's persons. At 12 o clock Capt [Rodgers, of *John Adams*] went on shore, with powers from the Commodore to open a negotiation. Capt [Rodgers] returned on board the same evening. On the 7th Commodore Morris, Capt Campbell [of *Adams*], the purser [Isaac Garretson], Mr Llewelen [Marine Lieutenant Samuel Llewellyn, on *New-York*], my self & 2 other officers from the Adams went on shore; we went to the [French] Consule's house who received us very kindly & about one hour after we waited on the prime minister's [representative], who invited the Commodore to come again at 6 o clock in the evening to began the negotiation. We waitit on him at that time & the next day the 8th at 10 o'clock, made his demands to the Commodore, which were as follows: 200,000 Spanish mill[ed] dollars, for the peace & all the expences of the war. Commodore Morris reply^d him the same day & offered him 5,000 Spanish mill dollars when [an American] Consule should be received in his dominion of Tripoly, & 10,000 Spanish mill dollars five years after, which was not agreed to. The Bashaw & the minister were very much affronted from the disproportion of the offer to the demand [however, a letter from the Prime Minister to Morris stuck in the back of St. Medard's journal hints that the minister will use his influence to persuade the Bashaw to lower his demands], & had it not been for the respo[n]sability of the [French] Consule who pledged his persone & his govenment, I have not the least doubt that we should all had been stopped on shore by [the Bashaw's] othority until Commodore Morris had complied with his extravagant demand. On that night, the white flag which had been kept up flying over his palaice as signal of truce & answered by our squadron during the negotiation was then struck & [the consul] considered us in his power [i.e., under his protection].

The next morning of the 9th the [French] Consule, who was responsable for our persons, sent to the minister & Bashaw and informed them of the impropriety of keeping the white flag struck & wished them to have it hoisted up again until we were safe on board of our squadron. The Bashaw, being afraid of the [French] Republic, suffered the flag to be hoisted again. At 9 o clock we took a [French] boat with its flag flying & returned on board of the squadron, the [Tripolitan] shore fortresses & gun boats being all covered with men armed, to shew us their strength as we passed them. At 12 o clock we arrived on board the Newyork. The same day at about 5 o clock p.m. we separated from the John Adams & the Adams, the Enterprise [sailing] with us for Malta.

Morris finally mollified the Tripolitans by promising that every time a new consul came to Tripoli he would bring a suitable gift for the Pacha, but not the thousands of dollars he had tried to extort from the Americans.

Thus ended the squadron's first attempt to blockade Tripoli, and to face down its ruler. Henry Wadsworth had had some "fun" as flashes of gunpowder illuminated the evening skies, David Porter had begun his journey to celebrity, and Direct Winds became the first—and only—member of the *New-York*'s crew to die by enemy action. On the other hand, the blustering Pacha had failed to intimidate the Americans completely, while Morris had continued his private policy of avoiding any substantial fight with the enemy, despite his orders from the Secretary of the Navy.

Leaving *Adams* and *John Adams* to patrol the coast of Tripoli, on 10 June *New-York* and *Enterprise* left for Malta, where they were quarantined for two weeks, justifying Morris's earlier fears of such a consequence if he and the other negotiators had gone ashore at Tripoli. While there the Commodore learned that his wife had delivered a son on 9 June, but he could not visit her until the quarantine had been lifted. There was some excitement on the 14th when Vice Admiral Lord Nelson, the hero of the battles of the Nile and Copenhagen, arrived on the 32-gun frigate *Amphion*. Morris saluted Nelson by firing 17 guns, which Nelson returned. St. Medard seems to have been pleased that Nelson had been sent to take command of all English naval forces in the Mediterranean, armed with authority to declare war against any of the Barbary states. Three days later Nelson went off seeking action, and soon sent two French prizes into Malta, just as *Enterprise* was sent back to cruise off Tripoli.

The only other excitement during the quarantine, as far as Henry Wadsworth was concerned, was the celebration of his eighteenth birthday on 21 June. He and his messmates observed the occasion over a dinner of "salt beef with wormy biscuits in which sport the Weevil & Maggot." Five days later the Commodore ordered Captain Rodgers to raise the seige of Tripoli and report to him at Malta—Morris was not yet aware that his reputation and career had come to an inglorious end. Nor did he know that the other three ships of his squadron, still at Tripoli, had blown up a 22-gun Tripolitan ship.

NOTES

The usual sources have been used to reconstruct the cruise of *New-York* and her crew, including the William Lewis letters cited in the Notes for Chapter 6. Henry Wadworth's MS. "Journal kept on board the United States Ship Chesapeake of Forty-Four Guns Richard Valentine Morris Esqr. Commander and Commodore of the American Squadron in the Mediterranean," and a typescript of his journal, are at the National Park Service's Longfellow National Historic Site, Cambridge, Mass.; much, but not all, of it was published in Dudley W. Knox, ed., *Naval Documents Related to the United States Wars with the Barbary Powers*, 6 vols. (Washington: Government Printing Office, 1939–1944). The birth of James Low's son is in Linda M. Moloney, "Doxies at dockside: Prostitution and American maritime society, 1800–1900," in Timothy J. Runyan, ed., *Ships, Seafaring and Society: Essays in Maritime History* (Detroit: Wayne State University Press, 1987), pp. 217–225. Mrs. John Newton Cannon is attested in McKee, *Edward Preble*, p. 216. *New-York*'s General Orders are preserved with John Rodgers's Quarter Bill for the ship in the Historical Society of Pennsylvania, no. AMN 300.

Chapter Nine

Abortion and Other Fevers
30 July–30 September 1803

T HE *New-York's* crew commemorated the Fourth of July 1803 at
Malta by dressing the ship with appropriately celebratory flags
and a 15-gun salute. The commodore gave a dinner for other senior officers in the squadron and local dignitaries, the ship's lieutenants gave
one for other lieutenants in the command, and the midshipmen entertained their counterparts from other ships. Henry Wadsworth recorded
the 17 toasts in which he and his fellows gloried; they included:

1. The day we celebrate may it never be blotted from the remem-
   brance of Americans. . .
4. The departed Washington: that virtuous & exalted man, who
   served his country as a warrior & statesman. . .
7. The Navy of the U.S. May it progress with our commerce & be
   the boast of our country & terror of our enemies. . .
9. Discipline & subordination the vital principles of a navy. . .
11. The Midshipmen of the navy: may their efforts to improve be
    in proportion to the "fostering care" of their country. Three
    cheers. . .
14. May the thunder of the American eagle always force an accep-
    tance of her olive branch. . .
16. The virtuous fair of America.
17. Steady.

These toasts summarize the mission of the United States Navy in the Mediterranean Sea that summer, and highlight the youthful enthusiasms that sometimes resulted in duels.

Five days later Wadsworth came down with what Dr. St. Medard labeled a "typhus fever"; it was not the highly infectious disease, produced by a rat-borne micro-organism, that is called typhus today, but simply a serious febrile illness accompanied by an unusually strong pulse. A week later the 20-year-old Wadsworth described the attack, which led to the only medical attention he received while in *New-York*:

> About 2 o'clock awoke with a violent fever—bilious it was & commenced the attack violently, but owing to the attention of Doctors St. Medard & Weems, it is conquered & your humble Serv[t] is in a fair way of recovery: discharged of great quantities of [bile]—I expect to be in prime health all summer.

Four enlisted men came down with the same symptoms that day. Dr. St. Medard first treated all five patients with tartar emetic, to stimulate removal of as much bile as possible. Over the next two days he prescribed more of the emetic, and added the cathartics calomel and jalap, to remove even more bile via the stool. St. Medard thought that their fevers had diminished by the fourth day; he discharged one man and prescribed Huxham's tincture, an all-purpose fever remedy whose chief ingredient was Peruvian bark, for the other four. Four men improved, but not at equal rates: Wadsworth was discharged back to duty after six days on the sick list, while 21-year-old Marine Private John Shinney was released only after 38 days.

The sickest of the five patients was 45-year-old Seaman Henry Bowdoin. He had been under medical care several times already during the cruise: for diarrhea, while they were still in the Potomac; for rheumatismus, an upper respiratory difficulty, while en route to Malta in early February; and for catarrhal fever, with chest pains, two months later. On 9 July Bowdoin showed signs of a more serious catarrhal fever, including chest pains and a fast weak pulse, and St. Medard soon realized that it had evolved into a typhus fever, a more serious complication. By the fifth day Bowdoin had developed signs of a further complication, scurvy, and he became progressively weaker. He died at 9:00 A.M. on 16 July, after only a week's illness, despite St. Medard's usual antiphlogistic treatment.

Mrs. Morris and her two young children boarded *New-York* on 11 July, and the squadron left Malta that evening. Although he was still sick, Wadsworth saw "Etna standing alone, vomiting black smoke" as they sailed around the southeast corner of Sicily toward the Straits of Messina. Peter St. Medard regarded Etna only as "a big & remarkable hill in Sicilie." Three days later *Enterprise* captured a small Tunisian vessel which then was taken in tow by the flagship, and the following evening the squadron came to rest at Messina.

Wadsworth reported that it was "necessary to pass the currents & contracurrents[,] the eddies & contraeddies, the whirlings & contra-whirlings" of the waters between Sicily and Italy. *New-York, Adams, John Adams, Enterprise*, and the prize ship, *Meshouda*, were caught up in the churning seas. "It could not have been a very pleasant sight to the Commodore to see his own ship in danger & the rest of his squadron dancing about the straits, governed neither by helm or canvass," wrote

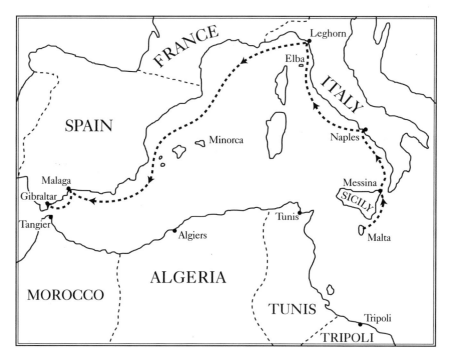

MAP 4.   Route of *New-York* from 30 July to 30 September 1803.

Wadsworth. The American ships took turns towing the prize, and finally escaped from the Scylla and Charybdis of ancient legend. *New-York* went after several other North African ships along the way, but they either escaped or were not legal prizes, which aggravated the crew because, as Wadsworth said, they "were all hot for battle, friends or foes. The sight of a turban soon enrages them."

At the same time, 29-year-old Seaman John Johnston was presenting another challenge to Dr. St. Medard's medical skills. He, too, had been admitted to the surgeon's care several times already: he was treated for "slow" fever for 20 days before his ship had even sailed from Washington; for dysentery over 35 days beginning in November; for diarrhea for a week in January; and for catarrhal fever in February, and again in March, athough he also had such debilitating diarrhea during the second bout that he spent a month on the sick list. Then, on 9 June, while the American squadron was at Tripoli, Johnston became so debilitated that he had to enter treatment again. St. Medard gave him various tonics to strengthen his system, but respiratory symptoms appeared. The surgeon first diagnosed consumption, but then the unmistakable signs of scurvy appeared after about 42 days on the sick list, and the seaman died five days later, as his ship entered the Tyrrhenian Sea.

The crew of *New-York* were treated to an astonishing sight as they headed north from Messina. On 19 July, St. Medard recorded that his ship was

> Close in with the island of . . . Stromboli, a noted place for volcanoes. Saw [for] four days & during the whole night the hill vomiting fire every 6 or 8 minutes, & in day time a large body of smoke coming out of it. The red [hot] lava runing down the hill from the crator about 2 thirds the way like a stream of fire about a mile long.

Wadsworth, who watched the volcano through two nights, thought it "indeed a most elegant sight: the blaze is exceedingly red."

Two days later—presumably during a lull in the sailing—St. Medard asked Captain Isaac Chauncey for permission to consolidate the contents of his original six chests of medicines into three. Not only had his own needs reduced the supplies on hand, he had also had to turn over some of his reserve stocks to the Surgeons on *Adams* and *John Adams* in May and July; the latter transfer had included some 200 lemons, so he may have had none on hand with which to treat Bowdoin or Johnston when they came down with scurvy. Because regulations required some form of supervision to insure that no medicines were improperly diverted, Lieutenant Porter and Sailing Master Lovell had to certify the final list of medicines on hand. Over the next two months the Surgeon would have to share more of his drug supplies with other ships in the squadron.

The Americans reached the Gulf of Naples on the 27th, and anchored near the Isle of Capri. Wadsworth was scornful of their mainland hosts:

> Our squadron furnishes much matter for observation to the Neapolitans, especially as we are accompanied by a Tripoline vessel, which to them is a rare sight, for in their wars with the Barbarians they have shewn themselves such infamous cowards, that a capture on their part seldom occurs.

The following day Dr. St. Medard went sightseeing. His account of his expedition ashore reveals more about his curiosity than either the rest of his journal or his medical notes:

> I went on shore & visited the antiquities & curiosities of [Naples] such as the King's palace at Portici about 6 miles from the city, the most brilliant palace in the world. At [a]bout half mile from the palace, [H]erculaneum & [P]ompeii, which are about 5 miles apart, were destroyed by the same eruption of Mount Vesuvius at which foot those cities are, about seventeen hundred and ten years ago [it was actually 1724 years]. The former was a town of much more magnificence than the other, but it is infinitely more difficult to be cleared of the matter which covers it. There are evident marks that the matter of six eruptions has taken its course over this city since the great explosion which involved the same fate with pompeii. The matter which immediatly covers the town & with which the theater & all the houses hitherto examined were found filled is not lava but a sort of soft stone composed of pumice & ashes intermixed with earth. This [mixture] has saved the pictures, manuscripts, busts, utensils & other antiquities which have been recovered out of Herculaneum from other destruction.
>
> In the afternoon I went to the westward of the city of Naples. Took a carage & rode about 4 miles out. I passed through the Grotto of Pausilippa, a subterraneous passage through the mountain near or about a mile in length & about 20 feet in breadth & 35 or 40 in height

everywhere, being about sun seting on my return. I was obliged to take torches to see my way through. There is two holes, skylights, pierced through the mountain near the middle of the grotto which afford a gloomy light in day time.

2 miles beyond this Grotta da Pausilipa is a Circular Lago d'Agonia [Lake of Death] on whose margin is situated the famous Grotta da Cani where so many dogs have been suffocated to shew the effect of a vapour which rises about a foot above the bottom of the cave and is destructive to animal life. I took a dog and tried the experiment. I held him for about 1 minute, with his nose at about 2 inches from the ground. By that time [he was] suffocated & lifeless. I put him out on ground in the open air and it took him near 5 minutes to come to again. A gentleman, Capt. Burgess from N. York, who was with me,

"La Grotte du Chien" near Naples, where Peter St. Medard and Captain Burgess experimented with the effects of carbon dioxide fumes on the dog, and the captain. Engraving from an unidentified *Voyage en Italie* published in the eighteenth century.

tried the experiment upon himself. In less than that time of one minute he was so senseless that we dragged him out of the Grotta, [he] fainted away & [it] took him likewise near 5 or 6 minutes to recover. It is therefor proved that this vapour convulses & kills every breathing animal, altho there is vegetation in the same place & at about 5 feet over the said vapour. A few rods from this Grotta in another direction & on the Lago there is a hot house with a number of rooms, say 5 or 6, which rooms are hotter & hotter as you go deep in them. The hearth is so [hot] that you cannot suffer your hand on it half a second, & are thrown in a violent sweat in less than 5 minutes. In 2 of the rooms you are obliged to put off your cloths to bare the heat half that time, occasioned by the sulphurous & nitrous [fumes].

The Grotto of Posilipo is actually a half-mile-long tunnel, cut through a promontory in the Gulf of Naples; Virgil's tomb was reputed to be at one end. The fumes that felled the dog—and Captain Burgess—were carbon dioxide which, being heavier than oxygen, effectively suffocates air-breathing animals—and men—placed close to the ground. St. Medard's surprise that no plants were affected by the poison hints that he was not, indeed, familiar with Lavoisier's demonstration that plants make oxygen from carbon dioxide, and, therefore, that he might have been unfamiliar with the new medical chemistry.

At Naples, Morris unsuccessfully sought the loan of ten gunboats and two bomb-ketches from the King of the Two Sicilies, although he did win permission to bring his squadron back for repairs and provisions if, for any reason, Malta became unsuitable for those purposes. At midnight on 4 August he signalled the squadron to unmoor, and it was underway for Leghorn (or Livorno) at sunrise the next day. The excitement of possible prize captures appeared from time to time as the squadron sailed north along the Italian coast, but all turned out to be ships of friendly powers.

Wadsworth regretted that their stay at Naples had been brief, and four days later he had to be content with seeing only the dome of St. Peter's in Rome as he stood on the deck of his ship. Later that day, as Captain Campbell's *Adams* sailed near Elba, she was fired upon by the island's French garrison, but was not hit. Campbell sent a boat on shore, to protest the unwarranted shooting, whereupon the French commander took Lieutenant John Dent hostage until Campbell paid for his release, ostensibly to compensate for the French cannon balls fired at the squadron. Wadsworth reported that Morris was furious with Campbell because he had "assum'd great liberty in transacting any affairs under the nose of the [Commodore]—& thro' his damn'd foolishness our country is insulted & we pay for it too, blast him—if I were Comr. I'd arrest him & pack him off to the United States for trial."

The squadron anchored at Leghorn at noon on the thirteenth. During much of the next two weeks Commodore Morris and James Leander Cathcart, the American consul at Tripoli, argued over which of them was authorized to negotiate with the ruler of Tripoli. Cathcart reported to Secretary of State Madison that Morris was obviously jealous "that any other person should be empower'd to negociate with the Barbary-States but himself." Morris further frustrated Cathcart by refusing to return to his assignment on the Barbary Coast, much less to take the consul there, as had been planned. The Commodore excused himself from that chore by claiming that

> The circumstances of the squadron prevent me from appearing before either Tunis or Tripoli at present, and render it necessary that other measures shou'd be pursued for the protection of the American commerce, & my presence is necessary at this time at Tangiers, in order to guard against the probable unreasonable demands and hostile threats of the Emperor of Morocco.

In short, Morris was determined to remain at Leghorn, then under French rule. In retaliation, Cathcart refused to let Morris see his instructions from the Secretary of State, and accused Morris of having escalated the hostility with the Sultan of Morocco by retaining the prize ship *Meshouda*, although she had a valid passport from Morocco. Morris finally sent *John Adams* to take *Meshouda* to Barcelona, where she was to wait for more American ships, and then on to Gibraltar, to arrange for her disposition as a prize. Cathcart was then allowed to return to Tripoli on *Adams*, carrying a letter to Mohammed Dghies, the Pacha's chief minister. It stated that both the Consul and the Commodore had full power to negotiate with Qaramanli.

St. Medard's sick list fell from thirteen to seven during the fortnight at Leghorn, so he might have had time for sightseeing there, but he recorded none in his journal. Perhaps he was fully occupied with his daily round of patients, one of whom was especially difficult. Lawrence

Conley, a 26-year-old Seaman, had been down with intermittent fever, complicated by diarrhea, for 22 days back in September; with catarrhal fever, for 48 days, beginning in November; and with scurvy, which had responded to "fresh fruits," for four days in late May. But symptoms of scurvy reappeared a couple of days later, presumably because St. Medard had recently given his last lemons to the Surgeon on *Adams*, and Conley became increasingly debilitated. His weakness increased, despite a daily dose of tonics, leading St. Medard to change his original diagnosis to consumption. Conley died at 10 A.M. on 19 August, 75 days after entering the sick list for the last time.

Jean Louis Benoît, a 36-year-old French physician whom St. Medard met at Leghorn, sought the Franco-American surgeon's help in arranging passage to America in *New-York*. At the same time he wrote to Commodore Morris, in the third person, saying that

> since the age of ten he has traveled so as to instruct himself in all [areas of] surgery. He remained two years in the Montpellier hospitals in France [Montpellier had been a leading medical school since the Middle Ages], where he completed his studies, and from there he continued to travel until this day. Finding himself in this city for the past eighteen days, with no acquaintances and no resources, he thought that he would do best to take the liberty of addressing himself directly to Your Excellency, who might have the kindness to employ him as [illegible] or other occupation on one of your frigates, with or without an appointment, so long as his meals and passage are gratis.

Perhaps Benoît feared political retribution if he returned to the France of the First Consul, perhaps he was destitute, or perhaps he was simply unable, for whatever reason, to settle anywhere on a permanent basis. There is no evidence that St. Medard was able to help his countryman, but by the time he neared Washington four months later he probably regretted that he had been unable to do so, because his daily sick list was rising to unprecedented numbers.

On the last day of August *New-York* departed from what Henry Wadsworth said was his "fav'rite part in the Mediterranean," perhaps because of the unspecified "pleasures of Leghorn" he had enjoyed there. According to St. Medard, while cruising north of Corsica three days later, they passed through a British fleet of seven ships of the line with 74 to 110 guns, and Commodore Morris spoke with Admiral Nelson on *Victory*. On 9 September the *New-York* anchored at Málaga. The schooner *Nautilus* arrived there the next day, bearing news that shocked Henry Wadsworth:

> We learn! strange to tell! we learn that the Commodore is order'd home: still more strange!! that he is unpopular with the people & with the government: we know that the orders from the Secretary came out to Capt. Rodgers & that the Comʳ has not even a line from the government. This is treatment for an officer! this is conduct towards the first in command in the American Navy!! Send orders out to an inferior to take command until Comʳ Prible arrives!! damnation! could they treat a malefactor worse: had he basely fled from Battle: had he cowardly shrunk from fight—could they have taken a step more mortifying, condemn him unheard, unseen. I know he has but to appear and be justified, but this damn'd cruel step—degrade him the eyes of the whole Mediterranean fixed upon him—sacrificed partly to the discontented officers under his command. Were I commodore & used thus, I'd raise such a dust about the Navy Office that one could not see the Capitol from the President's House. However let me observe that this is not official information but the news of the day.

The startling news might as well have been official—it was certainly true. Navy secretary Smith had written to Morris three months earlier, relieving him of command of the American squadron, and further ordering him to bring *Adams* home to Washington. At the same time, Smith instructed Captain John Rodgers to assume command of the squadron and its flagship. Morris was outraged on all counts: "The style of this letter and the manner in which it was transmitted are calculated to wound, as much as the occasion would permit, the officer to whom it was addressed." It never occurred to him that he had not carried out Smith's original orders.

Rodgers's *John Adams* and Isaac Hull's *Enterprise* were the only ships of the squadron remaining at Tripoli when Morris sailed for Malta on 10 June. Twelve days later a 22-gun Tripolitan warship began bombarding the two American ships, which delivered withering return fire. After 45 minutes the Tripolitans abandoned their ship. As Rodgers began recalling his own boats from the attack, a boatload of enemy sailors tried to return to their ship. They renewed their fire from her decks, but after a few minutes were forced to haul down their flag, while delivering two last broadsides at the Americans. At the same time the Tripolitan ship exploded, raising the main and mizzen masts and their sails 150 feet into the air. The Pacha was thus left with only one small warship, and she was off cruising in the Gulf of Venice.

Rodgers had first been marked for high command because of his efforts as First Lieutenant of *Constellation* during her celebrated capture of *l'Insurgente* during the Quasi-War with France. Because so far he been responsible for the one notable achievement of the U.S. squadron that was supposed to be blockading Tripoli, even though Smith could not have known that when he recalled Morris, it was not unreasonable to award the squadron to Rodgers, albeit only temporarily, until Preble reached the Mediterranean, at which time he would assume command of the American forces there.

New-York sailed from Málaga in company with *John Adams* to convoy six merchantmen, and on 14 September rendezvoused at Gibraltar with the rest of the new squadron under Preble, on *Constitution*. The squadron was further augmented by *Philadelphia*, commanded by William Bainbridge. *New-York* and *John Adams* were under orders to return home; Rodgers would remain a Commodore because he would still be commanding a squadron, albeit a small one, while Isaac Chauncey was still Flag Captain of *New-York*.

Two days later Henry Wadsworth moved his belongings to another ship:

> I have receiv'd orders from the Secretary of the Navy to join the Constitution: today I put them in execution, & I have gotten up very early this morning to bring my journal to a close. I shall send it to Papa at Washington by Dr St. Midard, Surgeon of the Newyork. . . .
>
> They receive me with open arms on board the Constitution; many of the officers are my acquaintances & five midshipmen accompany me from the ship: it is with regret I leave the officers of the Newyork, they have treated me with marked attention: the greatest harmony prevails & ever since I have been attached to this ship have lived very happyly. . . .
>
> Now here you have my journal, it cost me some trouble & I hope it will please. . . What I have written here, papa, is intended merely for the amusement of my friends. I trust it will go no farther.

Fortunately, it did—which means that Dr. St. Medard faithfully carried out his young friend's request.

William Lewis, too, was transferred to *Constitution*. He concurred with Wadsworth's opinion of Commodore Morris, writing that "He is a worthy man, and merits better treatment than he has received from our government," a comment that might, indeed, have been heavily influenced by Wadsworth. Lewis also agreed about the Commodoress; he described her as "the most amiable, accomplished woman I almost ever saw." Unfortunately for her husband, senior officers did not share the midshipmen's favorable opinion of Morris and his wife.

Dr. St. Medard's work had waxed and waned in intensity during the summer. Although the total sick list had been falling slowly since May, he treated nearly 20 new cases of influenza in July, and, after declining in August and September their number was rising again in October. He also had to treat ten new cases of diarrhea over the same months, as well as the usual assortment of other fevers and accidents.

What may have been the most dramatic case of the entire cruise began the day *New-York* reached Gibraltar, when Dr. St. Medard found that 19-year-old Nancy Staines had aborted a fetus, and was suffering from a "suppuration of the womb." Nancy's husband was John Staines, the 26-year-old Quarter Gunner who had caused the explosion that killed four men and forced *New-York* to undergo lengthy repairs at Malta in April. He had had influenza during the winter, during the ship's long stay at Malta, but had recovered quickly while receiving the same antiphlogistic treatment that Dr. St. Medard later prescribed for his wife's sore throat.

It is impossible to ascertain today whether the abortion was spontaneous or self-induced; that it could have been spontaneous might be suggested, but certainly not proved, by the fact that five months earlier she had had "angina"—a sore throat that may have been caused by streptococci, the bacteria that are also associated with puerperal, or childbed, fever. There is no obvious reason why she should have caused the abortion herself, inasmuch as enlisted men's wives did have babies on warships, as James Low's wife had on *Chesapeake* back in February. It is also possible that Nancy Staines's baby was not her husband's, but such situations occur most often in novels.

Whatever the immediate cause of her infection, she was quite ill with high fever and severe pain in the pelvis, due to inflammation and pus in the uterus. On the third day she began vomiting, diarrhea

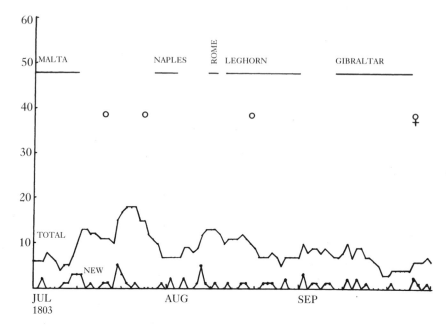

FIGURE 6.   Total sick list, new admissions, and deaths (circles) on *New-York* from 30 June to 10 October 1803. The female symbol on the far right indicates the death of Nancy Staines.

occurred, and she grew progressively weaker and light-headed. On the tenth day she became delirious, and gangrene developed in the uterus a day later. Mrs. Staines died at 3 o'clock the next morning.

St. Medard seems to have regarded her case as hopeless from the beginning: he did not prescribe his usual rather vigorous antiphlogistic treatment this time. He tried only to keep her quiet and as comfortable as possible, with an unspecified sedative mixture and a warm soothing medication that he probably forced into her uterus from a bag made from an animal bladder. As she weakened he tried to strengthen her with Peruvian bark, but it, too, was useless, as the surgeon probably suspected it would be. It was a supremely unlucky family.

On 17 September Morris hauled down the broad pennant that signified his command of the squadron, although he remained on board *New-York* for another week, and Rodgers broke out his own pennant on *John Adams*; he did not transfer it to *New-York* until 6 October. Rodgers and Preble were not on good terms: Rodgers, who was younger, outranked Preble in seniority. However, Preble, trying to avoid what might have been inevitable conflict, invited Rodgers, first on *John Adams* and then on *New-York*, to accompany him as he attempted to settle affairs with the Sultan of Morocco at Tangier.

Although the Sultan was not there at the time, the Moroccan officials who were there must have been intimidated by the combined force threatening them in their own harbor, consisting of *Constitution, John Adams*, and, sometimes, *New-York*, the latter under the temporary command of Hugh Campbell. All three American vessels were much larger than any of the Sultan's warships. Moreover, the Moroccans must have known that other American ships were close by, in the waters around Gibraltar. Anyone who has witnessed *Constitution*'s annual Fourth of July turnaround cruise from a boat in Boston Harbor in recent years has been impressed with what that 44-gun frigate's guns might have done to the stone fort on modern Castle Island near which she stops to fire a ceremonial salute; she would have looked much the same at the seawalls of Tangier in the fall of 1803. Peter St. Medard probably enjoyed the same view of his old ship from the deck of *New-York*. Besides, under Preble the American threat was not mere posturing.

Over the next three weeks Preble and Rodgers, in consultation with Tobias Lear, the American Consul General at Algiers (and formerly George Washington's private secretary), negotiated with the Moroccans through James Simpson, the Consul at Tangier, although he was under house arrest there. During this time the American ships shuttled back and forth to Gibraltar as the complex peace negotiations continued, although repeatedly frustrated by the Sultan's representative. Individual ships carried out other missions assigned by Preble, such as trying to intercept any Moroccan ships they might encounter on either side of the Strait of Gibraltar. Campbell and *New-York* cruised for a few days off Larache, a port on Morocco's Atlantic coast, while the squadron waited for the Sultan (the Americans called him Emperor) to arrive at Tangier.

During these weeks Drs. St. Medard and Weems had the additional burden of treating 18 Americans who were sent on board *New-York* from *Constitution* and *Philadelphia*. The latter was sent off to continue the blockade of Tripoli, but six patients were later returned to her, and two to *Constitution*. Weems also visited five enemy prisoners on *Meshouda* daily while at Gibraltar. During much of this time the number of sick among *New-York*'s crew dropped from ten to four or five, but it was soon to rise astronomically as they recrossed the Atlantic. This would affect St. Medard's work load drastically, especially because Weems, too, was transferred to *Constitution,* and Dr. Archer, who was informed by dispatches brought on one of the newly arrived American vessels that he had been promoted to Surgeon in July, was reassigned to *Argus.*

Notes

This portion of the cruise of *New-York* has been reconstructed from sources already cited, including the William Lewis letters cited in the Notes for Chapter 6. Other manuscript sources include the 22 August 1803 letters to PSM and Morris (therein addressed as "His Excellency the Commanding Admiral of the American Navy Fleet stationed at Livorno") from Jean Louis Benoît, and certificates of medicines requisitioned from *New-York* on 1 May 1803, 25 May 1803, 6 July 1803, 22 and 27 August 1803, and 22 September 1803, all of which are in the EBA collection. For Commodore Preble and, especially, the complex negotiations with the Sultan of Morocco, see McKee's *Edward Preble,* pp. 139–172, which includes the background of the Barbary prisoners treated by the surgeons on *New-York.*

Suzanne J. Stark has described the many roles of women on contemporary British warships, which set the patterns for life on American ships, in "Women at sea in the Royal Navy in the age of sail," *American Neptune 57* (1997): 101–120.

Chapter Ten

An Epidemic of Scurvy

1 October–9 December 1803

S<small>T.</small> M<small>EDARD</small> <small>RECORDED</small> in his journal that at 4 A.M. on 6 October his ship arrived before Tangier, where *Constitution, John Adams,* and *Nautilus* had already assembled. The Moroccan prime minister released Consul Simpson and allowed him to go out to *Constitution* later that morning, bearing news that the Sultan still wished to re-establish peace with the United States. The three frigates offered 21-gun salutes the next day as he led his court down to the beach to inspect the American warships. In the afternoon the Sultan sent ten bullocks, twenty sheep, and forty-eight fowl to the American fleet, his customary gift to visiting dignitaries; of this, *New-York* received three bullocks, four or five sheep, and twelve fowl. Four days later, Preble and a small party that included Henry Wadsworth, who was already at work on an account of his adventures with his new commander, went ashore to meet with the Sultan.

The next day the Sultan re-ratified the treaty his father had negotiated in 1786, and agreed to swapping a captive American merchant ship for *Meshouda* and one other Moroccan ship; the Sultan promised that the captain of *Meshouda* would lose his head for having attempted to run the blockade of Tripoli illegally. The Sultan further stipulated that Mr. Simpson had not been detained on his own orders; he could hardly admit that the detention had been illegal. A week later all the formalities had been completed and the Americans could finally leave Tangier.

A few days before Preble and the American diplomats finished negotiating with Mulay Sulaiman, *New-York* suffered another accident, although it was not as devastating as the explosion in April. She was at Gibraltar when, at nearly 2 A.M. on 11 October, while the brig *Syren* was signalling that she wanted *New-York* to take dispatches to Washington, heavy seas caused the two ships to collide. Although it appeared to the men in the smaller vessel that her total destruction was imminent, she suffered only minor damage, but the fore, main, and spritsail yards of the frigate were broken. One man in *Syren* appears to have lost his hand as a result of the accident, but no other casualties were reported.

After taking on water and provisions at Gibraltar, *New-York* and *John Adams* returned to Tangier, where the small squadron took on firewood and livestock. Dr. St. Medard's sick list had been as high as 20 a few days before, but was now falling. Although Commodore Preble had planned to send eight invalids each from *Constitution* and *Philadelphia* home on *New-York*, only seven or eight of them were still under St. Medard's care when his ship finally sailed for Washington on 19 October.

The homeward voyage must have been a professional nightmare for him. Not only had Drs. Weems and Archer been transferred to other ships, leaving the additional invalids from other ships that had been Weems's charges while they were still at Gibraltar under St. Medard's care, he now had the additional challenge of treating the multiple injuries suffered by William Pitman, a 16-year-old boy who had fallen from the mizzenmast to the taffrail two weeks earlier. He had suffered a compound fracture of the right leg, fractures of the lower jaw and the left femur near the greater trochanter, and dislocation of his right wrist. St. Medard set the fractures and reduced the dislocation. Although he bled the young man at the beginning, to lessen the risk of inflammation that almost always accompanied compound fractures, most of his treatment consisted of simple wound dressings, and occasional doses of Peruvian bark if fever seemed to be threatening, or a cathartic when Pitman became constipated. The usual treatment of compound fractures at that time was amputation, to prevent gangrene, but St. Medard's more conservative treatment seems to have been successful—perhaps he intuitively kept the surface wound unusually clean. Because it was clear that Pitman would be crippled for the rest of his life, St. Medard gave him a medical discharge when they returned.

Seaman John Fenner (or Tenner) died at the age of 23 on 2 November, of a catarrhal fever that had escalated into a typhus fever. He had

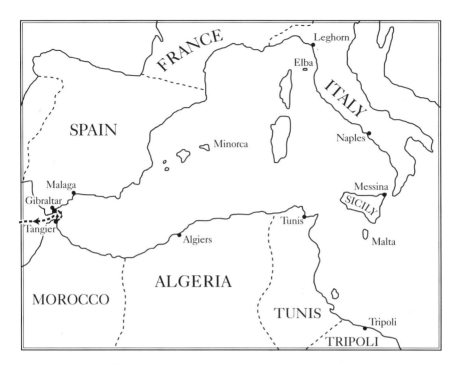

MAP 5.   Route of *New-York* from 1 October to 9 December 1803.

already had several illnesses, including dysentery and several bouts of rheumatismus, that had kept him on the sick list for a total of 146 days. A month later 24-year-old Seaman Hugh Scott died with catarrh and rheumatismus, both of which had occasioned his assignment to the sick list nine times, for a total of 61 days over the past 13 months.

But the most serious problem Dr. St. Medard faced was the rising number of scurvy patients, beginning in late October, just after a minor epidemic of catarrhal fever seemed to have abated. Without a Surgeon's Mate to assist him, he scarcely had time to make all the usual daily entries in his patient log; he compromised by entering the full data for all new admissions to the sick list, and for his non-scorbutic patients, but he had time to record only the numbers of his scurvy patients, on loose scraps of paper. In a memorandum to Commodore Rodgers he wrote, on 11 November:

> I . . . think it highly necessary to inform you that from the 23th of October last, the scorvy of a most malignant character & with the

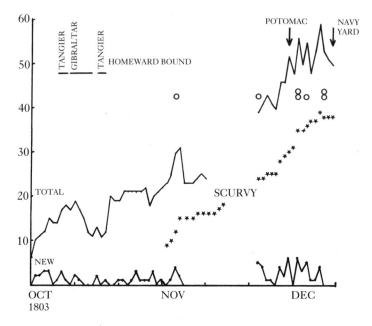

FIGURE 7. Total sick list, new admissions, and deaths (circles) on *New-York*, 1 October to 9 December 1803; the stars represent the total number of scurvy patients on the sick list each day.

highest symptoms has broken out among our ship's company & increases dayly.

This disease arising from a source of causes, such as an inactivity, a want of a cleir circulation of air, laying on a bare damp deck, turning in to their hamacks with damp clothes, a long use of salted provisions & cooks slush, a want of greens & vegetables &c. &c. (a complication of causes too tedious to enumerate), are such as will originate this disease, which in its nature is of a very difficult cure particularly at sea, & which when extended becomes epidemical & [carries] its calamity through a whole ship's company; sixteen of this complaint are on this day's list, & some of them very ill.

As a result of this memorandum, the next day Captain Chauncey issued the following orders, dictated by Commodore Rodgers, as recorded by the ship's surgeon:

The wind sails are to be kept up constantly in good weather to admit a free circulation of air;

No man to be suffered to lay upon decks or turn in their hamacks with wet clothes [when stowing them each morning];

No person to be suffered to make use of slush in any way. The officer of the watch will be held respons[ible] for the execution of the above orders; the Commodore is determined to take serrious notice of any neglect thereof, as the Doctor has *lately discovered* that the people [i.e., the crew] are suffered to be *idle, sleep upon wet decks*, turn in with *wet* cloths on, &c. &c. &c.

The foul air emanating from unwashed bodies and stagnant bilge water, and worsened by accumulated candle smoke, was most likely to accumulate below decks when the gun ports and hatchways had to be closed because of bad weather, especially on decks below the water line, such as *New-York*'s berth deck, which had no openings to the outside. In fair weather, air could be kept moving with windsails, large canvas tubes that led down through hatchways so as to funnel fresh air below decks when the upper opening was adjusted so as to face the wind. They performed that task more efficiently and less unpleasantly than traditional fumigation with vinegar, sulfuric acid, or arsenic, or by burning charcoal, sulfur, tar, tobacco, or damp gunpowder. However, windsails were less effective than a ventilator with a large fan that brought fresh air in and removed foul air. This device, invented in 1741 by the Reverend Stephen Hales, a pioneering experimental biologist, required considerable human effort to power them. Although the British navy required their use in 1756, they were not used routinely in many warships before 1793. Nevertheless, Commodore Preble required use of both windsails and ventilators on *Constitution*; *New-York* had only windsails.

Neither Dr. St. Medard nor other physicians of his time knew, of course, that scurvy is caused, in the first instance, by a deficiency of the essential nutrient vitamin C, ascorbic (literally, "anti-scurvy") acid, in the diet, much less that the vitamin is a cofactor necessary for the optimal function of several enzymes involved in the manufacture of collagen, the chief supportive protein of the body. Instead, they could only associate the disease with easily observable conditions like those listed by St. Medard, such as dampness, dirt, foul air, or eating certain foods, especially slush, the fat skimmed off the water in which salted meat was boiled in order to make it palatable, and which, when made into a sort of suet pudding, was highly prized by seamen.

The medical profession was well aware that contagious diseases were defined as those that spread through the air (miasmas) or from one person to the next (contagions). Moreover, both laymen and doctors were aware that most contagions, whatever their ultimate causes, were characterized by gradually increasing numbers of affected patients as they spread through a community. The most feared epidemics ashore in early America were small pox and yellow fever; outbreaks of scurvy had occurred during the first century of exploration and settlement of North America, but were seldom seen on land there by the eighteenth century. Small pox had been preventable since 1721, but yellow fever vaccine was not developed until the twentieth century.

Many maritime historians and other writers seem to have assumed that their readers understand scurvy as well as the people in their books, but the clinical features of the disease are unfamiliar today, thanks to the nearly ubiquitous presence of ascorbic acid in vitamin pills and many processed foods. Therefore, despite its length (which alone suggests the importance of scurvy at the time), it seems important to use a late eighteenth-century description of scurvy to illustrate why it was so fearsome to seamen during the early years of the American republic. The following account from the 1771 first edition of the *Encyclopædia Britannica*, written by an anonymous physician, was intended for non-physicians, but at the same time it shows that the diagnosis was easy to make, and why the inexorable progression of the disease was so horrifying to men at sea in the age of sail:

This distemper chiefly affects the inhabitants of cold northern countries, and especially those who live in marshy, low, flat and moist soils, near stagnating water, whether fresh or salt. Those who live idle sedentary lives are most subject, chiefly in the winter, to the attacks of this disease; as also those who feed upon salted and smoak-dried flesh or fish, sea biscuit, stinking water, unfermented farinaceous [starchy or mealy] vegetables, pease, beans, sharp salt old cheese; like wise those who are subject to melancholie, maniacal, hysteric, or hypochondrial disorders.

It is known by spontaneous weariness, heaviness of the body, difficulty of breathing, especially after bodily motion; rottenness of the gums, a stinking breath, frequent bleeding of the nose, difficulty of walking; sometimes a swelling, sometimes a falling away [i.e., wasting] of the legs, in which there are always livid, plumbeous [leaden], yellow, or violet-coloured spots; the colour of the face is generally of a pale tawney [yellowish brown].

The first state of this disease begins with unusual laziness, spontaneous weariness; the patient loves to be in a sitting or lying posture; there is a pain in all the muscles, as if he was over tired, especially of the legs and loins; when he wakes in the morning, all his joints and muscles seem to be tired and bruised.

In the second state, the gums swell, grow painful, hot and itching, and bleed upon the least pressure; the roots of the teeth become bare and loose; he feels pains in all the external and internal parts of the body, imitating distempers proper to the various parts.

In the third state, the gums at length grow putrid, with a cadaverous smell; when they are inflamed, blood distils from them, and a gangrene ensues; the loose teeth by degrees grow yellow, black, and rotten; the sublingual veins become varicous [i.e., enlarged], and like rings; there are often fatal hæmorrhages, which break out from the external skin, without any appearance of a wound from the lips, gums, mouth, nose, lungs, stomach, liver, spleen, pancreas, intestines, womb, kidneys, &c. Obstinate ulcers [of the skin] arise, of the very worst kind, which no applications will cure, and which are apt to turn to a gangrene; they break out in all parts, but especially the legs, and are attended with a stench. There is a kind of an itch and dry scabs, with a dry and mild leprosy [i.e., not true leprosy, but resembling it on the surface]. The blood drawn from a vein is black, grumous, thick, and yet wants its due consistence in the fibrous part [the clot]; the serum is salt, sharp, and abounding with a yellowish green mucus on its surface. There are gnawing, rending pains, quickly shifting from place to place, which grow more violent in the night, affecting all the joints, bones, and viscera.

In the fourth state, there are fevers of various kinds, which bring on an atrophy; sometimes diarrhœa, dysenteries, or violent stranguries [painful urination]; as also faintings and mortal anxieties, a dropsy, consumption, convulsions, trembling, a palsy, contractions [of the limbs], black spots, voiding of blood upwards and downwards, a putrefaction and consumption of the liver, spleen, pancreas, mesentery. Now the contagion spreads very quick. . . .

The skin is dry throughout the whole course of this disease, except towards the last, and in many it is rough. In some it appears like the skin of a goose, but it is most frequently smooth and shining.

It is stained with blue, purple, livid, or black spots; some of which are small [petechiae], and others of a hand's breadth, when the disease is advanced. They are chiefly on the legs and thighs, but sometimes on the arms and trunk of the body. Some have a swelling of the ankles in the evening, which disappears in the morning. In a little time it advances gradually up the leg, and the whole member becomes œdematous. Hurts, bruises, wounds healed up, and fractured parts, always become scorbutic first. Old ulcers will emit a thin fetid sanies [watery yellowish fluid], mixed with blood, and at length coagulated gore will lie on the surface of the sore like a cake. As the disease increases, they shoot out a soft, bloody fungus [i.e., an amorphous growth] resembling bullock's liver, which sometimes will rise to a monstrous size in a night's time. The slightest bruises and wounds of scorbutic persons degenerate into such ulcers, and are easily distinguished from all others, by being putrid, bloody, and fungous.

Thus, the signs and symptoms of scurvy were unambiguous to eighteenth-century seamen. The only other equally easily recognizable diagnosis among those St. Medard made on *New-York* was intermittent fever; the various pulmonary, gastrointestinal, and febrile disorders were, by contrast, more subjective interpretations of their correlative symptoms.

Since scurvy is now known to be caused by a dietary deficiency, not by a transmissible microbe, one must ask why Dr. St. Medard and his colleagues considered it a contagious disease that occurred in epidemics. The answer emerges when the numbers of new scurvy cases (the stars in Figure 7) are separated from the other illnesses that appeared among the closed community of about 350 men in *New-York* in the fall of 1803 (as shown in Figure 8). That is, the steady increase in the number of scorbutic patients would have appeared to most observers to follow the familiar pattern—a gradual increase—seen during epidemics of illnesses such as small pox and yellow fever.

St. Medard lacked the one sure remedy for scurvy. The citrus fruits he had bought in Malta back in May must have sufficed only for immediate needs, and he had had to turn over many lemons—probably his last—to another ship shortly before leaving the Mediterranean. Although a supply of limes and lemons had become standard on British ships after 1795, citrus fruits would not be issued regularly on American warships until just in time for the War of 1812. That was, at least in part, thanks to efforts by John Rodgers, who in January 1812 wrote to the influential American naval surgeon William P. C. Barton about his own observations of the efficacy of limes and sour oranges when scurvy broke out among the crew of the sloop *Maryland* while cruising off Guiana in 1800–1801, just before his assignment to the Mediterranean squadron that eventuated in his command of *New-York*. Later that year, after Congress had declared war on Britain, Barton caused citrus fruits to be issued routinely to American warships.

On 1 November, St. Medard recorded in his patient log that his usual "antiscorbutic treatment" consisted of Peruvian bark, wine, elixir vitriol (dilute sulfuric acid), and "vinegar lemonade," along with liniments for the characteristic skin ulcers and "diet adapted to the disease," although he did not specify the ingredients of the diet. But five days later his treatment no longer included the "vinegar lemonade," for reasons that are not apparent unless he had simply run out of lemons, which seems likely, and he added a mouthwash. In any event, the "vinegar lemonade" may not have contained sufficient vitamin C to provide effective prophylaxis or therapy; we do not know how it was made.

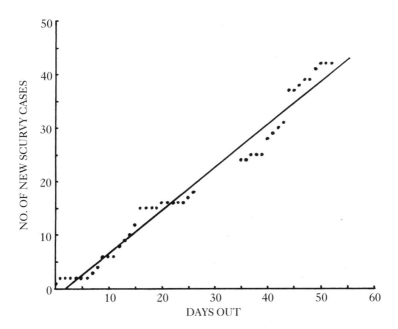

FIGURE 8. Cumulated numbers of patients newly diagnosed as having scurvy on the transatlantic voyage of *New-York* from mid-October to 9 December 1803.

In 1747 James Lind, soon to be England's leading naval surgeon, had compared the efficacies of six putative antiscorbutic remedies in six groups of two scurvy patients each; all were in the same stage of the disease, and all were kept in the same place and given the same diet. The six remedies were cider, elixir vitriol, vinegar, sea water, a lozenge made with garlic, myrrh, and other ingredients plus cremor tartar (sodium potassium tartrate), and citrus fruits (two oranges and one lemon daily); only the latter provided any discernible relief. Although some historians have succumbed to the retrospective temptation to conclude that Lind had used five negative controls in his clinical trial of the efficacy of citrus fruits, he really intended only to compare six acid remedies, inasmuch as contemporary chemical theories postulated that purulent illnesses were alkaline in nature—as Dr. St. Medard would have agreed. Indeed, he may have thought that the major "active ingredients" in his "vinegar lemonade" were the acids inherent in ordinary vinegar and lemon juice. Lind himself was not sure that he had proved the superiority of citrus fruits, and he could not confirm it in studies he carried out 25 years later at the Haslar naval hospital. He continued to suggest a range of acids as antiscorbutic remedies, although at the same time William Cullen, the influential professor at the medical school at Edinburgh, was arguing that only the highly acid citrus fruits could provide truly optimum therapy. Consequently, it is not surprising that the British navy did not adopt lemons and limes as standard issue antiscorbutics before 1795.

Modern experimental data showing the relationship between the rate of disappearance of the body's total pool of vitamin C and the order of appearance of those symptoms of scurvy that characterized the disease for eighteenth-century physicians are shown in Figure 9. In that graph, the middle curve shows that, on the average, it takes about 21 days for the body to be depleted of half its stores of the vitamin, and about 33–43 days to reach vitamin C levels that are generally associated with symptomatic scurvy; the other two curves delineate the expected statistical extremes of vitamin C depletion rates. It should be noted that the experimental subjects from whom the data in Figure 9 were obtained were relatively healthy and not subject to the stresses, especially the physical labor and restricted diet, found on ships in 1803, which means that the rates of ascorbic acid disappearance used to construct the curves are likely to have been somewhat slower than those among St. Medard's scurvy patients on *New-York*, but the conclusions to be drawn are probably not affected to any significant extent.

The data in Figure 8 permit us to calculate that the number of those patients was doubling approximately every twelve days on the transatlantic voyage. At the same time, the data used to construct Figure 9 can be used to calculate the expected rate of appearance of scorbutic symptoms in a normal population deprived of further replenishment of its stores of vitamin C: under such conditions, the number of affected patients would be expected, on average, to double approximately every twelve days, as occurred in *New-York*. Thus, it seems that that ship's

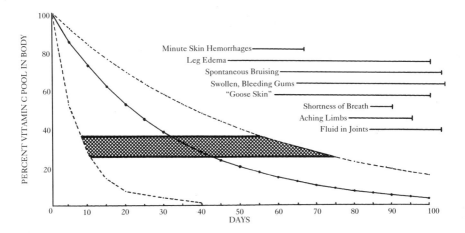

FIGURE 9.   Summary of modern experimental data for the disappearance of vitamin C from the body after its complete removal from the subjects' diet. The middle curve represents the average disappearance rate in 41 experimental subjects reported in eight studies; the other two curves represent the expected statistical extremes, so that 95% of the population would be expected to lose vitamin C at rates between those two limits.

The scorbutic symptoms in the upper right portion of the figure are given in terms used by naval surgeons of the late eighteenth century. The time span (in days) over which each could be expected to appear runs from the initial letter of each symptom to the end of the bar after it. Each time span represents the period after experimental deprivation of vitamin C in which the symptom was observed in the 1971 study by Hodges, *et al.*, the only study of its kind. The hatched area represents the time span over which body stores of vitamin C can be expected to fall to the critical levels between its upper and lower limits; thus, other factors being equal, the entire crew of a ship with no dietary sources of the essential nutrient might be expected to have scurvy in a maximum of about 75 days.

crew developed the disease at about the rate that would be predicted on the basis of the body's usual handling of the vitamin when the diet lacks any biologically useful supplies of it.

The official diet for enlisted ranks on American warships in 1803 had not changed since that authorized for the Continental Navy (see p. 18). It probably provided sufficient calories for men doing heavy work under the usual conditions at sea, but it did not provide for regular supplies of fresh fruits and vegetables, the sources of most vitamins. Instead, it was assumed that ship captains would lay up such supplies, and replenish their stores of salted meat with fresh meat, preferably still on the hoof, when they were able. (Officers, who had their own cooks, messed separately from the enlisted men, and provided food and drink, including fine wines, for themselves whenever possible.)

The eighteenth-century naval diet perhaps does not seem appetizing in terms of today's tastes, but it was not much different from most working-class menus of the day, it did have some variety, and its caloric value was almost certainly sufficient for hard-working men at sea. Its chief virtue was that it could be preserved fairly well under the primitive storage conditions available before refrigeration replaced salting. Only when stores were reduced, as during an unexpectedly long cruise, or if they became infested with insects or other vermin, were reduced rations likely to speed the appearance of scurvy among a ship's crew. There is no evidence that that occurred on the return voyage of *New-York*. Indeed, it seems most likely that an otherwise healthy crew of mostly young men who were constantly at work simply lost their bodies' stores of vitamin C at about the expected rate, resulting in a frightening epidemic of scurvy that would have become much worse had their ship not reached Chesapeake Bay by 2 December.

Word of the epidemic seems to have reached the Secretary of the Navy by then, because that same day he ordered that fresh provisions be sent aboard her at Norfolk as soon as possible. As his ship continued up the Potomac, Dr. St. Medard recorded that she fired a salute to "General Washington's mansion" as she passed Mount Vernon on the 8th, and at 4 P.M. that afternoon she anchored in the East Branch of the Potomac, where *John Adams* had already come to rest.

The next day *New-York* was "laid up in ordinary," and most of the crew were paid off and discharged. Those on the sick list, however, were retained, under an order issued by the Secretary nine months earlier, so that they could, eventually, be discharged, but also be paid in full until they were discharged (unless, like William Pitman, they were to be discharged for permanent physical disability, for which a life pension was allowed if the injury was incurred in the line of duty, as it was in his case). On the twelfth, President Jefferson with his cabinet and "nearly all of Both Houses of Congress" visited the newly arrived ships, and three days later the Secretary permitted Dr. St. Medard and his fellow officers to go on furlough "until called upon."

DISEMBARKATIONS

Several officers and midshipmen had already left *New-York* when she was at Gibraltar in September and October. For instance, Lieutenant David Porter, who had been wounded in the small fight at Tripoli, remained behind, reassigned to Preble's squadron. He was among the crew of *Philadelphia* captured by Tripolitans in 1803 and imprisoned for 19 months. During the War of 1812 he distinguished himself by leading the first American squadron to cruise the Pacific, and was again captured, by a British ship, in 1813. Ten years later he commanded a squadron sent to suppress piracy in the Caribbean, but after being court-martialed and suspended from duty because he took action against the Spanish at Puerto Rico, he resigned from the navy in 1826, although he later held several diplomatic posts, including one tour of duty at Algiers. He died in 1843.

Nathaniel Weems, who had been assigned to *Argus* after his promotion to Surgeon in July 1803, switched places with the surgeon of *John Adams*, so that he could remain in the Mediterranean squadron for the final assault on Tripoli. When his new ship returned to the United States in February 1805, Weems was furloughed to his home in Maryland in order to settle his father's estate. In April he asked the navy secretary for more than his current half pay, but his request was denied, and in February 1806 Smith accepted Weems's resignation, ostensibly so that he could devote more time to family matters. In 1809 he was granted a pension of $15 per month because of the injuries he had received in the gunroom explosion on *New-York* in April 1803. A year later he asked the Secretary's help in securing a federal appointment, at a salary of at least six to eight hundred dollars, to help make ends meet.

Neither the outcome of this plea nor the date of his death is known, but Weems was still on the list of federal pensioners in January 1814.

Henry Wadsworth ended his naval career on *Constitution*. According to a letter to a female cousin, he had been appointed to just the kind of expedition he most coveted when, on 16 February 1804, men from his ship, led by Stephen Decatur, burned *Philadelphia*, still held captive by the Tripolitans, before the Pacha could turn it against the American squadron—but at that time he was confined to quarters with an illness he did not disclose to his cousin. The diagnosis—venereal disease, probably syphilis—was revealed only in *Constitution*'s log four months later. In the meantime, however, Wadsworth had been promoted to Lieutenant on 23 December; his enthusiasm for the stalemated war had not waned. He wrote home that he had "been so long in the Mediterranean that I have acquired an habitual hatred of the Bashaw our enemy, & I feel as much interested in punishing him as if he had personally insulted me."

In August 1804 Commodore Preble conceived a plan of rigging the ketch *Intrepid*, formerly a Tripolitan vessel, as a fireship which would be sent into the harbor at Tripoli, where it would explode and set the Pacha's flotilla on fire. After the American ships had made several attacks on the city, the *Intrepid* was sent on her way on the evening of 3 September. Among the officers who steered her through the dark night were former *New-York* Midshipmen Wadsworth and Joseph Israel. For reasons that have never been fully explained, the fireship exploded prematurely, before her crew could get safely away, and all thirteen Americans aboard were killed. After news of Henry Wadsworth's death reached his family in Portland, Maine, lawyer Stephen Longfellow named his next son for the infant's maternal uncle who had died so heroically. A monument to Wadsworth, Israel, and their fellow officers who died on *Intrepid* is on the grounds of the U.S. Naval Academy at Annapolis. A treaty with Tripoli was signed on 10 June 1805, largely as a result of Preble's challenge to the Pacha, and ratified by the U.S. Senate the following April.

William Lewis, who had been hurt in the April explosion, was reassigned to *Constitution* in September 1803. Like Wadsworth, he regretted that he could not participate in the burning of *Philadelphia*, because, he said, "no volunteering was allowed." Except for a few months at home, he was continuously assigned to squadrons in the Mediterranean, and was promoted to Lieutenant as he returned to Virginia, again on *Constitution*, in 1807. Still in the navy, he disappeared at sea in 1815. A fellow midshipman, James T. Leonard, who was treated on five occasions by Dr. St. Medard for the most common illnesses on *New-York*—intermittent, catarrhal, and typhus fevers, as well as diarrhea and scurvy—died a captain in 1832, aged 54.

Captain James Barron, who left *New-York* in March 1803, and Lieutenant Stephen Decatur, who was sent home on *Chesapeake* after seconding Joseph Bainbridge's duel in Malta, had been friends and colleagues since 1798. Decatur was rewarded with promotion to Captain after leading the party that burned *Philadelphia* under the noses of the Tripolitans, thus depriving the Pacha of a potentially valuable war machine, and in 1806 Barron became Commodore of a new squadron which he commanded from *Chesapeake* (Charles Gordon, who had been Second Lieutenant on *New-York* under Morris, was his Flag Captain), although he was ruined professionally when he lowered his colors so that his 38-gun ship could be searched for presumed British deserters by the 50-gun British ship *Leopard* in 1807.

By this time the ten-year cordial relationship between Decatur and Barron had degenerated into ill-concealed enmity. The precipitating cause of their rupture seems to have been Decatur's embarrassment when Barron told him that it was dishonorable for the younger man to break off his engagement with a young lady in Philadelphia in favor of one he had just met in Norfolk, and whom he married soon after. Decatur was further incensed when, after Captain John Rodgers challenged Barron to a duel, Barron's second defused the issue, effectively precluding any passage of arms. Thus, Decatur was convinced, by the evidence presented at the court of inquiry called to investigate Barron's behavior in the *Chesapeake-Leopard* affair, that his former friend and mentor had acted improperly. The subsequent court-martial suspended Barron from all commands and pay for five years. After a long self-imposed exile in Copenhagen, he returned to Washington, only to find that an unsubstantiated accusation prevented his being given another command even five years after the term of the original sentence had expired, and Decatur continued to taunt his former mentor. Finally, on 22 March 1820, Barron met Decatur on a field of honor at nearby Bladensburg, Maryland, where Decatur was fatally wounded by the man whom he had once regarded as "more than a father." Barron later commanded various navy yards and in 1845 he retired to Norfolk, where he died six years later.

Richard Valentine Morris went home in disgrace following his suspension from command of the Mediterranean squadron. When he arrived at Washington, in *Adams* on 21 November 1803, he was asked to explain his failure to accomplish his assigned mission. Because his answers were not satisfactory to the Navy Department, a court of inquiry was convened at Stelle's Hotel in Washington on 3 April 1804. The court was almost certainly aware of rumors that Morris had dallied at the great British ports in the Mediterranean at the insistence of his wife, and they may have seen the letter to Consul William Eaton in which First Lieutenant Thomas W. Hooper, the marine commander on *New-York*, outlined several errors of Morris's military judgment.

The court found that Morris was "censurable for his inactive and dilatory conduct of the squadron under his command," especially citing the long periods he spent at Malta and Gibraltar "without necessity, or any adequate object," and for his delay in proceeding to Tripoli, as well as for raising the blockade there without good reason. He was also reprimanded for having prevented Lieutenant Porter from carrying out the raid on Tripoli he had proposed, and for mounting only an "unskilful and awkward" attack with his gunboats. Morris rebutted the charges, saying that

> if the disposition of the ships was not at one time exactly as I could have wished it to have been [when one American ship prevented two others from firing because it was between them and their targets], still I cannot impute it to myself as an offence, but to causes I could not controul. . . . the escape of the enemy, under their batteries, was intirely owing to the calmness of the weather, and the fast approach of night.

In his book-length defense of his conduct in the Mediterranean, published after the inquiry, Morris blamed the vagueness of his orders from Washington, which left it up to him to choose "the ground you are to occupy," as well as the necessity for repairs to his ship, lack of adequate provisions in early 1803, and the outbreak of influenza among the ship's company in the spring of 1803. He was also proud of his record of safely convoying American merchant ships in the Mediterranean. Still, the court concluded that the squadron's failure is to be ascribed, not to any deficiency in personal courage on the part of the commodore, but to his indolence, and want of capacity. He might have acquitted himself well in command of a single ship, under the orders of a superior, but he was not competent to the command of a squadron.

The Secretary of the Navy chose not to take the findings of the inquiry to a court-martial, but he did inform Morris that the President had revoked his commission, although early naval historians agreed that his abrupt dismissal was excessive punishment. He retired to his family seat in Westchester County, New York, and died while attending a meeting of the state legislature at Albany in 1814.

In Ordinary

New York City's once proud contribution to the young nation's wars was again put to rest in the Eastern Branch of the Potomac under a new Naval Peace Establishment, although she was supposed to be kept in a state of readiness should the need arise. Indeed, the navy secretary reported to the Speaker of the House that the annual cost of her upkeep was $102,252.76 as of 27 January 1806. Two weeks earlier the Secretary had ordered her to be prepared for sea duty. Repairs had been completed by November 1807, when she was being readied for recoppering and the erection of new masts. However, by May 1809 *New-York*'s hull, masts, and yards required extensive replacement, at an estimated cost of $21,234.39. The projected repairs seem not to have been carried out, because in January 1810 the Secretary appointed a committee, including two of her former officers, John Rodgers and Isaac Chauncey, to consider the merits of repairing *New-York* and three other frigates.

On 3 December 1811, as war with Great Britain seemed to be a real possibility, the Secretary informed the Speaker of the House that it would require $120,000 and six months to bring her into fighting shape again, and resurrected his earlier estimate that it would still cost over $102,000 a year to maintain her. The Secretary seems to have authorized repairs to the decrepit frigate once shooting began in the summer of 1812. In December 1812 five gun boats were ordered to convoy *New-York* to Baltimore, where a builder had been engaged to make her seaworthy again, but the convoy ships themselves proved unfit to travel any distance, so the frigate remained at Washington. Thomas Tingey, commanding officer of the Navy Yard there, next proposed to use her as temporary quarters for men who had been recruited for assignment to *Adams*, although it is uncertain whether that plan was carried out.

On 24 August 1814 naval authorities burned several ships at Washington to prevent them from falling into the hands of the enemy force then marching toward the city. The next day the British did burn some Navy Yard buildings and several ships moored there, including *Boston*. Many historians have reported that *New-York*, too, was burned in that attack, but the little frigate actually escaped the British flames and remained floating at anchor in the Potomac without repairs for many years. But by January 1830 she was resting on the bottom of the river, her upper structures still visible above the surface of the water. Divers could not be sent down to explore the hull that winter. An attempt to raise her eight months later met with disaster, and she sank further than she had been lifted. Although a second attempt was successful, it was finally decided that the entire project was too expensive, and *New-York* once again settled into the floor of the Potomac, where she remains to this day.

Notes

The popular description of scurvy is extracted from *Encyclopædia Britannica, or, a Dictionary of Arts and Sciences, Compiled upon a New Plan*, 3 vols. (Edinburgh: A. Bell and C. Macfarquhar, 1771), III:106–107. For contemporary professional criteria for the diagnosis of scurvy, see the following works by doctors who had worked at sea: Gilbert Blane, *Observations on the Diseases of Seamen* (London: John Murray and William Creech, 1785), pp. 460–477; William Northcote, *The Marine Practice of Physic and Surgery*, 2 vols. (London: T. Becket and P. A. De Hondt , 1770), II:354–363; and [anonymous], *Medical Advice to Masters of Ships* (Lancaster, England: n. publ., 1799), pp. 59–61. James Lind's 1747 experiment is described in his *A Treatise on the Scurvy*, 3rd ed. (London: S. Crowder, D. Wilson, G. Nicholls, T. Cadell, T. Becket and Co., G. Pearch, and W. Woodfall, 1752), pp. 149–153. William Cullen recommended citrus fruits in his *First Lines of the Practice of Physic*, 4 vols. (Edinburgh: C. Elliott and T. Cadell, 1786), IV:424. For the evolution of the British navy's approach to scurvy, see Christopher Lawrence, "Disciplining disease: Scurvy, the navy, and imperial expansion, 1750–1825," in David Philp Miller and Peter Hans Reill, eds., *Visions of Empire: Voyages, Botany, and Representations of Nature* (Cambridge: Cambridge University Press, 1996), pp. 80–106. The adoption of lemon juice by the British navy is summarized in Christopher Lloyd, "The introduction of lemon juice as a cure for scurvy," *Bulletin of the History of Medicine 35* (1961): 123–132, and the introduction of citrus fruits as standard issue for U.S. warships is described in William P. C. Barton, *A Treatise Containing a Plan for the Internal Organization and Government of Marine Hospitals in the United States* (Philadelphia: Edward Parker and Philip H. Nicklin, 1814), pp. 145–159. Captain John Rodgers's letter of 6 January 1812 to Barton is in the Joseph C. Trent Collection in the History of Medicine, Medical Center Library, Duke University, Durham, N.C.

The early history of below-decks ventilation is described in F. P. Ellis, "Victuals and ventilation and the health and efficiency of seamen," *British Journal of Industrial Medicine 5* (1948): 185–197, and in Richard L. Blanco, "The soldier's friend—Sir Jeremiah Fitzpatrick, Inspector of Health for Land Forces," *Medical History 20* (1976): 402–421. Preble's rules on ventilation are in Knox, *Barbary Wars Documents*, III:34. The diet is abstracted from *Statutes at Large of the United States of America, 1789–1873* (Washington, D.C.: Government Printing Office, 1850–1873), 1:523, and is quoted in William M. Fowler, Jr., *Jack Tars and Commodores: The American Navy, 1783–1815* (Boston: Houghton Mifflin, 1984), p. 137.

The most complete history of scurvy is Kenneth J. Carpenter, *The History of Scurvy and Vitamin C*, 2d ed. (Cambridge: Cambridge University Press, 1988), and modern concepts of the biochemical role of the vitamin are succinctly reviewed in Mark Levine, "New concepts in the biology and biochemistry of ascorbic acid," *New England Journal of Medicine 314* (1986): 892–902. Other relevant stories on which I have drawn are told in Leonard G. Wilson, "The clinical definition of scurvy and the discovery of vitamin C," *Journal of the History of Medicine & Allied Sciences 30* (1975): 40–60, and John Norris, "The 'scurvy disposition': Heavy exertion as an exacerbating influence on scurvy in modern times," *Bulletin of the History of Medicine 57* (1983): 325–338. I re-examined the rationale behind Lind's 1747 clinical trial in "Making therapeutic decisions with protopharmacologic evidence," *Transactions & Studies of the College of Physicians of Philadelphia, n.s. 1* (1979): 116–137.

The data used to construct Figure 9 were collated from G. L. Atkins, Betty M. Dean, Wendy J. Griffin, and R. W. E. Watts, "Quantitative aspects of ascorbic acid metabolism in man," *Journal of Biological Chemistry 239* (1964): 2975–2980; Leon Hellman and J. J. Burns, "Metabolism of L-ascorbic acid-1-C^{14}

in man," *Journal of Biological Chemistry 230* (1958): 923–930; E. M. Baker, H. E. Sauberlich, S. J. Wolfskill, W. T. Wallace, and E. E. Dean, "Tracer studies of vitamin C utilization in man," *Proceedings of the Society for Experimental Biology and Medicine 109* (1962): 737–741; Arthur F. Abt, Susanne von Schuching, and Theodore Enns, "Vitamin C requirements of man re-examined," *American Journal of Clinical Nutrition 12* (1963): 21–29; Robert E. Hodges, James Hood, John E. Canhan, Howerede E. Sauberlich, and Eugene M. Baker, "Clinical manifestations of ascorbic acid deficiency in man," *American Journal of Clinical Nutrition 24* (1971): 432–443; A. Kallner, D. Hartman, and D. Hornig, "Determination of bodypool size and turnover rate of ascorbic acid in man," *Nutrition and Metabolism 21*, supplement 1 (1977): 31–35; Anders Kallner, Dieter Hartmann, and Dietrich Hornig, "Steady-state turnover and body pool of ascorbic acid in man," *American Journal of Clinical Nutrition 32* (1979): 530–539; E. M. Baker, J. C. Saari, and B. M. Tolbert, "Ascorbic acid metabolism in man," *American Journal of Clinical Nutrition 19* (1966): 371–378; John H. Crandon, Charles C. Lund, and David B. Dill, "Experimental human scurvy," *New England Journal of Medicine 223* (1940): 353–369. The difficulty of coming to the realization that a dietary deficiency of anything can cause disease is outlined in Richard H. Follis, Jr., "Cellular pathology and the development of the deficiency disease concept," *Bulletin of the History of Medicine 34* (1960): 291–317.

New-York's return to Washington is documented in Knox, *Barbary Wars Documents*, II:137, 386, and III:263; National Archives Microfilms M149, roll 6, p. 263 and M209, roll 3, vol. 7, p. 3; and PSM's private journal, cited earlier.

Henry Wadsworth's illness is in Dudley W. Knox, ed., *Naval Documents Related to the United States Wars with the Barbary Powers*, 6 vols. (Washington: Government Printing Office, 1939–1944), III:472 and III:495. The story of the *Intrepid* is in McKee, *Edward Preble*, pp. 298–306. Nathaniel Weems's career is in Dudley W. Knox, ed., *Register of Officer Personnel, United States Navy and Marine Corps, and Ships' Data, 1801–1807* (Washington: Government Printing Office, 1945), p. 58; National Archives Microfilm M149, roll 1, items 43 and 86, and roll 6, p. 533. Professor McKee furnished his files on Leonard and Wadsworth. The Barron-Decatur story is told by W. M. P. Dunne in his "Pistols and honor: The James Barron-Stephen Decatur conflict, 1798–1807," *American Neptune 50* (1990): 245–259. Commodore Morris's later career is documented in Knox, *Naval Documents*, II:526–531. He attempted to exculpate himself in his *A Defence of the Conduct of Commodore Morris during his Command in the Mediterranean, with Strictures on the Report of the Court of Enquiry Held at Washington* (New York: I. Riley and Co., 1804).

The last years of *New-York* are chronicled in Dunne's *Resource Data File*, pp. 84–88. Those historians who assumed she was burned by the British seem to have overlooked a near-contemporary chronicler who pointed out that she did escape: [A. Bowen, ed.,] *The Naval Monument* (Boston, 1816), p. 306

Chapter Eleven

Final Reports

ETER ST. MEDARD's clinical records for *New-York*'s crew provide a new window on daily life among all ranks aboard a warship in the days of sail, a picture uncomplicated by the rapid loss of life—or at least of blood—usually associated with battles at sea. Indeed, navy secretaries valued such overviews, inasmuch as one school of thought (not shared by enthusiastic midshipmen like Henry Wadsworth) acknowledged that a primary function of any navy is to maintain peace. In addition, St. Medard's comprehensive and systematic clinical notes permit a systematic evaluation of the response of a well-defined closed group of patients born over 200 years ago to their medical and surgical treatments. Conversely, the same data permit us to evaluate the efficacy of an eighteenth-century physician's treatments.

Although St. Medard probably did send the required final report of his observations and professional activities during the 435-day voyage of *New-York* to the Secretary of the Navy, it has not surfaced in naval archives or among his own draft documents. In fact, no such document for any American warship dated from before the War of 1812 is known to have survived. (From 1731 to 1808 the British Admiralty required its surgeons to keep day-books identical to those mandated by the U.S. Navy in 1802, but the earliest surviving example dates only to 1793, and no systematic study of them seems to have been published.)

It has been possible to reconstruct, from St. Medard's *Physical and Chirurgical Transactions*, the information about the impact of disease and trauma on his ship that would have been of most importance to the Secretary, who would have wished to collate it with comparable data from other ships when planning for future cruises to the Mediterranean, and for the general medical needs of the navy. The degree to which *New-York*'s experience is representative of the entire navy is, of course, moot, in the absence of comparable data from her sister ships. Moreover, as contemporary data from British ships demonstrate, several variations can be attributed to geographic theaters of operation, since disease burdens differed among the North Atlantic, West Indian, Mediterranean, and Pacific stations. Nevertheless, many generalizations can be drawn from St. Medard's clinical observations.

THE DISEASE BURDEN AT SEA

The 239 men (and one woman) that Drs. St. Medard and Weems admitted to their ship's sick list represent 64 percent of the 370 men assigned to *New-York* in 1802–1803. Conversely, 36 percent of those men required no, or only minimal, medical attention during their tour of duty on the ship. The 18 men from other American vessels and the five "Arab" prisoners treated in *Meshouda* at Gibraltar in September 1803 are not included in the following summary analyses, although they are included in Appendix II.

Table 1 shows that, of the patients treated on board *New-York*, just over half (53 percent) suffered only one illness or injury during the voy-

TABLE 1.   Numbers of admissions per patient during the cruise of *New-York*.

Number of Admissions	Number of Patients
0	133
1	126
2	56
3	24
4	11
5	15
6	3
7	3
9	1
10	1

age, while 23 (10 percent) were on the sick list five or more times. The total number of individual admissions, or illnesses, was 487, for an average of 1.1 new patients per day during the entire voyage. They ranged in age from 13 to 50; about two-thirds were in their twenties, as was true for most seamen of the time. As seen in Table 2, the ship's officers were somewhat less likely to need medical attention than the enlisted ranks.

The officers, marines, and enlisted seamen differed more in their respective illness burdens than mere morbidity rates might suggest. As Table 3 shows, the enlisted seamen were sick more often, and for longer periods of time, than the marines. The seamen were also sick for twice as long, and twice as often, as their own officers. Although men from all three groups were in daily contact with the others, which would have permitted, or even facilitated, the transmission of infectious diseases, all three messed and were berthed separately.

The officers and enlisted men also differed somewhat in the frequency of the diagnoses that Dr. St. Medard assigned to each rank group, as seen in Table 4, in which the diagnoses are grouped by organ system or by the pathological processes involved, especially in the case of the febrile illnesses. (Patients in whom St. Medard diagnosed "rheumatismus" were included among the catarrhal fevers if it was clear from his notes that their complaints were referable to the respiratory system, not the joints.)

Catarrhal fever, which usually meant bad colds and other upper respiratory complaints in which the temperature was probably not significantly elevated (which is why such "fevers" were also called "colds"), was the most frequent diagnosis on *New-York*. It was less frequent

TABLE 2.   Numbers of crew members admitted to the sick list of *New-York*, by rank.

Ranks	Number Never Sick	Number Sick	Percent Sick
Officers, Related Professionals, and Midshipmen	20	24	55
Enlisted Marines	14	34	71
Enlisted Seamen and Petty Officers	99	180	65
TOTALS	133	238	—

TABLE 3. Average numbers of admissions, sick days, and length of stay on *New-York*'s sick list, by ranks.

Average No. of:	Officers and Midshipmen	Enlisted Marines	Enlisted Seamen
(N)	(24)	(34)	(180)
Admissions	1.2	1.6	2.4
Sick Days	8.3	16.3	28.4
Sick Days per Admission	6.7	10.3	12.1

among officers than enlisted patients, and was by far the least frequently fatal illness among all those that caused any deaths. Other potentially fatal febrile illnesses, such as influenza and consumption, caused no deaths while the ship was at sea. Nor did intermittent fever (i.e., malaria), which affected officers more frequently than enlisted men. It is not likely that any of the crew were exposed to malarial parasites during this voyage unless they went ashore, as some of the officers and midshipmen did; most cases were probably recurrences of earlier bouts with the disease. If we leave aside infected gunshot wounds, the most devastating infection during the entire voyage was the septic abortion that killed Nancy Staines, but death claimed one in five patients with the serious generalized fevers that could be found in virtually any population—typhus, slow, and nervous fevers, illnesses that today cannot be definitively linked with corresponding modern diagnoses.

Diarrhea (another term St. Medard used for this was "lientaria") and dysentery (painful bloody diarrhea), the most common illnesses of the gastrointestinal tract, affected enlisted men far more often than officers, while the most serious illnesses of the digestive system—the "bilious" diseases that often produced jaundice because they caused liver obstruction—were more likely to affect officers, and killed one in five of their victims, regardless of rank. Cholera morbus was not true cholera but a relatively mild form of diarrhea often called "summer diarrhea," characteristically diagnosed in children in early America. However, the one case in *New-York*, that of a 24-year-old midshipman, must have been more serious; it led to his discharge from the navy before his ship left the Potomac.

TABLE 4. Frequencies of diagnoses made at admission by Dr. St. Medard on *New-York*, and their respective death rates.

Diagnosis	Frequency among					Death Rates
	Officers	Marines	Enlisted Naval	All Ranks	All Admission Diagnoses*	
Catarrhal fever	26.83 %	37.88 %	40.09 %	38.87 %	44.73 %	0.9 %
Influenza	0	1.52	0.65	0.71	0.84	0
Pulmonic fever	0	0	0.22	0.18	0.21	0
Pleurisy	0	0	0.22	0.18	0.21	0
Consumption	0	0	0.65	0.53	0.42	0
Typhus,	2.44	4.55	1.31	1.77	1.48	19.0
Slow, &	0	0	0.65	0.53	0.63	
Nervous fevers	0	0	0.22	0.18	0.21	
Fever, unspec.	0	1.52	0	0.18	0.21	0
Intermittent fever	19.51	12.12	8.06	9.36	10.76	0
Diarrhea	2.44	9.09	9.59	9.01	8.23	2.5
Dysentery	0	7.58	8.06	7.42	5.91	18.4
Cholera morbus	2.44	0	0	0.18	0.21	0
Bilious fever, bilious colic, & liver obstruction	9.76	6.06	2.83	3.71	4.22	20.0
Rheumatic complaints	2.44	7.50	8.50	7.96	3.59	0

Lues, venereal disease	0	4.88	2.18	2.12	1.05	0
Strangury & dysuria	0	0	0.44	0.36	0.42	0
Dropsy (severe edema)	0	0	0.22	0.18	0.21	0
Debility, cachexia, & "invalid"	0	0	1.96	1.59	1.27	0
Abscesses & boils	0	0	0.65	0.53	0.42	0
Ulcers & Sores	0	2.44	0.44	0.53	0.21	0
Pain in the Side	0	2.44	0	0.18	0.21	0
Tumor, benign	0	0	0.22	0.18	0.21	0
Accidents, flogging, beatings, & gunshot	3.03	7.32	1.53	2.12	2.53	15.4
Hurt in explosions	1.52	17.07	0.87	2.12	2.53	33.3
Scurvy	7.58	0	10.02	9.01	8.65	15.4
Angina (sore throat)**	0	0	0.22	0.18	0.21	0
Abortion**	—	0	0.22	0.18	0.21	100

*Excludes additional diagnoses that later complicated the condition for which the patient was originally admitted to medical care.

**Both entries are for St. Medard's single recorded female patient.

Enlisted men suffered rheumatic joint pains at least three times more often than officers, probably because many of the affected men were older and had spent more years doing heavy work at sea. On the other hand, lues—syphilis—was more common among officers, presumably because they were more likely to be able to go ashore while in port. The two other cases of urinary tract afflictions that St. Medard diagnosed were, in all likelihood, caused by bladder stones. Generalized debility and related non-specific weakness, due to unrecorded underlying causes, were diagnosed only in enlisted seamen, and never resulted in death.

The one instance of dropsy (excess fluid in the chest, abdomen, or legs, now attributed to failure of the heart, kidney, or liver) occurred during the illness of 23-year-old Seaman Henry Thomas. He originally reported to sick bay with catarrhal fever and joint pains in February 1803. Two days later St. Medard was puzzled that he had become partially paralyzed and was having difficulty urinating. The surgeon inserted a catheter into Thomas's bladder, which relieved his dysuria within a day or two, and the paralysis disappeared within another week. The patient was recovering, albeit slowly, when, on the thirty-fourth day of his illness, fluid reaccumulated; again, St. Medard does not specify where. He prescribed jalap (a cathartic) and calomel (a mercurial, used in this case as a diuretic) to get rid of the excess fluid, and within a week it had disappeared, although Thomas did not return to duty until fifty-one days after he had been admitted to the sick list. The true cause of his dropsy cannot be ascertained, but a few hints in the record suggest that it was not related to heart or liver disease.

Minor surgical problems, such as abscesses, boils, a sprained ankle, the bruises that St. Medard suffered in a fall down a hatchway, and a small tumor (probably an abscess or other non-painful swelling) of the upper jaw, were few and far between; all were treated successfully. So was the man who traumatized his testes while straddling a yard, a common shipboard accident. The major injuries caused by accidents, beatings, and gunshot wounds were not rare, and occurred principally among the officers. (It is perhaps surprising that drunkenness does not appear among the diagnoses made on board *New-York*, even as a cause of injury or illness. However, if alcohol was not a problem on the ship, it may reflect as much about the collective contentedness of the crew as the fact that few floggings were inflicted on any of its members.)

St. Medard successfully reduced Seaman Henry Whitny's dislocated hip, but he remained on the "lame list" for nearly three months. The surgeon's treatment of the multiple injuries that William Pitman sustained when he fell from a considerable height was only partially successful (see p. 150). The most serious wounds were those that resulted from Henry Vandyke's duel in January 1803 (he actually died of overwhelming secondary infection; see pp. 105–108); the storeroom explosion in April (see pp. 120–122); and the bullet wounds inflicted during the skirmish off Tripoli in June (see pp. 127–129).

Scurvy was diagnosed only in enlisted men, and its progress to death was inexorable, unless checked by the timely administration of citrus fruits. Its 15 percent death rate in *New-York* would surely have been much higher had the ship not reached home—and fresh fruits and vegetables of any kind—when she did. Scurvy alone, among all the

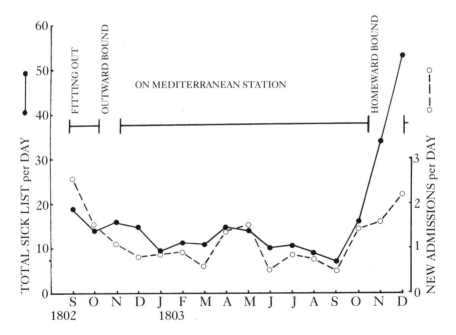

FIGURE 10. Monthly averages of number of new admissions per day, and total patients seen per day, during each month of *New-York*'s voyage. The dashed line with open circles (○) represents the new admissions daily, and the solid line with filled-in circles (●) represents the total daily sick list.

conditions Peter St. Medard treated, save for the most severe infections, had only one possible cure, and he had no supplies of it for the homeward voyage, probably because he—or the captain—had insufficient funds for purchasing new medical supplies, including lemons and oranges, before the ship left Gibraltar for home.

Figure 10 shows that the sick list averaged 19 a day in September 1802, while the ship was being readied for her Mediterranean assignment. Naval surgeons and commanders usually expected a high burden of disease at the beginning of any assignment, as new recruits from different places brought aboard diseases to which men from other areas had never been exposed.

The number of new admissions began to fall as cooler weather replaced the stifling heat of summertime Washington. In addition, the

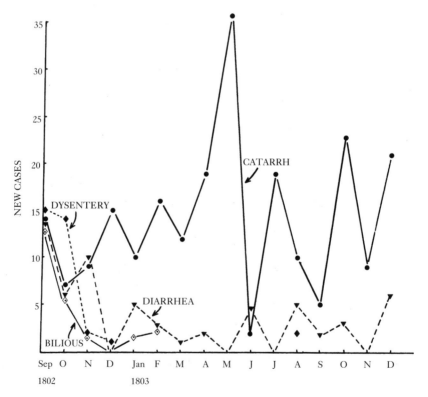

FIGURE 11.   Numbers of patients with catarrh, diarrhea, dysentery, and bilious fevers admitted to *New-York*'s sick list each month.

declines in the numbers of new cases of diarrhea, dysentery, and bilious fever (see Figure 11), which St. Medard blamed on bad water, is another clue that cool weather had returned. The sick list remained low until a major epidemic of catarrhal fever (sometimes lumped with influenza by St. Medard and Commodore Morris) broke out in April and May, as the ship shuttled around the Mediterranean. Catarrhs and scurvy, as well as a few cases of diarrhea, accounted for the resurgence of both admissions and the sick list as *New-York* sailed home in the fall.

Table 5, with Figure 11, shows the impact of the most common diseases on *New-York*'s mission. Navy secretaries would have been aware that they could not extrapolate the disease burden of any one ship to the entire fleet any more than we can, nor could they do so from data collected during missions to different parts of the world. For instance, yellow fever was typical of Caribbean assignments, but was seldom encountered in the Mediterranean. However, naval administrators could surely have expected to make useful predictions by accumulat-

TABLE 5. Morbidity and mortality data for the diseases Dr. St. Medard diagnosed most commonly on *New-York*, along with their respective contributions to work time lost to illness during the 435-day voyage.

Diagnosis	Percent of Total	Mean Duration	Percent Dying	Percent All Man–Days Lost
Catarrhs	44.6	8.7 days	0.9	31.7
Intermittents	10.5	8.9	0	7.7
Typhus, Slow, & Nervous fevers	1.6	13.9	37.5 +	1.9
Pulmonic fevers	1.6	36.4	0	4.9
Diarrhea	8.2	10.6	2.5	7.1
Dysentery	7.8	15.7	18.4	10.0
Bilious diseases	4.1	20.3	20.0	6.8
Rheumatism	3.7	16.7	0	5.0
Lues	1.2	11.0	0	1.1
Scurvy, without complications	8.0	18.9	15.4	12.4
All Others	8.7	—	—	11.4

ing data from as many ships as possible, taking into account factors such as the size of their crews and where they were deployed.

Of the 487 admissions to the ship's sick list, 84.4 percent terminated in return to duty, 6.6 percent terminated in death, 2 percent terminated in medical discharges, and 6.1 percent (mostly scurvy cases) were hospitalized when *New-York* reached her home port. In the aggregate, approximately 11 percent of the work days that should have been expected from the crew of 370 men over 435 days were lost to illness and injury.

From the Secretary's point of view, catarrhs had the greatest impact on the ship's function. On the other hand, there was little he or anyone could do to prevent such illnesses, they were rarely fatal, and most cases required little in the way of prolonged or unusual, expensive, treatment. Diarrhea and dysentery, on the other hand, had high mortality rates, but at least, insofar as Dr. St. Medard's recommendations could be taken into account and implemented, they could probably have been reduced by providing clean fresh water to the crew before they left home waters.

The physicians who examined new recruits were expected to reject those with potentially disabling conditions such as liver disease and arthritic rheumatism, as well as lues, but they were not always successful at that task, and nothing prevented those illnesses from first appearing during a voyage. Enlisted men seldom enjoyed shore leave in foreign ports, so they were less likely than their officers to contract venereal and other communicable diseases there, but most such stays were far shorter than *New-York*'s protracted visits to, for instance, Malta, where it would have been difficult to confine so many men in a ship anchored in the protected harbor for as long as a month.

Finally, inasmuch as Americans turned to British medicine for much of their clinical information, they were undoubtedly aware—as St. Medard certainly was—that citrus fruits provide sure protection from scurvy. Since the Royal Navy had adopted them for that purpose in 1795, it is not clear why the American navy did not officially adopt that method of protection from a major medical scourge until 1812. In the absence of data from other ships, the outbreak of scurvy on board *New-York* may have been unique among American warships of the time, but that seems doubtful. By contrast, the crew's collective experience with both upper respiratory and diarrheal illnesses was probably typical for contemporary warships.

The Efficacy of Ineffective Drugs

Navy secretaries were more interested in the impact of disease on the efficiency of their warships than in the efficacy of the remedies used to treat illness at sea. Indeed, their only real concern when it came to medicines was their price; even their purity was only one aspect of their cost. Indeed, like physicians at sea as well as ashore, the secretaries could only assume that all medicines were effective, at least as long as they could be assured, by the required oral examination, of the professional competence of the surgeons who prescribed them.

Today it is easy to recognize that few of Dr. St. Medard's drugs could have had much in the way of truly beneficial effects on his patients' recoveries—yet, as his clinical notes on *New-York* show (and as they are summarized in Appendix II), the vast majority of them did recover enough of their health to return to their assigned duties. When exploring the reasons for this therapeutic paradox, we must keep in mind that the notion of specific diseases with specific causes and specific treatments that is inherent—or at least assumed—in the modern use of the word "diagnosis" was not important to his contemporaries, nor had it been for 2,500 years. Instead, physicians used drugs to alter, to fine tune, their patients' internal equilibria, as reflected in their putative humors, tones, and acid-base balances, and in their correlative excretions and secretions such as urine, feces, saliva, and sweat. That is, physicians trained during the eighteenth-century Enlightenment treated their patients' symptoms, not their diseases.

Table 6 shows St. Medard's general approach to rebalancing humors and tones when he treated patients with catarrhs. At the same time, the table shows that he did not employ the same therapeutic regimen for all patients with the same diagnosis—the same symptoms. Rather, he tailored his treatments to each patient's individual characteristics—not only his pulse and respiratory rate but also his age, habitus, skin color, and so on, although, unfortunately, the patient record does not include those details. Nevertheless, it does reveal many aspects of an eighteenth-century practitioner's prescribing patterns, and illustrates the day-to-day application of the traditional two-step antiphlogistic treatment.

For instance, on the first day of admission to the sick list, St. Medard prescribed emetics and diaphoretics for about 40 percent of his

TABLE 6.   Fractions of 210 patients with catarrhs on *New-York* treated with major drug classes while on the sick list. The average duration of illness was nine days, and 0.9 percent died.

	Day on Sick List					
	1st	*2nd*	*3rd*	*4th*	*5th*	*6th*
Emetics	39%	13%	3%	2%	2%	1%
Cathartics	17	36	17	10	7	10
Diaphoretics	42	20	15	9	7	11
Bark	1	15	25	43	43	53
Bleeding	20	3	3	0	0	0
Average Amount Removed (ounces):	20	11	9	—	—	—

catarrh patients, cathartics for some, and bleeding for the most seriously ill patients. The next day he prescribed fewer emetics and diaphoretics, and fewer cathartics after the second day; he even removed less blood, on average, after the first day. Although some patients received more than one kind of drug on the first two days, on subsequent days they rarely received more than one. And, as was true for all the major illnesses he treated, each patient usually received a different drug each day, even from within the same drug category, although for long-term admissions Peruvian bark or mercurials, especially calomel, were repeated *ad infinitum*. That is, in the case of the catarrhs in particular, tonic drugs such as the bark, which has little obvious effect on the body's secretions and excretions, were substituted for those with clear effects such as vomiting, catharsis, and sweating.

As shown in Table 7, St. Medard prescribed emetics as initial therapy for the majority of his patients with intermittent fevers and then, as in other illnesses, some were given cathartics for the next couple of days, although Peruvian bark preparations were administered to increasing numbers of patients from the second day on. The bark, now known to contain quinine, was highly selective for killing malaria parasites, which made it one of the very few drugs with truly beneficial effects—but for intermittent fever only. However, because it had been found to be so effective in that illness as early as the 1630s, doctors concluded that it

182

would be effective in all other fevers as well, which led to its use in catarrhs and most febrile illnesses, to strengthen bodies that had been weakened by disease. St. Medard also prescribed absorbents to remove excess water from the intestinal tract. These remedies included clays such as kaolin, still found in over-the-counter diarrhea remedies.

Typhus, slow, and nervous fevers were the most serious illnesses among the non-gastrointestinal disorders that Dr. St. Medard treated on *New-York*. For them he relied on the same constellation of drugs he used when treating catarrh and intermittent fever, and most other illnesses for that matter, while altering his prescriptions day by day to help restore each patient's own special physiologic equilibria, as seen in Table 8. However, for these most serious conditions he also relied on febrifuges to reduce body temperature (he did not measure it directly with a thermometer but indirectly, by counting the pulse, which was known to be correlated with body temperature), while continuing to rely heavily on Peruvian bark to strengthen body tone. He did not specify which drugs he called "febrifuges," those that reduced body temperature, but they were most likely flavored cooling drinks made with various inorganic salts, some of which resemble the hydrating drinks favored by athletes today. The regulation of evacuations clearly was not as important as strengthening body tones in the treatment of such potentially devastating illness, which killed about a fifth of those afflicted.

Dr. St. Medard began treating his diarrhea patients with emetics or, less often, cathartics, in order to hasten removal of whatever noxious matter had disturbed the responsible humors. At the same time, he could assume that some of his emetics and cathartics also reduced the

TABLE 7. Fractions of 43 patients with intermittent fever on *New-York* treated with major drug classes while on the sick list. The average duration of illness was 19 days, and none died.

	Day on Sick List					
	1st	*2nd*	*3rd*	*4th*	*5th*	*6th*
Emetics	81%	20%	5%	3%	0%	0%
Cathartics	5	23	21	5	0	11
Bark	5	43	62	84	72	74
Absorbents	0	0	5	3	4	11

TABLE 8. Fractions of 16 patients with typhus, slow, or nervous fevers on *New-York* treated with major drug classes while on the sick list. The average duration of illness was 18 days, and 19 percent died.

	Day on Sick List					
	1st	*2nd*	*3rd*	*4th*	*5th*	*6th*
Emetics	56%	13%	0%	0%	0%	0%
Cathartics	6	31	7	8	8	0
Diaphoretics	31	6	7	0	15	17
Febrifuges	0	13	47	8	15	17
Bark	13	13	33	100	77	100

hyperactive tones that were assumed to be responsible for the bowel's excessive irritability. As seen in Table 9, he continued, or even initiated, cathartics longer than was customary in non-gastrointestinal illnesses, and he added bark preparations later, but for fewer patients with simple diarrhea than with the fevers. Finally, he added absorbents for up to a third of his diarrhea patients.

Although dysentery was a more prolonged diarrhea syndrome that was further characterized by bloody stools and abdominal pain, St. Medard used the same drugs as for diarrhea alone, as seen in Table 10. He began by first treating the diarrhea with emetics or, less frequently, with cathartics. He followed these with absorbents, although more

TABLE 9. Fractions of 42 patients with simple diarrhea on *New-York* treated with major drug classes while on the sick list. The average duration of illness was 11 days, and 2.5 percent died.

	Day on Sick List					
	1st	*2nd*	*3rd*	*4th*	*5th*	*6th*
Emetics	71%	2%	3%	7%	0%	5%
Cathartics	24	68	37	10	12	5
Bark	0	7	20	21	36	33
Absorbents	5	10	29	35	24	24

often than he prescribed them for diarrhea alone, and Peruvian bark, which he gave less often than in diarrhea. In addition, he ordered enemas for some of his dysentery patients, to speed recovery of their intestinal disequilibria. Despite his efforts, mortality from dysentery was seven times that from simple diarrhea. Ironically, one 30-year-old seaman was recovering from dysentery when, on the fifteenth day of hospitalization, he died immediately after falling from his hammock and breaking a vertebra.

Dr. St. Medard's treatment for bilious disorders was by far the most complex of all those he prescribed on *New-York*. These devastating illnesses, which were assumed to arise in the liver, were usually characterized by serious diarrhea and abnormal stools, and often by jaundice, all caused by an excess of bile among the humors. Although he prescribed emetics and cathartics among the mainstays of his initial therapy, as shown in Table 11, he also employed diaphoretics and bleeding, especially when fever was present, to further adjust the disequilibrium produced by too much bile. Over subsequent days he added Peruvian bark and febrifuges for the same reasons as in other conditions. He prescribed opiates for the relief of pain, although in most non-gastrointestinal disorders he gave them to control diarrhea whenever it complicated the principal illness. As noted earlier, St. Medard treated most of these patients in the first few weeks after *New-York* had been commissioned, while she was still in the Potomac being readied for sea. Not only did the bilious disorders and dysentery have high mortality rates, they led to more medical discharges than any other diagnostic categories.

TABLE 10. Fractions of 40 patients with dysentery on *New-York* treated with major drug classes while on the sick list. The average duration of illness was 16 days, and 18 percent died.

	Day on Sick List					
	1st	*2nd*	*3rd*	*4th*	*5th*	*6th*
Emetics	65%	8%	3%	3%	4%	7%
Cathartics	25	61	29	30	7	4
Bark	3	10	10	13	18	18
Absorbents	0	14	56	43	61	48
Enemas	3	0	6	10	7	7

TABLE II. Fractions of 21 patients with bilious disorders on *New-York* treated with major drug classes while on the sick list. The average duration of illness was 20 days, and 20 percent died.

	Day on Sick List					
	1st	*2nd*	*3rd*	*4th*	*5th*	*6th*
Emetics	29%	16%	11%	0%	0%	0%
Cathartics	19	21	32	11	12	19
Diaphoretics	38	53	21	21	0	6
Febrifuges	0	21	16	11	6	0
Bark	5	5	11	21	47	56
Absorbents	0	5	5	16	12	13
Opiates	0	32	16	5	12	6
Bleeding	27	16	0	0	0	0
Average Amount Removed (ounces):	12	10	—	—	—	—

In contrast to his treatments of acute illnesses such as fevers and gastrointestinal complaints, St. Medard did not adjust his treatments of patients with "rheumatic compaints" in the limbs on a day-by-day basis. Instead, he chose a single remedy for each patient, and continued to prescribe it until the patient was discharged from his care. Of the 32 patients with rheumatism, he treated 56 percent with liniments, 21 percent with oral doses of gum guaiac (an all-purpose tonic originally promoted as an antisyphilitic remedy), 12 percent with diaphoretics, and 5 percent with cathartics; he gave the last two only at the time of entering the sick list. For the few patients whose complaints became complicated by fever, he added blisters and various preparations of Peruvian bark, but most anti-rheumatic therapy was less specifically targeted than those two remedies.

Similarly, for his 12 syphilis patients, he prescribed "mercurial" drugs alone—he didn't specify which, but calomel was popular with many physicians of his day—until they recovered. He never specified whether these patients were in the first or second stage of the disease, and in only five patients was it the only diagnosis made. However, because the chancres that occur in the primary phase, and the rash, fever, and other manifestations of secondary syphilis are now known to resolve spontaneously, in the absence of any treatment, St. Medard could only have concluded that his mercurials were, indeed, effective remedies.

As outlined in more detail earlier, the surgeons on *New-York* were called upon to treat only 29 "surgical patients," comprising 6 percent of all 487 admissions. Most required conventional dressings for burns, trauma, minor operations, or immobilization of fractures and dislocations to facilitate healing. Some were given cathartics during their recoveries—probably the only instances in which such remedies were used specifically to remove constipation. Bark was prescribed for another few surgical patients, apparently when they felt weak during recovery, or if they were feverish as sepsis overtook them.

Table 12 lists the drugs that St. Medard prescribed most often during *New-York*'s cruise.

St. Medard reserved two treatments—blisters and bleeding—for his most seriously ill patients, usually those with fevers. He applied blisters to eleven patients all together; they included three of 210 catarrh patients, two of 43 with intermittent fever, one of 16 with typhus and related fevers, two of 42 with diarrhea, one of 40 with dysentery, one of 21 with bilious disease, and one of 32 with rheumatism.

Nor did he rely heavily on therapeutic bleeding. He removed an average of 12 ounces in 86 cases, representing 17 percent of all admissions but only 1.4 percent of all the treatments he prescribed. St. Medard ordered bleeding for all five patients with influenza or pleurisy, 48 percent of those with bilious disorders, 23 percent of those with catarrh, 5 percent with intermittent fever, 4 percent with dysentery, and one each with rheumatism, sore throat, and scurvy accompanied by a "full pulse." He also prescribed it for four men with bullet wounds, two who were injured in falls (he ordered it for himself because of the resulting contusions), and one each with burns, injury to the testicles, and a dislocated hip.

All the evidence available to Peter St. Medard—and to the Secretary of the Navy—clearly demonstrated to them that contemporary medical and surgical practices contributed directly to the recovery of the sick or wounded at sea—and comparable data permitted doctors ashore to come to the same conclusion. That is, in the absence of epidemics of the most serious contagious illnesses, the vast majority of adult patients, about 19 out of 20, survived their illnesses and wounds, which was accepted as ample evidence of the efficacy of eighteenth-century therapeutic practice.

TABLE 12.   Individual drugs most commonly prescribed by Dr. St. Medard on *New-York*.

Cathartics:	*19.3% of all treatments*
Calomel (mercurous chloride)	2.8 %
Jalap (usually with calomel)	1.9 %
Rhei (medicinal rhubarb)	3.3 %
Ricini (castor oil)	2.1 %
Stomachics (e.g., rhei + aloes + myrrh + mint, or gentian + canella)	6.2 %
Elixir proprietatis (aloes + myrrh)	0.7 %
Enemas (e.g, soap and/or olive oil)	0.6 %
Nitre (potassium nitrate, saltpeter)	0.6 %
Glauber's salt (sodium sulfate)	0.5 %
Balsam of Capivi	0.5 %
Glycerrhiza (licorice)	0.2 %
Senna	0.03 %
Cremor tartar (sodium potassium tartrate)	0.02%
Emetics:	*5.6% of all treatments*
Tartar emetic (antimony potassium tartrate)	3.0 %
Ipecac	2.6 %
Diaphoretics and Febrifuges:	*4.9% of all treatments*
Antimony salts in wine	4.8 %
Peruvian Bark preparations (regarded as Tonics):	*26.5 % of all treatments*
Bark in red wine	1.6 %
Cortex Peruviana (essentially the same)	5.5 %
Huxham's tincture	4.3 %
Opiates:	*2.3 % of all treatments*
Laudanum, Paregoric, and Thebaic tincture	2.14 %
Opium pills	0.19 %
Absorbents (magnesium carbonate or perhaps kaolin):	*5.5 % of all treatments*

But we must still resolve the paradox presented by this conclusion when now, two centuries later, we can recognize that Dr. St. Medard's remedies were, by and large, ineffective, and could have had no selective therapeutic effect on his patients. Perhaps the single greatest value of his clinical notes during *New-York*'s only voyage is that they permit us to develop an answer to that question—or at least a working hypothesis.

It begins to unfold when the medical histories summarized in Appendix II are used to outline the progress of patients with each of the major illnesses treated on *New-York*. Indeed, St. Medard's clinical records provide what is, so far, a unique opportunity to study the effect of day-to-day medical practice on any early modern population. In this case, the task is simplified, and even enhanced, by the fact that *New-York* never engaged another ship in battle, an event that would have seriously disturbed the normal equilibrium of health and disease among her crew. In short, the crew can be taken as representative of any population on land or sea, subject only to the disequilibria imposed by disease or everyday occupational hazards. Although it is unrepresentative in that this particular population included almost no women, the most common illnesses that affected it are not specific to either sex.

Figure 12 shows the percentage of patients with each of St. Medard's seven most frequent diagnoses who remained on the sick list at each of the first ten days following admission to his care. Patients with catarrhs were discharged back to duty sooner than all the others: 50 percent had been discharged by the fifth day, 80 percent by the tenth day, and the remainder were either convalescing uneventfully or went on to develop complications, such as rheumatism or diarrhea, that required additional treatment. A high proportion of men with intermittent fever stayed on the list for the first four days. Because malaria symptoms often recur in three-day cycles, four days would have been the minimum time required before recovery—absence of previously periodic chills and fever—could have been observed. Afterward such patients were discharged as soon as those with catarrhal fevers, and those with diarrhea were not far behind. The average duration of illness was about nine days each for catarrhal and intermittent fevers, for which deaths were rare (see Table 5, p. 179), and almost eleven days for diarrhea, which was fatal only when complications ensued, in 2.5 percent of those afflicted by it.

By contrast, dysentery patients were discharged almost equally rapidly at first, but in general were unable to return to duty for much longer than those with uncomplicated diarrhea: 60 percent were still on the sick list as long as ten days after admission. The average duration of dysentery symptoms was 15 days, and the death rate was high, over 18 percent. Bilious disorder patients were sick for even longer initially, but at ten days 60 percent of them, too, were still under the Surgeon's care. They were sick on average for more than 20 days, and 20 percent

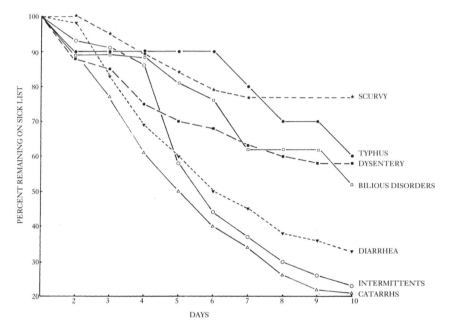

FIGURE 12.   Rates of removal from the sick list of all men in *New-York* who came under Dr. St. Medard's care for the seven leading diagnoses he made during her voyage, and for whom the eventual outcome of their illnesses is known.

of them died. Patients with typhus and other serious fevers remained in treatment for at least a week, and two-thirds were still on the sick list after ten days. Over a third of them died, which kept their average duration of illness as low as two weeks. As with the less serious illnesses, those still under treatment after ten days were chiefly those who developed complications.

Finally, scurvy patients required longer treatment than all the others. It was the only one among *New-York*'s most common afflictions that Dr. St. Medard could not treat effectively on the long voyage home, because he had no citrus fruits available. He had been able to treat two men successfully back in January, and eleven in May, with fresh oranges and lemons purchased at Gibraltar and Valetta, but he had none for the epidemic that felled 38 men in the fall. Even without complications, scurvy was fatal to nearly 19 percent of its victims, and more would have died if their ship had not reached home when she did. Scurvy was, of course, the only one of the principal diseases in

New-York, save the most devastating infections, that the body could not eventually correct by itself—that is, without receiving new supplies of vitamin C.

In short, because Dr. St. Medard's remedies cannot have contributed much to his patient's recoveries, his clinical notes have permitted us to reconstruct the natural history of the major diseases he treated with those remedies on the otherwise fruitless mission of *New-York*. There was nothing "wrong" with his therapeutic reasoning; indeed, his practice was entirely consistent with those of contemporary physicians at sea and on land, in France, Britain, and America.

In 1778, James Lind had noted that ". . . the best proof of the efficacy of any method [of treatment], is the success with which it is attended." Lind, probably the most celebrated naval surgeon of Dr. St. Medard's time, would have recognized the American's treatments as entirely successful. In this respect, neither surgeon would have recognized the relevance to evaluating drug efficacy of the *vis medicatrix naturae*, "the healing power of nature."

Although the concept was accepted by eighteenth-century physicians, its overall importance and implications were not yet widely recognized; doctors who relied on it alone would soon have been out of business. For St. Medard's contemporaries, a remedy was effective if it released the secretions or excretions it was supposed to, especially if the patient survived his illness (and even if he was not completely cured of all signs of it). That is, if the remedy assisted nature in restoring the patient's physiological imbalances to their natural state.

In 1785, the British naval surgeon Gilbert Blane recognized that

> There is a tendency in acute diseases to wear themselves out, both in individuals that labour under them, and when the infection is introduced into a community [i.e., a ship's crew]. Unless there were such a *vis medicatrix*, there would be no end to the fatality of these distempers . . . and those who happen not to be infected at first, become in some measure callous to its impression, by being habitually exposed to it. . . Thus the most prevailing period of sickness is when men are new to their situation and to each other.

Dr. Blane's last sentence helps explain the high incidence of disease among *New-York*'s crew before she even left the Potomac; Dr. St. Medard may not have had enough practical experience on ships being readied for sea duty to recognize that factor, since he blamed foul water for all the gastrointestinal compaints he treated during those two months.

On the other hand, Lind, Blane, and St. Medard could not have known about microbial sources of infection, much less about the principles of immunity that underlie today's approach to protection from infectious disease, nor about the processes involved in the repair of damaged tissue, including the vitamin C-dependent production of collagen. However, Blane clearly understood the epidemiology of shipboard disease, and St. Medard probably did. Thus, in the absence of truly beneficial remedies, the data in Figure 12 show the rates at which the human body is able to repair the damage inflicted by the six most common infectious illnesses in *New-York*, thanks to the immune and other protective mechanisms, even under the marginally adequate dietary conditions that prevailed on the ship. By contrast, scurvy, in which tissue repair mechanisms fail because collagen cannot be synthesized, could not be reversed without continuing supplies of vitamin C, leading to its reputation among the most feared illnesses to strike any ship. Indeed, not only had Blane explicitly omitted scurvy from his epidemiologic generalization, in 1795 he caused the Royal Navy to issue citrus fruits as protection from the disease.

The successes attributed to eighteenth-century "internal medicine" should, in reality, be attributed to the body's innate ability to heal itself, not to the therapeutic skills of physicians. By contrast, the clinical successes of contemporary surgery—that is, in patients who did not succumb to post-operative infections—can truly be attributed to surgeons' operative skills. Or, as 21-year-old John Moore wrote in 1784, soon after completing his training under the pioneering experimental pathologist John Hunter in London: "The art of medicine has this advantage over the art of surgery, that the means it uses to accomplish its ends are less painful; but surgery, on the other hand, has this superiority over medicine, that it is more certain."

St. Medard's patient records for 16 months in America's most forgotten war, on an equally unremembered ship, have thus yielded new insights into life and death in the U.S. Navy when it was still under sail—as well as into the remarkable results of the medical practices of his time. Indeed, of the practices of all times and places before the introduction of selective drugs of previously proved therapeutic value, as demonstrated by negatively controlled double blind studies, in the middle of the twentieth century.

NOTES

The first clear explanation of the efficacy of ineffective remedies was developed by Charles E. Rosenberg in "The therapeutic revolution: Medicine, meaning, and social change in nineteenth-century America," *Perspectives in Biology & Medicine* 20 (1977): 485–506; St. Medard's data provided my first opportunity to test Rosenberg's hypothesis—and, ultimately, to validate it. I presented early reports of my conclusions at the annual meeting of the American Association for the History of Medicine on 14 May 1981, and at the Naval History Symposium at the U.S. Naval Academy, Annapolis, on 2 October 1981. Those papers were published as J. Worth Estes, "Naval medicine in the age of sail: The voyage of the *New York*, 1802–1803," *Bulletin of the History of Medicine* 56 (1982): 238–253, and J. Worth Estes, "A naval surgeon in the Barbary Wars: Dr. Peter St. Medard on *New York* 1803–3," in *New Aspects of Naval History* (Baltimore: Nautical and Aviation Publishing Company of America, 1985), pp. 81–92.

For a comparable study of the disease burden at sea, albeit on voyages from Scandinavia to the Danish Virgin Islands (now the U.S. Virgin Islands), at about the same time as the cruise of *New-York*, see: Øivind Larsen, *Schiff und Seuche, 1795–1799. Ein medizinischer Beitrag zur historischen Kenntris der Gesundheitsverhältnisse an Bord dänisch-norwegischer Kreigsschiffe auf den Fahrten nach Dänisch-Westindien* (Oslo: Universitetsforlaget, 1968), kindly brought to my attention by Neale W. Watson.

For comparable survival rates in civilian populations ashore, see J. Worth Estes, "Making therapeutic decisions with protopharmacologic evidence," *Transactions & Studies of the College of Physicians of Philadelphia*, n.s. 1 (1979): 116–137, and Guenter B. Risse, *Hospital Life in Enlightenment Scotland: Care and Teaching at the Royal Infirmary of Edinburgh* (New York: Cambridge University Press, 1986), pp. 228, 365.

The quotation from James Lind is in his *An Essay on the Most Effectual Means of Preserving the Health of Seamen*, 3rd ed. (1757; London: J. Murray, 1778), pp. 254–255. Gilbert Blane's generalization is in his *Observations on the Diseases Incident to Seamen* (London: Joseph Cooper, John Murray, and William Creech, 1785), pp. 66–67. I have treated typhus, slow, and nervous fevers together, partly because there were few of each on *New-York*, but chiefly because contemporary observers did; see, e.g., Thomas Trotter, *Medicina Nautica: An Essay on the Diseases of Seamen*, 3 vols. (London: T. Cadell, Jun. and W. Davies, 1797–1803), 1:252.

For more on survival as the chief criterion of medical efficacy in the eigtheenth century, see Ulrich Tröhler, *Quantification in British Medicine and Surgery, 1750–1830, with Special Reference to its Introduction into Therapeutics* (Ph.D. dissertation, University of London, 1978), pp. 93–186.

For details of contemporary clinical applications of the drugs St. Medard prescribed, see, in addition to the works of Lind, Blane, and Trotter just cited, William Turnbull, *The Naval Surgeon* (London: Richard Phillips, 1806); Robert Robertson, *An Essay on Fevers* (London: G. G. J. and J. Robinson, 1790); [anonymous], *Medical Advice to Masters of Ships* (Lancaster, England: 1799); Edward Cutbush, *Observations on the Means of Preserving the Health of Soldiers and Sailors* (Philadelphia: Thomas Dobson, 1808); and Usher Parsons, *Sailor's Physician* (Cambridge, Mass.: Hilliard and Metcalf, 1820). Although each author usually had his own favorite remedies within any one drug class, they did not differ markedly in their uses of each class, and all prescribed drugs for different disease categories in the same sequences that St. Medard followed; even if they do not explicitly state that they did so, their recommendations, especially for fever remedies, were solidly based on the two steps inherent in the solidist approach to therapy. Using other, more detailed, eighteenth-century data, I have been able to report not only the same sequence but also the precise indices that physicians used in both planning and assessing their fever remedies day by day—the pulse and respiratory rates; those data are in J. Worth Estes, "Drug usage at the infirmary: The example of Dr. Andrew Duncan, Sr.," Appendix D to Risse's *Hospital Life*, pp. 351–384, and J. Worth Estes, "Quantitative observations of fever and its treatment before the advent of short clinical thermometers," *Medical History* 35 (1991): 189–216; the latter paper shows the relationship between body temperature and pulse and respiratory rates.

John Moore's comparison of medicine and surgery is in his *A Method of Preventing or Diminishing Pain in Several Operations of Surgery* (London: T. Cadell, 1784), p. 4. The true efficacy of antisyphilitic mercurials has been argued for some years, but there is little convincing evidence that they have any pharmacological selectivity for the responsible bacteria. A good recent review of the disease is by Edward W. Hook, III, and Christina M. Marra, "Acquired syphilis in adults," *New England Journal of Medicine* 326 (1992): 1060–1069.

For more on any of the diseases discussed here, see any current textbook of internal medicine, and the corresponding entries in Kenneth F. Kiple, ed., *The Cambridge World History of Human Disease* (Cambridge: Cambridge University Press, 1993).

Chapter Twelve

Epilogue in Boston

ETER ST. MEDARD returned to Boston when he was furloughed after leaving *New-York*. At the end of December he asked Navy Secretary Smith to assign him to the medical care of the officers, seamen, and marines attached to the Charlestown Navy Yard (renamed Boston Navy Yard after Charlestown was annexed to the larger city in 1873). In February 1804 Smith ordered St. Medard to the care of all navy and marine personnel in Boston and its vicinity, at full pay.

The Seamen's Sickness and Disability Act of 1798 had established the Marine Hospital Service to provide medical care for sick merchant seamen arriving from foreign ports, and for U.S. Navy personnel, financed by a deduction of 20 cents a month from their pay. The funds could be used to build new hospitals, or to pay for care at civilian facilities. The first Marine Hospital established under this legislation opened in 1801 at Norfolk, Virginia. The second, which began operation at the Charlestown Navy Yard a year later, moved into a handsome new building in the Federal style completed about 1805 on the point of the Charlestown peninsula, well away from the yard's ship-building and repair facilities, but within its confines.

By 1810 some senior physicians in the U.S. Navy had come to regard such hospitals as less than ideal for the care of navy men. Consequently, in 1811 Congress passed an Act Establishing Naval Hospitals, which remained in effect until 1943. Its major innovation was to fund hospitals for naval personnel entirely from the department's own budget, not from pay deductions. That meant that men in the U.S. Navy would no longer be treated at facilities of the Marine Hospital Service, which in any event was originally intended to serve primarily sailors in the merchant marine. (The Service eventually evolved into today's Public Health Service.)

When the new Marine Hospital burned in 1818, it was the largest in the system; 487 patients had been treated there in a recent year, and its average in-patient census was about 32. Later that year one observer complained that its loss had forced the navy to hospitalize its sick in "the hulk of an old merchant vessel, and. . . the frigate *Java*, lying in ordinary. The unsuitableness of these places to accommodate sick men is too apparent to require any comment." In 1824, two years after Peter St. Medard died, the Navy built its own new hospital across the Mystic River in Chelsea. It continued in operation into the 1970s, while the Boston Marine Hospital, rebuilt in the Brighton section of Boston, died along with other Public Health Service Hospitals in 1981, when Congress discontinued medical entitlements for the country's merchant seamen.

When St. Medard acknowledged Smith's orders to assume the care of sailors stationed at Boston, he added that Dr. Charles Jarvis (one of young Peter's mentors and a member of Boston's medical elite), who was in charge of the Marine Hospital, had been surprised at St. Medard's appointment, "fearing an interference in his department," presumably because it was on the grounds of the navy yard. St. Medard went on to say that he had tried to reassure Jarvis that their respective responsibilities were entirely separate, and that if he needed to send any patients to the Marine Hospital (at that time there was no hospital directly under naval jurisdiction at the yard), he would first discharge them from his own care; in short, there would be no grounds for inter-ference. Just to make sure, Smith replied that St. Medard was not to attend at the Marine Hospital—but the surgeon already knew this.

A month after Dr. St. Medard took up his new duties at Charlestown, which was within easy travel distance of his home in the North End of Boston, both he and the Jefferson administration were unpleasantly surprised. First, on 19 March 1804, Secretary Smith and the President learned that the frigate *Philadelphia* and its crew had been captured at Tripoli back on 31 October. Concluding that the United States must respond more effectively to the still piratical Pacha of Tripoli than had Commodore Morris, a new squadron was ordered to supplement the forces under Edward Preble, who was still in the

Mediterranean in *Constitution*. Consequently, two days later Smith ordered St. Medard and other surgeons to Washington for assignment to duty on the ships being readied for the new squardron.

The Boston doctor, who had just celebrated his forty-ninth birthday, asked to be excused from sea duty on grounds of ill health, but the Secretary rejected his plea and once more ordered him to report, "without a moment's delay." When St. Medard again asked for exemption, he enclosed a certificate from Dr. Benjamin Shurtleff of Boston, a former U.S. Navy Surgeon, who wrote that St. Medard is "unable at present to undertake a long journey or to perform the duties of his office at sea without great injury to his health as he is now labouring under a complaint of the chest which appears to be of a chronic nature." However, knowing that St. Medard had recently returned from sea duty, the secretary seems to have interpreted his request as a refusal to obey orders, and the Surgeon lost his leading position at the Navy Yard. On 12 May the Secretary wrote to inform him that it had been given to Dr. Jarvis.

This was almost certainly an act of political retribution. St. Medard's political leanings—at least, his known professional associations—were with Federalists. He may not have realized that Jarvis would have been preferable to the administration in any event because Jarvis, like the Secretary, was an outspoken Jeffersonian Republican. So was his successor at the Navy Yard, Dr. Benjamin Waterhouse, who took the post after Jarvis died unexpectedly in 1807. But it was the fact that neither Jarvis nor Waterhouse had seen military duty on land or sea during any of the new nation's recent conflicts that hurt St. Medard more than his dismissal alone.

However, he remained on active duty, apparently attending ambulatory patients at the Navy Yard, perhaps because the Secretary knew he had influential friends among the navy's senior officers. Moreover, St. Medard was among the most senior Surgeons in the entire navy. In March 1805 Smith placed him under the command of Lieutenant George G. Lee, then at Boston, for reassignment to New York, where he was to determine whether men recruited there were healthy enough for service in *John Adams*, then being readied for duty in the Mediterranean. Smith didn't tell St. Medard that he was to replace Nathaniel Weems, his former Surgeon's Mate, who had been furloughed so that he could visit friends. This was probably another politically motivated attempt to remove St. Medard from a coveted paying position at Boston.

Once more he wrote to Smith, asking to be excused from further sea duty because of ill health, and for assignment to some appropriate duty on shore, preferably as superintendent of the Navy or Marine hospitals at Boston. This time he enclosed two Boston doctors' certificates as evidence of his poor health. One was written by Dr. Jonathan Sprague, who reported that he has "witnessed [St. Medard's] excrutiating pains in the course of last winter in consequence of a sciatica induced by a long sea faring and advanced life." In the other, Dr. John Warren stated that an inguinal hernia made it "dangerous for him to expose himself to the hardships of very active professional exertion." St. Medard concluded his request for shore duty near his home by arguing that it was justified because "it is a rule, in all governments, to provide for surgeons in hospitals on shore (when infirmed or advanced in life in the service of their country) allowing they are qualified for, and worthy of such trust."

Although his letter was more than a little whiny, St. Medard was asking no more than some of his contemporaries did: he had done his best for his adopted country, and had become disabled while performing that service. Therefore, like many other Americans, he readily concluded that the government owed him a good job. The letters of Edward Cutbush, for instance, reveal much the same story, at least until he published his influential *Observations on the Means of Preserving the Health of Soldiers and Sailors* in 1808, which led to major new appointments. Although the Secretary did not give St. Medard what he regarded as a suitable appointment, neither did Smith accept his resignation from the navy, and St. Medard retained his commission for the rest of his life, albeit at half pay, and he did return to full-time work from time to time, especially during the War of 1812.

St. Medard continued to seek a permanent medical assignment in Boston for the rest of his life. He must have felt some optimism—and perhaps glee—when in November 1807 he informed Smith of Jarvis's sudden death, and asked to be reappointed to that position, but in vain. He wrote to each of Smith's successors—Paul Hamilton, William Jones, Benjamin Crowninshield, and Smith Thompson—and even went so far as to make the two-day journey by coach to New York to meet personally with Thompson in June 1820. But it was all to no avail. In 1813, Benjamin Homans, Chief Clerk of the Navy Department, promised to try to obtain a suitable position for the Bostonian. If he did, the attempt was fruitless, as was St. Medard's gift of several delicacies for Homans's table four years later.

In late April 1812, Dr. St. Medard asked Captain William Bainbridge, commandant of the Charlestown Navy Yard, but not yet the hero of the fight between *Constitution* and H.M.S. *Guerriere* on 19 August, for an essentially *ad hoc* appointment as examiner of new recruits, since war with Great Britain was imminent. Bainbridge agreed to ask President Madison's Secretary of the Navy, Paul Hamilton, to authorize the appointment, because "I know of no complaint against you as surgeon in the navy," and because, "believing that your character and capability stands fair, I think it no more than common justice that you should have employment given to you, when your services are required."

Bainbridge seems to have put the surgeon to work immediately. However, nearly a year later St. Medard needed official confirmation of his appointment from Washington in order to be paid. The letter he wrote to newly appointed Navy Secretary William Jones, six months after the War of 1812 had begun, is typical of all those he wrote to successive Secretaries—although atypical in that this letter was answered by confirmation of a coveted appointment:

> Your appointment at the head of the Navy Department imposes on me the duty of reporting myself to you as one of the Surgeons attached to that Department.
>
> Permit me, at the same time, to state to you, that as an old servant of the government when seemingly forgotten, I may presume to crave your indulgence and to recall to your mind a series of services and applications hitherto neglected. I observe with pain, from the unvoluntary shade of retirement, that young men who never had the honor of bearing a commission, young surgeons without the heavy charge of a family, and with hardly more than two years service; receive appointments, and are placed in stations particularly adapted to reward the services of one who has spent his whole life, and sacrificed his health and comfort in wars* and in the dangers of a sea service, from the dawn of the Revolutionary War in the service of the United States. Several years have elapsed since the date of my furlough, which has left me in a state of inactivity from public employment; but on the 22^{d} of April last, Commodore Bainbridge was pleased to order me on the recruiting service in this town, and until the pleasure of the Honble. Secretary of the Navy is known (which it appears has been exprecced by the government), and I take the liberty to inclose a copy of that order for your perusal. You have therefore

before you the opinion and orders of Comodore Bainbridge; conscious as I am that I never disgraced the commission I have the honor to bear, and ignorant of ever having given voluntary offence, you will pardon me; if I inquire, why am I thus consigned to oblivion. My services during and since the Revolution are sufficiently known to government; as they were rendered in a professional line, they would not have been continued so long had I been deficient in skill and capacity. The confidence which the Overseers [of the Poor] of this town have put in me for two years as a Physician and Surgeon of their hospital is a convincing proof of their knowledge of them, my character as a gentleman cannot be impeached. [Y]ou have in your Department sufficient proofs of my assertions; forgive me then if with the utmost anxiety, I pray you to give me a place on the list of those candidates, to whom you destine some appointment on shore, where ever you may judge I may be most usefull. . .
*Revolutionary [wars]
French wars
Mediteranean [i.e., Barbary] [wars]

Although this letter was successful—the Secretary really had no choice but to ratify a *fait accompli*—the reader will note that the surgeon no longer had children to support, since two had died and the third was in the army at the time.

In early 1815 three naval surgeons, led by Edward Cutbush, formed a committee which began to argue for improving their colleagues' rank and pay. St. Medard, now second only to Cutbush in seniority, and five other naval surgeons stationed at Boston drafted a letter supporting the committee's goals. The Bostonians' recommendations clearly echo requests St. Medard had been making for twelve years:

Boston June 23th 1815
The undersigned Surgeons in the Navy of the United States, and attached to the squadron now in this port, having learned that a Board has been formed for the purpose of receiving and organising the medical establishment and placing it on a better and permanent foundation, respectfully invite the attention of those gentlemen to whose judgment this important trust is confided, to a few suggestions which the united opinion of the undersigned think important in the consideration of the subject and which they have deemed proper to

place before the Board; the undersigned at the same time beg the gentlemen to believe that while they are activated by a wish to advance that part of the service to which they belong and to offer their thoughts on a subject which so nearly concerns them, they feel proud in appreciating the talents and respectability which compose the selection to whose wisdon and experience this duty is assigned. In considering a subject which involves so many important points, and which is so susceptible of various opinions, the undersigned do not wish to extend their remarks beyond a plain view of the subject, and in the observations they have now the honor to make, they only offer those hints, which from length of service has thought, and which they [consider] good policy might sanction.

The following are the points to which the undersigned refer —

1st that our pay be increased one hundred or seventy five per cent;

2d in sharing prize money, to be clas[s]ed with Lieutenants;

3th that each vessell or station to which a Surgeon is attached be furnished with medical books;

4th that it be defined how far we are amenable to the authority of junior sea officers;

5th that no appointment of Surgeons be made withought a privious service as mates for a certain time; nor no promotion be made withought an examination of their professional qualifications;

6th that senior or [distressed] Surgeons have the preference of shore stations;

7th that the pay and rank of Surgeon's Mates be placed on a more respectable footing;

8th that our former uniforms be established with a distinction to be made in the dress of Hospital Surgeons.

The first, second, fifth, and sixth suggestions here offered are those [in] which we feel the strongest interest. We however submit the whole, with deference to your consideration and subscribe ourselves

Most respectfully
Yr obed Humble Servants

Peter St Medard Surgeon, Recruiting Service

Saml. R. Trevett Surgn. of the Station Boston

A[mos]. A. Evans Surgn. Independence 74

Robert J. Kearney	Surg^n. Frig^t. U. States
	Surg^n. Ship Erie
	Surg^n. Frigate Congress
John A. Kearney	Surg^n. Frigate Constitution
Thos Chicester	Surg^n. Brig Enterprise
	Ac^t. Surg^n. Brig Prometius

Although the fate of the Boston naval surgeons' letter is not known, it was probably typical of those received by Cutbush and forwarded to the navy's new Board of Commissioners. The Board's chairman, John Rodgers, should have recognized St. Medard's name from their days together on the return voyage of *New-York*. In presenting the Board's case, Rodgers argued that surgeons, currently authorized to receive about one percent of each prize award, should not be classified with the commissioned officers entitled to about two percent as the Boston letter implicitly recommended. However, the rest of the recommendations submitted by St. Medard and his colleagues were seconded at other levels in the naval hierarchy, and all were presented to a Congressional committee in January 1817. But there the matter of naval medical reform died, for unknown reasons. It must have been frustrating to Dr. St. Medard, who had placed so much faith in a republican government.

St. Medard again conjured up his first service to America in his saddest—and whiniest—letter, to navy secretary Crowninshield, on 20 December 1818, in which he sought a minor appointment as the official medical purveyor for the port of Boston, "considering this as a retreat and compensation to be preferred to an old and faithful Revolutionary Surgeon, *who is in need*, and still honored with a commission." However, if he had been pressed to do so he probably could not have documented any actual "need" for additional income.

For instance, he continued to receive half-pay of $148.80 every six months, even though he had to write to the Accountant of the Navy or to the Fourth Auditor of the Treasury in order to receive it. He also earned full pay for the few days on which, for unknown reasons, he treated naval personnel. But his steadiest protracted period of naval income was the $1.50 a day he received for examining new recruits during the War of 1812. Thus, in June 1814 he received what must have been a windfall of $1,092 for 728 days spent examining recruits during the recent war. Moreover, his half-pay increased afterward, so that by 1819 the Boston surgeon was earning about $1,000 annually from the navy, in addition to whatever income he earned from his civilian practice and, perhaps, from his properties in France and the West Indies.

Beginning in 1819 Constant Freeman, the Fourth Auditor of the Treasury, began questioning some of St. Medard's accounts. It began when the surgeon passed a new recruit, Alexander Eagles, as "sound and healthy." Freeman noted that the recruiting lieutenant and sailing master, on the advice of a Dr. Gordon, had discharged Eagles a week later as unhealthy. When Freeman informed St. Medard that the $24.00 advanced to Eagles upon his recruitment would be withheld from the Surgeon's pay because it was not recoverable from Eagles, the indignant Surgeon replied that Eagles had been perfectly well at the time of his examination, that he had merely spent his recruitment advance in drinking, the result of "the natural propensity of a sailor towards intemperance, &c." He included certificates attesting to Eagles's similar exploits at other times, and one from the assistant recruiting officer seconding his appearance as healthy the day Eagles signed on. Although the surgeon successfully defended himself from Freeman's later questions, the auditor never authorized payment of the $24.00 he considered the price of St. Medard's poor judgment in Eagles's case.

During these years St. Medard was also occupied with his civilian medical practice, which must have produced some income, although none of his personal or professional account books have surfaced. Probably in order to solidify his position among Boston physicians, and to insure his share of referrals, he joined two local professional organizations, the Massachusetts Medical Society and the Boston Medical Association. However, he could never have been accepted into the town's elite medical establishment, controlled by the men who dominated Harvard's medical faculty as well as the two professional societies. The brief autobiography he submitted in 1812 with his application for membership in the state society reveals more of his professional life than the more military curricula vitae he had sent to Secretaries of the Navy:

> to the Honorable Gentlemen, Counsellors & Sensors [Censors, or Examiners] of the Massachusetts Medical Society, Boston
>
> Gentlemen
>
> Doc^t. Peter S^t. Medard an inabitant of Boston every since 1778, has the honor of laying before the honorable Boards, a corect statement of his regular studies of physic & surgery in Europ, & genuine certifi-

cates of the physicians & surgeons of the [French] King's hospitals & others, likewise a certificate of interogations before the surgeons of the admiralty [i.e., his examination for admission as a Surgeon in the U.S. Navy] on different subjects, and a diploma of his reception therein; likewise copies of certificates of different commanders under whom he has had the honor of serving during the revolutionary war, in the contest with Great Britain, & in the late contest with France; copy of his warrant of surgeon in the service of the general government dated Octob^r 1781; certificates from a number of respectable gentlemen, physicians & surgeons, of this town; togather with his commission of Surgeon in this new Navy of the United States dated July 1799; certificates from the Selectmen; idem from the Overseers [of the Poor] of this town, at the time of having been honored with their confidence for two years in the charge of the Almshouse hospital; a certificat from the French Consul of his confidence in the discharge of his duty as surgeon and physician of the French hospitals in this town; all those documents being from respectable gentlemen & eminent physicians & surgeons both in Europ & Boston in America, of the faithfull discharge of his trusts, of the skilfulness of his profession, & of the gentleman-like conduct, are humbly submited to the honorable gentlemen of the Boards for their consideration & satisfaction; as Doc^t. Peter S^t. Medard humbly pray[s] & solicits for a license in the practice of physic & surgery under the patronage of the Massachusetts Medical Society.

Doc^t. Peter S^t. Medard flatters himself & hopes, that they will be sufficient recommendation to grant his request as he further trusts & again flaters himself that he is not a stranger (after thirty three years of residence in the town of Boston & twelve years of service in the United States Navy) to the gentlemen (in general) members of the Massachusetts Medical Society, particularly those residing in the town [of] Boston.

His word "license" near the end of the application was not a license in the modern sense of a document issued by a state agency that was required before one could practice medicine in Massachusetts. Indeed, he had been exercising his profession since he arrived in 1778. In the early republic, Massachusetts practitioners won "approval" for their practices either by graduating from the only medical school in the state, at Harvard, or by being accepted as a member of the state medical society, but neither was required for any legal purpose. St. Medard had been able to practice since he arrived in Boston simply because he wanted to; the examination he underwent before receiving his warrant in the Continental Navy may have served as an additional level of approval. Unfortunately, none of the supporting documents he listed survived with his application, but they were sufficient to win his admission to the Society.

At about the same time, St. Medard joined the Boston Medical Association. Like other local medical societies, its primary goals were to protect the economic interests of its members, who were required to forswear the following activities: consulting with practitioners who were not members of the Association (i.e., itinerant healers, quacks, or other irregular practitioners); contracting with a family for providing its medical needs for a year, an early form of prepaid care; and accepting fees less than those prescribed for services listed in the Association's fee table. Some representative professional fees in Boston in 1806, early in Peter St. Medard's post-Barbary Wars career, and in 1819, near the end of his life, are given in Table 13.

Although charges for most operations did not increase between 1806 and 1819, charges for ordinary house calls and for bleeding did, as did those for attendance at deliveries. The perhaps surprisingly high cost of care for patients with venereal diseases reflected both the cost of prolonged treatment and a sort of punishment for having contracted such an immoral disease in the first place, as was also true in the navy. The costs of certain drugs were specified in the fee bills for other years, inasmuch as doctors often dispensed them, against the protests of local apothecaries. However, because most drugs were still being imported at this time, their prices could vary independently of the doctors' wishes. The greatest fee increase, for house calls at night, was probably intended to discourage frivolous or unnecessary summonses by overwrought family members. Although members of the Boston Medical Association agreed on this fee schedule, each was free to charge less to patients who could not afford to pay the standard rate, but only after a bill for the set fee had been presented to the patient. Unlike some (but not all) other local medical societies, the Association made no pretence of holding regularly scheduled meetings in order to discuss new developments or share professional experiences and observations; it was formed exclusively to regulate the economics of medicine in Boston.

TABLE 13. Selected professional medical fees established by the Boston Medical Association in 1806 and 1819.

	1806	1819
First visit [i.e., house call] for a given illness	$ 1.50	$ 2.00–5.00
Subsequent visits	—	1.50
Visit at night (i.e., between 11 P.M. and sunrise)	3.00	8.00
Visit on a vessel at a town wharf	2.00	2.00
Visit, for every mile from Boston	1.50	1.50
Case of midwifery in the day	12.00	15.00
Same, if any part of attendance is in the night	15.00	20.00
Capital operations [e.g., amputation of large limbs, lithotomy, trepanning, extirpation of large tumors)	40.00	40.00
Reducing dislocated or fractured large bones, or tapping for dropsy	10.00	10.00
Amputation of fingers or toes, removing small tumors	8.00	8.00
Bleeding (plus fee for house call)	1.00	1.50
Gonorrhea	10.00	10.00
Syphilis	15.00	15.00

In June 1805 the Overseers of the Poor recommended to Dr. James Jackson that St. Medard be appointed the physician to the new Boston Almshouse on Leverett Street, near Long Wharf, for the following year; he seems to have retained the post for a second year as well. The job would have attracted St. Medard largely because such appointments were highly desirable sources of steady income, worth usually about $150.00 a year in surrounding towns half as large as Boston. Because that city's population was now nearly 30,000, its Almshouse Physician was probably paid proportionately more than those in other New England ports. The Bay Town's almshouse, which had an average census of about 50 at any one time, admitted about 350 persons a year on average. Although such institutions were not designed primarily to deliver medical care, their inmates did need frequent professional attention because many of them were elderly or infirm or both.

Although St. Medard's income from the property he inherited in France fell, by an indeterminable amount, during the deflation that accompanied the first years of the Revolution there, his agents at Bordeaux and La Rochelle continued to manage his overseas properties to their client's advantage as best they could. The few surviving documents indicate that they continued to forward revenues to the expatriate doctor in Boston until the end of his life. He seems to have had smaller returns from his properties in Haiti and Martinique, but over the years the income from his combined overseas investments may have been substantial.

Sometime in early 1816 St. Medard began to add to his income when he became the Boston agent for the line of proprietary remedies promoted by a M. Ligneau, another French expatriate, whose office was on Pearl Street in New York. His leading products included:

— Consumptive Pectoral Syrup of Mou de Veau [Calves' Lungs], "invented and composed by the celebrated MACORS, so universally used in France for curing the *Consumption*, and other diseases of the breast, caused by colds and accidents, and which complaints are so frequent and dangerous, owing to the sudden changes of the temperature in this climate," as St. Medard's advertisement in a Boston newspaper proclaimed. Ligneau himself was proud that this remedy contained no opium, the usual cough suppressant of the day. $1.00 a bottle.

— Vermifuge Syrup, "so generally known in France and the West Indies. Its exclusive property is to cure every kind of sickness arising from worms... It is also aemployed with efficacy in putrid fevers, pains in the stomach, pregnancy and confinements, and particularly the vomiting amongst children, in the bginning and at the end of the small pox, either natural or inoculated." $0.50 a bottle.

— Oxygene Syrup, "Anti-venereal remedy, composed by the principles adopted by modern chemistry, without mercury, and its principal action is to neutralise the siphylitic virtues, without occasioning to the patient the least contrariety in his manner of living, nor in any of his ordinary vocations." That is, this medicine would not cause either the diarrhea or the excessive salivation ordinarily produced by the mercurial drugs, such as calomel, that were regular medicine's chief weapons against syphilis and, by extension, other sexually transmitted diseases such as gonorrhea. $2.00 a bottle.

— The Antisiphyletic Pill, which "does not leave any sign of the wants which one feels, nor even a suspicion of the disorder which has been the cause of it." $4.00 a box.

— *"The Infallible Dupurative [Purifier] of Woeugil which has never been known to fail in its effects,* and which no diseases, whether *Venereal, Ringworm, Itch* or *Scurvy,* even of the most desperate kind, ever resisted, *and which also cures, radically, every disorder of the Skin,* whatever be their date, nature, and cause." $3.50 a bottle.

St. Medard retained a 10 percent commission on these products, and on Ligneau's other wares, which were less expensive. They included scurvygrass (an antiscorbutic remedy), eau de meisse (Meissen water, made with mint), orange flower water, brandy bottled in 1801, a dentifrice, tarragon vinegar, vinegar à la ravigote (made with ground hard-boiled eggs and shallots), Orleans vinegar, and vinegar à la Ninou (the composition of the last two vinegars is not known).

Ligneau and St. Medard corresponded frequently, the proprietor seeking to be paid, his Boston agent to complain about spoilage in many of the bottles he received by ship from New York. While most of Ligneau's letters repeatedly proclaim his satisfaction with his own products, he also asked St. Medard to procure some enthusiastic testimonials from satisfied customers, although he insisted that they be witnessed and notarized. St. Medard was able to send at least three such notices, including the following:

> Boston October 16th 1816
>
> I the Subscriber, do hereby Certify that on the 10th instant I was violently seized with cold, frequent shivering, violent and frequent Cough, with spitting of blood and fever; on the 12th a physician [presumably St. Medard] was sent for, who administered to me, the pectoral Syrup *de mou de veau, Calves lungs, of Mr. Macors* so called, which after having taken about half of the phial, (by spoon full) in about four hours, I was perfectly relieved from all those accidents, and am now quite recovered; Witness my hand attested —
>
> Charlotte Foster
> Elijah Cleveland [witness]

However, St. Medard informed Ligneau that he could not have the signatures on the testimonials validated because Boston had no notary.

It is not possible to determine the extent to which St. Medard profited from retailing Ligneau's remedies, but a rough estimate based on the accounts exchanged between the two principals suggests that they might have netted the Boston agent as much as three hundred dollars over the first year, a not insubstantial amount at the time, and possibly even more. But in the late summer of 1817 it became apparent that his sales were falling off. He told Ligneau that the prices were too high, and hinted that perhaps the medicines were not as effective as their proprietor claimed. Ligneau replied that his Boston agent should increase his promotional activity. St. Medard did continue to order additional supplies, but he now subtracted a 37 percent commission from the amounts he sent Ligneau.

By the spring of 1819, less than three years after the venture began, Ligneau was reporting that his own sales in New York (and possibly those of his agents in other places) were down, and in June he informed St. Medard that he was selling his entire stock and going out of business altogether so that he could retire to his country home in New Jersey. However, it was probably not their lack of efficacy that forced Ligneau's products off the market—after all, few of the medicines prescribed by regular physicians had any truly beneficial effect on their patients—but the financial collapse of 1818–1819 which followed the instability created by the nation's attempts to recover from the economic effects of the War of 1812. That is, people simply didn't have the money to spend for expensive over-the-counter panaceas, and it would be another twenty years before proprietary medicines such as Ligneau's began their astonishing ascent into the lore of patent medicine excesses.

*   *   *

Peter St. Medard died, after a short illness, on 28 March 1822, at the age of 67. He was barely able to make his mark, a rather wobbly X, after dictating his will the day before he died. The funeral procession went from his house on Back Street to Holy Cross Cathedral on Franklin Street, where Bishop Cheverus, a fellow French Catholic expatriate, conducted the service. The cortege included six physicians as pall bearers, followed by clergy, the St. Medard family, military officers, "civil authorities," members of the Massachusetts Medical Society, and "citizens, &c." His coffin was then returned to the North End, where it was placed next to those of his children in the family tomb under Christ Church (Old North) that he had bought in 1808. It was most likely Susannah St. Medard's parish; she joined her second husband there two weeks later.

The probate inventory of Peter's estate shows that he and Susannah had lived comfortably. Their house had six rooms on the first floor, five on the second, and a cellar that boasted two barrels of cider as well as a "shower bath." The first floor reception rooms were filled with card tables, "alabaster ornaments," and all the appurtenances needed for gracious entertaining. The master bedroom and Peter's study were also on the first floor. Three upstairs rooms had beds; one or more of those upper chambers was probably where John Andrews (or perhaps his son John, who married Susannah St. Medard's granddaughter Susan Masson in 1816) lived for three years before Peter died, for $200 a year. The only clues to Peter's profession in the inventory were his books and surgical instruments, but they were not listed individually.

The value of his estate appears substantial on the surface. The inventory shows it was appraised at $6,537.92 (approximately $76,000 in 1991 dollars, but even that may be an underestimate), of which the house accounted for about 80 percent. Two bills for repairs suggest that he owned two other houses that he rented out. But most of the liquid assets were owed to fourteen creditors. The United States paid the estate $157, for back pay and expense reimbursement, and some of the furniture was sold at auction. Susannah (or, more likely, her daughter Sally Farrington Masson) gave the property that Peter had inherited from his parents on the Ile d'Oléron, and which he still owned, to his sisters Victoire and Eustelle. Their other brother, the Abbé, had recently died of a "putrid and malignant fever" accompanied by delirium—their branch of the St. Medard family was now extinct.

* * *

Peter St. Medard is typical of medical practitioners trained in the late eighteenth century. Unfortunately for him, he lived into the nineteenth, only to find the world changing a bit too fast for him. However, it was not his medical world that had changed. The remedies on which he and his professional contemporaries relied continued to be prescribed throughout much of the nineteenth century, even if their popularity waxed and waned. We cannot know if he mastered the medical correlates of the new chemistry that emerged between 1770 and 1800, or if he was aware that the next generation was beginning to take its cues from the newly emerging Paris school, which emphasized close clinical observation of patients before and after death, especially increased attention to physical diagnosis at the bedside. Inasmuch as he came from a seafaring tradition as well as a medical one, it is not surprising that his autobiographical memoranda reveal that he thought of himself primarily as a sea surgeon, nor that he identified as closely as he did with the town and the new republic in which he was set down after what can only have been a harrowing experience as a British prisoner of war. He seems to have succeeded, on at least a modest scale, as a physician on both land and sea; he does not seem to have aspired to any greater position in life, although he certainly aspired to a grander life style supported by a commensurate income.

He would, however, probably be surprised at the historical value of his major legacy—his clinical notes on the otherwise forgettable voyage of the U.S. frigate *New York*. Not only do they give us a rare firsthand glimpse into the professional thinking of a doctor trained during the Enlightenment, but they also furnish an equally rare look at day-to-day life—and the deaths that accompanied it—on a ship in the days when all ships were under sail.

Notes

The story of PSM's naval service after 1803 was reconstructed from several sources. Many are in National Archives Microfilm Publications, including (1) *Letters Received by the Secretary of the Navy from Commissioned Officers below the Rank of Commander, 1802–1884*, M-148, Record Group 45: PSM to Robert Smith, 23 March 1805 (roll 1, p. 63); William Bainbridge to PSM, 22 April 1812, with PSM to William Jones, 15 February 1813 (vol. 1, p. 64); PSM to Smith Thompson, 20 April 1820 (roll 24, p. 44); Isaac Hull to Smith Thompson, 25 May 1820 (National Archives, locus unknown); PSM to Smith Thompson, 29 May 1820 (roll 24); (2) *Letters from the Secretary of the Navy to Officers, 1798–1868*, M-149, Record Group 45: Robert Smith to PSM, 15 December 1803 (roll 6, p. 243); Robert Smith to PSM, 17 February 1804 (roll 6, p. 293); Robert Smith to PSM, 15 March 1804 (roll 6, p. 305); Robert Smith to PSM, 21 March 1804 (roll 6, p. 317); Robert Smith to PSM, 19 April 1804 (roll 6, p. 384); Robert Smith to Lt. George G. Lee, 6 March 1805 (roll 6, p. 523); Robert Smith to PSM, 6 March 1805 (roll 6, p. 524); Robert Smith to PSM, 13 March 1805 (roll 6, p. 530). Some of these letters are reproduced in W. M. Kerr, "Peter St. Medard, surgeon in the navy of the United States,

1756–1822," *U.S. Naval Medical Bulletin 16* (1922): 867–874; some of the additional information presented therein is erroneous, but most of it is accurate.

Approximately 300 letters and other documents that PSM drafted or received are in the EBA collection. Many either confirm the evidence from naval documents listed above or fill in some of the gaps. Because this collection has not been catalogued, it would be improvident to list its contents individually here. However, the dates given in the text will permit finding them, especially because an early custodian of the papers, perhaps even PSM himself, segregated most of them by correspondent: Navy Secretaries (29 items), [Thomas Turner], Accountant of the Navy (67 items), [Constant Freeman], "4th Auditor of U.S. Navy," actually of the U. S. Treasury (37 items), [Benjamin Homans], "First Secretary of Navy Office," actually chief clerk of the Navy Department (6 items), [Thomas T. Tucker], Treasurer of the U.S. (8 items), M. Ligneau (52 items, plus four advertisements and a handbill in English and French), letters to and from PSM's agents in France and the West Indies (5 items), and miscellaneous household bills, mostly for hiring horses and carriages (38 items).

The appointments of Drs. Jarvis and Waterhouse are noted in the following letters reproduced in the National Archives microfilm of *Miscellaneous Letters Received by the Secretary of the Navy*, M-124: Benjamin Waterhouse to Robert Smith, 4 March 1808 (reel 20, p. 129); and Francis Johonnot to Robert Smith, 11 March 1808 (reel 21, p. 9). PSM's work at the Charlestown Navy Yard in 1804 is evident in two reimbursements by James T. Loring, Navy Agent, for drugs PSM bought for use there from April through August, in box 4 of the Samuel Brown Papers at the Massachusetts Historical Society.

PSM's application to the Massachusetts Medical Society is in the Society's *Miscellaneous Papers*, 3 vols., I, f. 180, at the Boston Medical Library. His membership in the Boston Medical Association is dated 1812 in the *Rules and Regulations of the Boston Medical Association* (Boston: Dutton and Wentworth, 1838), p. 24. The 1819 fees were extracted from the 1819 edition of the same work (printed by J. T. Buckingham), p. 6. The entire story of the Boston Medical Association, and the 1806 fee table, are in Mark S. Blumberg, "Medical fees in Boston, 1780–1820," *Journal of the History of Medicine and Allied Sciences 39* (1984): 303–338. PSM's appointment to the Boston Almshouse is attested in a letter from Edward Proctor, chairman of the Overseers of the Poor, to Dr. James Jackson, 19 June 1805, in the Jackson Papers, Massachusetts Historical Society.

The following are in the EBA collection: PSM's will, dated 27 March 1822, and the certificate of probate, dated 15 April 1822; the probate inventory of his estate, by William Clouston, William Andrews, and Martin Bicker, dated 6

May 1822; two pages titled "Dr. The Estate of the late Doct^r. St. Medard in acct. Current with John Andrews," listing debts and credits to the estate; bills, and notation of their settlement, from Dr. John Pronk for attendance on Susanna Farrington [St. Medard]; and a letter from Eustelle St. Medard to Susanna Farrington [St. Medard], 1 July 1823, accompanied by an undated contemporary translation by an unknown person. (It is thanks to John Andrews that so much of PSM's correspondence has been preserved.) PSM's brief death notice is in the *Columbian Centinel* for 30 March 1822, page 2, column 5.

The essential source for all aspects of the medical corps of the early navy is Harold D. Langley, *A History of Medicine in the Early U.S. Navy* (Baltimore: Johns Hopkins University Press, 1995); the abortive 1815 attempt at reform is outlined on pp. 244–248. Additional information about Cutbush's attempts to enhance the status of naval surgeons in 1815 is in F. L. Pleadwell, "Edward Cutbush, M.D.: The Nestor of the medical corps of the U.S. Navy," *Annals of Medical History 5* (1923): 337–386; information about Charles Jarvis, and Cutbush's own failed attempts at naval preferment, are also outlined therein. The development of medical services at U.S. Navy Yards, including the one at Charlestown, is described in Hans A. Brings, "Navy medicine comes ashore: Establishing the first permanent U.S. naval hospitals," *Journal of the History of Medicine and Allied Sciences 41* (1986): 257–292; and Richard A. Bienia, Emanuel Stein, and Caroline H. Bienia, "United States Public Health Service Hospitals (1798–1981)—The end of an era," *New England Journal of Medicine 308* (1983): 166–168. The naval facilities in Charlestown are described in Bettina A. Norton, *The Boston Naval Shipyard, 1800–1974* (Boston: Bostonian Society, 1974).

For the structure, and political correlates, of the Boston medical scene, see Philip Cash, "The professionalization of Boston medicine, 1760–1803," in Philip Cash, Eric H. Christianson, and J. Worth Estes, eds., *Medicine in Colonial Massachusetts, 1620–1820* (Boston: Colonial Society of Massachusetts, 1980), pp. 69–100. A brief description of the Boston Almshouse is in Francis D. Moore, "In medicina veritas: The birth and turbulent youth of the Faculty of Medicine at Harvard College," *New England Journal of Medicine 307* (1982): 917–925. Approximations of current dollar values are possible using the tables in John J. McCusker, "How much is that in real money? A historical price index for use as a deflator of money values in the economy of the United States," *Proceedings of the American Antiquarian Society 101* (1992): 297–373. For the postwar economy, see Douglass C. North, *The Economic Growth of the United States, 1790–1860* (1961; rprt. ed. New York: W. W. Norton, 1966), especially pp. 182–184.

Appendix One

Drugs and Surgical Equipment for New-York

L ISTED BELOW are the medicines and medical instruments that Dr. Peter St. Medard requisitioned for *New-York*'s cruise to the Mediterranean. Except when he specified only the number of bottles, the amounts of drugs have been recalculated in drachms (1 ounce = 8 drachms). A later document suggests that the entire order was packed in six large boxes. From: [Peter St. Medard], "Estimate of Medicine, Instruments &c. furnished the frigate New York," MS., 3 pp., U.S.S. *Constitution* Museum Archives, vol. 4, no. 19. Unless specified here, definitions and further details can be found in J. Worth Estes, *Dictionary of Protopharmacology: Therapeutic Practice, 1700–1850* (Canton, Mass.: Science History Publications, 1990).

A. DRUGS

ABSINTH, sal	384
Absinth, leaves	192
Agaric	18
Aloes, gum	24
Alum/Alumen [potassium aluminum sulfate]	192
Ammonia, volatile spirits of	48
Ammoniac, gum	96
Ammoniac, sal [ammonium chloride]	192

Angelica, crocus [probably a mixture of aloes and rhubarb]   4
Anise oil   8
Anise seeds   96
Antimony in wine [made with an antimony salt or ore]   384
Arabic, gum   96
Assafetida   96

BARK, Peruvian [Cinchona], red, powdered   960
   Bark, Peruvian, yellow, powdered   960
   Bark, Peruvian, cortex   288
   Bark, as Huxham's Tincture [a mixture of Peruvian bark,
     orange peel, serpentina, cochineal, and saffron in wine]   384
Benzoin, flowers of [benzoic acid, extracted from the
   Benjamin tree]   2

CALAMINE, powdered [zinc silicate]   144
   Calamine, in cerate [beeswax]   480
Calomel [mercurous chloride]   288
Camphor, gum   384
Cantharides ["Spanish flies," *Lytta vesicatoria*], powdered   192
   Cantharides, or unguent plaster of   480
Capivi/Copaiva, balsam of   192
Castor oil [= Ricini], bottles   12
Caustic, lunar [silver nitrate]   2
Cerate [beeswax], white   144
Cerate, yellow   192
Chalybeate/Chalybis [usually ferric oxide, rust]   96
Chamomile, flowers of   576
Cinnamon oil   4
   Cinnamon, powdered   96
Columbo root   96
Corrosive sublimate [mercuric chloride]   24
Cremor tartar [sodium potassium tartrate]   960

EMPLASTRUM [plaster], adhesive   144
   Emplastrum, diachylon [a plaster made of olive oil
     and white lead (lead monoxide)]   96
Emplastrum, diachylon, with gum   96

GALLS, powdered   96
Gamboge   24

Gentian, powdered	288
Glauber's salt [sodium sulfate]	4512
Glycerrhiza [licorice] extract	768
Guaiac, gum	96
IPECAC, powdered	96
JALAP, powdered	480
KINO, gum	48
LAVENDER, spirits of	192
Linseeds	1056
Linseed oil	8
Litharge [white lead, lead monoxide]	1152
Litharge salt	192
Litharge plaster	480
MAGNESIA alba [magnesium carbonate]	128
Manna, gum	288
Mel [honey], clarified	288
Melissa balm [mint water]	192
Mentha piperita oil [peppermint]	8
Mentha piperita, Essence of [a proprietary brand], (bottles)	12
Mercuric precipitate, red [red mercuric oxide]	48
Mercury ointment [usually made with metallic mercury]	480
Mercuric ointment, citrinum [probably made of lead acetate, rose water, frankincense, and citron bark as well as mercury]	384
Mercury plaster	192
Myrrh, tincture of	48
NITER [saltpeter, potassium nitrate]	384
Niter, dulcified spirits of [niter in alcohol]	384
Nitric/Nitrous acid	96
Nutmeg/Nux moschata	4
OLIVE OIL (bottles)	12
Opium gum, purified	144
Opium, as Paregoric [also = Thebaic tincture]	120
Orange peel	192

PROPRIETATIS, Elixir [alcohol extract of aloes, myrrh, and
    saffron]   288

QUASSIA   96

RHEI (= Rheum, Rhubarb), powdered root   384
Ricini [see Castor Oil]   96
Roses, conserve of   96

SALEP [orchid root]   394
Sarsaparilla root   576
Seneca root   96
Senna leaves   192
Serpentina Virginia/Serpentaria root   192
Soap liniment   672
Spermaceti [sperm whale oil]   96
Squills, root   96
Stomachic elixir [aquaeous extract of gentian, coriander,
    and orange peel added to 100 proof alcohol]   576
Styptic water [solution of copper sulfate and alum]   96
    Styptic, Ruspini's (bottles) [a proprietary brand]   2
Succini oil [oil of amber]   12
Sulphur, flowers of [purified sublimated sulfur]   576

TARTAR EMETIC [antimony potassium tartrate]   48
Tartari, sal [potassium tartrate]   96
Terebinth [turpentine]   192
    Terebinth, Venetian/Turpentine [i.e., highest quality]   384
Traumatic balsam [made of 27 ingredients, chiefly oils
    extracted from various evergreen trees]   96

UNGUENTS/OINTMENTS (also see Calamine, Cerate,
    Litharge, Mercury):
    Basilicon [probably made of Canada balsam oil, lard, yellow
        beeswax, and sometimes olive oil]   912
    Simplex [made of white beeswax and olive oil]   480

VITRIOLIC acid [sulfuric acid]   96
Vitriol alba [zinc sulfate]   72
Vitriol coerulea [copper sulfate]   48

Vitriol, elixir of [made of sulfuric acid, cinnamon, and ginger in wine]	192
Vitriol, ether of [ether, sulfuric ether]	96
Vitriol viride [probably copper sulfate]	72
WINE, rectified	960

B. INSTRUMENTS

Amputation set	1
Bandages, compress	6
Bandages, head	3
Bandages, 2-headed	12
Bandages, 4-headed	9
Bandages, scapulary	4
Bandages, T-	3
Bandages, 12-tailed	6
Bandages, 18-tailed	6
Barley, pearl (pounds)	20
Bolus knives	2
Bone nippers	1
Bougies, in a case	24
Box (storage)	1
Brush, flesh	1
Case with large pockets	1
Catheters, silver	2
Clyster pipe with bag	6
Corks (for vials)	144
Dissecting set	1
Flannel (yards)	6
Forceps, bullet	1
Forceps, crooked	1
Funnels, tin	1
Gallipots	10
Inhaler, Mudger	1
Keg, cask	1
Lancets, spring	2
Lancets, thumb	12

Linen (yards)	15
Linen, old (pounds)	16
Lint, common [bandaging, rags] (pounds)	6
Lint, patent (pounds)	2
Measure, graduated	1
Medicine chest, mahogany, small	1
Medicine chest, mahogany, large	1
Mortar & pestle, bell metal	1
Mortar & pestle, glass	1
Mortar & pestle, marble	1
Muslin (yards)	36
Needles, common	50
Oil cloth (yards)	6
Paste board (sheets)	12
Pill boxes, papers	2
Pillows	4
Pins (papers of)	4
Plaster, court	3 pieces & 6 boxes
Pocket instrument set	1
Probang	1
Probe (crooked) scissors	1
Sago (boxes)	2
Scales and weights, sets	2
Seton needle	1
Sheepskins	6
Silk (ounces)	2
Soap, Castilian (pounds)	5
Spatula, fire	1
Splints, whalebone	8
Sponges (pounds)	1/2
Spruce, essence of (pounds)	10
Stove chest	2
Sugar (pounds)	200
Syringe, pewter, penis	24
Syringe, 2-pint (clyster)	2
Tape, narrow (pieces)	2
Tape, broad (pieces)	2
Tapioca (pounds)	19

Thread (ounces)	4
Tiles	2
Tooth set	1
Tooth-key, common	1
Tourniquet, Petit's or field	1
Tow, surgeon's (pounds)	6
Towels	6
Trephining set	1
Trocars & cannulas	2
Trusses, elastic steel	6
Twine (pounds)	1/2
Urinals	2
Vials	144
Writing paper (reams)	1

For other estimates of the various medical supplies required for warships of the same period, see William P. C. Barton, *A Treatise Containing a Plan for the Internal Organization and Government of Marine Hospitals in the United States* (Philadelphia: Edward Parker and Philip H. Nicklin, 1814), pp. 176–177; Aug[ust] C. Beers, Surgeon, to Capt. Edward R. McCall, commanding U.S. Ship *Peacock*, requisition for drugs, New York, 31 August 1829, MS. in G. W. Blunt White Library, Mystic Seaport, Conn.; Edward Cutbush, *Observations on the Means of Preserving the Health of Soldiers and Sailors* (Philadelphia, 1808), pp. 248–252; J. Dobson, "The pernicious remedy of the naval surgeon," *Journal of the Royal Naval Medical Service 43* (1957): 23–28; Benjamin Kissam, surgeon on U.S.S. *Constitution*, MS. drug list, 1816, in U.S.S. *Constitution* Museum Library; Usher Parsons, *The Sailor's Physician* (Cambridge, Mass.: Hilliard and Metcalf, 1820), pp. 192–195; and William Turnbull, *The Naval Surgeon* (London: Richard Phillips, 1806), pp. 312–314, 338–339. Some of these requirements must be prorated for the number of men on a ship of given size to be comparable to St. Medard's requisition, but they are approximately equivalent when this is done.

Pictures of many items in St. Medard's list can be found in several illustrated histories of medicine and surgery. A representative assortment recovered from a small vessel that sank in the Patuxent River, south of Annapolis, in 1814, can be seen at the Calvert Museum in

Solomons, Maryland. Those items, which include surgical and pharmaceutical artifacts, are illustrated in Fred W. Hopkins, Jr., and Donald G. Shomette, *War on the Patuxent, 1814: A Catalog of Artifacts* (Solomons, Md.: Nautical Archaeological Associates, Inc., and Calvert Marine Museum Press, 1981).

Appendix Two

Health Records of the Crew of New-York

T HE CREW of the U.S. Frigate *New-York* between September 1802 and December 1803, and their illnesses, if any, as recorded by Dr. St. Medard. All appear to have been on board for the entire 16-month voyage, with the exceptions noted. Collated from St. Medard's *Physical and Chiurgical Journal* on *New-York*; John Rodgers's Quarter Bill for *New-York*, in the Historical Society of Pennsylvania, no. AMN 300; and Dudley W. Knox, ed., *Naval Documents Related to the United States Wars with the Barbary Powers*, as supplemented by biographical files compiled by Professor Christopher McKee.

Abbreviations

E	Enlisted, exact rank unknown
OS	Ordinary Seaman
S	Able Seaman
M	Marine
Pvt	Private (Marine)
Mt	Mate
D	Died
d/d	discharged back to duty
d/c	discharged from the navy
hosp/	hospitalized at—
→	indicates change of rank while on *New-York*
f	fever

passenger home: men from other ships who were sent on *New-York* for the voyage home, in September–October 1803

Name	Age	Rank or Position	Entered on Sick List	Diagnosis	Days Sick	Outcome	Notes & Remarks
ABBERT, Jacob	—	M, drummer	— Sep 02	Rupture	?	*dlc* 28 Sep 02	
Ackerman, Jacob	17	Boy, gunroom	26 May 03	Catarrhal fever	1	d/d	
Alexis, Lewis	—	Midshipman	25 Apr 03	Hurt in explosion	7+	d/d	hosp/Malta
Allen, Reuben	—	Landsman	— Sep 02	Paralysis of left arm and leg	?	*dlc* 29 Sep 02	
Anderson, Aguilla	—	M Pvt	—	—	0	—	
Anderson, James	—	E → Sailmaker	—	—	0	—	
Anderson, John	26	M Pvt	19 Mar 03	Catarrhal fever	2	d/d	
Anderson/Henderson, John	16	Boy	4 Feb 03	Catarrh, rheumatismus	8	d/d	
			13 Sep 03	Catarrhal fever	21	d/d	
Anderson, Samuel	—	E	—	—	0	—	
Angus, Samuel	19	Midshipman (aide to Commodores)	—	—	0	—	D 1840
Archer, Starling	20	Surgeon's Mt	—	—	0	—	on *N-Y* 3 Dec 02 to 6 Oct 03; D 1806
Archibald, Robert	—	E	—	—	0	—	
Atterford, Peter	—	E	—	—	0	—	
Atwood, William	21	OS	21 Nov 02	Concussion from fall	20	d/d	
BAINBRIDGE, Joseph	—	Midshipman	—	—	0	—	left *N-Y* 5 Apr 03; D 1824

Name	Age	Rank or Position	Entered on Sick List	Diagnosis	Days Sick	Outcome	Notes & Remarks
Baker, John	18	OS	17 Sep 02	Catarrhal fever	4	d/d	
			7 Nov 02	Diarrhea	1	d/d	
			19 Feb 03	Catarrhal f., diarrhea	3	d/d	
Baker, Philip	—	E	—	—	0	—	
Barnet/Bernard, John	24	S	15 May 03	Catarrhal fever	1	d/d	
Barrington, Joseph	30	S	1 Nov 02	Intermitent fever	1	d/d	
			4 Nov 02	Diarrhea	5	d/d	
Barron, James	34	Captain	—	—	0	—	left N-Y 22 Mar 03; D 1851
Bashe, George	25	S	24 Sep 02	Dysentery	3	D 26 Sep 02	
Batton, Richard	—	M drummer	—	—	0	—	
Beattie, Abraham	—	E	—	—	0	—	
Bellamy/Bellona, Michael	—	Gunroom steward	—	—	0	—	
Benning, Henry	—	OS; gunner	—	—	0	—	
Berry, Thomas	30	S	19 Nov 02	Diarrhea, dysentery	26	D 18 Dec 02	at Mahon
Bilboa, Thomas	—	OS	—	—	0	—	
Bishop, Levi	19	OS	3 Nov 03	Scurvy	35+	hosp/US	
Bitter, Michael	30	OS	6 Sep 02	Diarrhea	2	d/d	
			6 Oct 02	Dysentery	15	D 20 Oct 02	broke vertebra in fall
Blake, Henry	—	E	—	—	0	—	
Blanchard, Samuel R.	—	E	—	—	0	—	

Name	Age	Rank or Position	Entered on Sick List	Diagnosis	Days Sick	Outcome	Notes & Remarks
Bowdoin, Henry	45	OS	21 Oct 02	Diarrhea	3	d/d	
			8 Feb 03	Rheumatismus	6	d/d	
			10 Apr 03	Catarrhal fever	7	d/d	
			9 Jul 03	Typhus fever; scurvy	7	D 16 Jul 03	
Bowie, Michael	35	M Pvt	22 Sep 02	Bilious fever	2	D 23 Sep 02	
Bowman/Bauman, John	22	S	22 Dec 02	Rheumatismus	1	d/d	
Brannan/Brennan, Neal	25	OS	29 Sep 02	Dysentery	11	d/d	
			6 Jan 03	Catarrh, rheumatismus	2	d/d	
Broudy (?), Lewis	24	OS	11 Jul 03	Catarrhal fever	3	d/d	
Brown, George	—	Boy → Gunner	—	—	0	—	
Brown, Joseph #1	22	M Pvt	23 Sep 02	Dysentery	11	d/d	
			14 Oct 02	Intermittent fever	8	d/d	
			27 Oct 02	Intermittent fever	4	d/d	
Brown, Joseph #2	—	E, holder	—	—	0	—	
Brown, Temple	—	M Pvt	—	—	0	—	
Buck, Samuel/Lemuel	23	S → Carpenter's Mt	7 Sep 02	Diarrhea	8	d/d	
			6 Oct 02	Dysentery	3	d/d	
			31 Oct 02	Catarrh, rheumatismus	12	d/d	
			9 May 03	Catarrh, rheumatismus	3	d/d	
			4 Aug 03	Scurvy	6	d/d	
Bumpus, Nathaniel	22	M Pvt	8 Sep 02	Dysentery	13	d/d	
			13 Oct 02	Dysentery; rheumat.	49	D 30 Nov 02	at Mahon

Name	Age	Rank or Position	Entered on Sick List	Diagnosis	Days Sick	Outcome	Notes & Remarks
Burgis, Henry	16	Midshipman; Idler	16 Sep 02	Bilious fever; boils	10	d/d	
			18 Jan 03	Influenza	7	d/d	
			21 Mar 03	Catarrh, rheumatismus	15	d/d	
			9 Aug 03	Catarrhal fever	4	d/d	
Butler, William Smith	17	Midshipman	26 Sep 02	Intermittent fever	5	d/d	
			22 Nov 02	Intermittent fever	9	d/d	D 1809
Byrnes, Charles	—	E	—	—	0	—	
CAMPBELL, Daniel	—	Cabin steward	—	—	0	—	
Campbell, Hugh G.	43	Captain	—	—	0	—	on N-Y 25 Sep to 6 Oct 03; D 1820
Campbell, James	27	OS	9 Sep 02	Catarrhal fever; lues	1	d/d	
			17 May 03	Catarrhal fever	1	d/d	
			20 Jul 03	Catarrhal fever	8	d/d	
			8 Aug 03	Catarrhal fever	13	d/d	
			31 Oct 03	Scurvy	39+	hosp/US	
Campbell, John	24	S	3 Jun 03	Catarrhal fever	10	d/d	
			19 Nov 03	Intermittent fever	20+	hosp/US	
Canada, John	18	S	16 Mar 03	Catarrhal fever	1	d/d	
			3 Oct 03	Diarrhea	2	d/d	
Canon, John Newton	36	Boatswain	15 Oct 02	Leg ulcers	12	d/d	
			30 Oct 02	Catarrh; biliary colic	7	d/d	
			25 Dec 02	Catarrhal fever	3	d/d	
			7 Sep 03	Catarrhal fever	2	d/d	
			26 Sep 03	Rheumatismus	5	d/d	left N-Y 18 Oct 03

Name	Age	Rank or Position	Entered on Sick List	Diagnosis	Days Sick	Outcome	Notes & Remarks
Carling, Robert	22	S	19 Nov 03	Scurvy (?)	5	d/d	
Carnes, John	24	OS	20 May 03	Catarrhal fever	4	d/d	
			20 Jul 03	Catarrhal fever	43	d/d	
Carpenter, David	20	M Pvt	12 Jan 03	Catarrhal fever	2	d/d	
Carr, James	24	OS	26 Nov 02	Lues	25	d/d	
			11 Feb 03	Catarrhal fever	8	d/d	
			5 Jun 03	Scurvy; sores	5	d/d	
Cecil (?), Matthew T.	—	Boy	—	—	0	—	
Chapple, Jonathan (?)	—	Cabin cook	—	—	0	—	
Chauncey, Isaac	31	Lieutenant (Flag Captain)			0	—	on *N-Y* 6 Apr 03 to 7 Oct 03; D 1840
Cheeseman, John	38	S, Quarter Master	4 Sep 02	Bilious fever	10	d/d	
			23 Dec 02	Catarrhal fever	6	d/d	
Clark, Michael	20	Capt's steward	5 Feb 03	Catarrhal fever	5	d/d	
Clark, Winlock	24	Midshipman	3 Sep 02	Cholera morbus	1+	d/c 28 Sep 02	liver disease, invalid; D 1810
Clay, Charles	—	Captain's hold	—	—	0	—	
Cockburn, Andrew	21	S	9 Sep 02	Diarrhea; lues	5	d/d	
			24 Jan 03	Lues; debility	9	*d/c*	
Cockburn, Charles	—	E	—	—	0	—	unfit for 25 lashes

Name	Age	Rank or Position	Entered on Sick List	Diagnosis	Days Sick	Outcome	Notes & Remarks
Collins, Earl	24	M Corporal	29 Sep 03	Fever, ? catarrhal fever	17	d/d	
			24 Oct 03	Catarrhal fever	10	d/d	
Collins, Matthew	26	OS	23 Feb 03	Catarrh, rheumatismus	7	d/d	
			3 May 03	Catarrhal fever	8	d/d	
			20 Oct 03	Catarrhal fever	3	d/d	
Collins, Thomas	16	Boy	27 Sep 03	Catarrhal fever	15	d/d	
Conley, Lawrence	26	OS	10 Sep 02	Intermit. fever, diarrhea	22	d/d	
			7 Nov 02	Catarrhal fever	48	d/d	
			28 May 03	Scurvy	4	d/d	
			5 Jun 03	Scurvy; consumption; debility	75	D 19 Aug 03	
Conway, John	—	E	—	—	0	—	
Conway, Peter	25	OS	4 Jan 03	Catarrhal fever	8	d/d	
			6 May 03	Catarrhal fever	3	d/d	
			12 May 03	Catarrhal fever	1	d/d	
			3 Oct 03	Catarrhal fever	9	d/d	
			22 Nov 03	Catarrhal fever	8+	hosp/US	medical d/c
Cook, Aaron	—	Cook's Mt	—		0	—	
Cooney, James	22	OS; Steward's Mate	13 Sep 02	Dysentery	9	d/d	
			7 Oct 02	Dysentery	4	d/d	
			14 Oct 02	Dysentery	19	d/d	
			10 Nov 02	Diarrhea	34	d/d	
			4 Feb 03	Catarrh, rheumatismus	9	d/d	
Cooper, Horatio	25	Master's Mt	24 Sep 02	Bilious fever; rheumatic gout	12	D 6 Oct 02	

Name	Age	Rank or Position	Entered on Sick List	Diagnosis	Days Sick	Outcome	Notes & Remarks
Cousins/Couzens, George	22	M Pvt	2 Dec 03	Catarrhal fever	7+	hosp/US	
Craddock, Edward	—	Cooper	—		0	—	
Crawford, John	—	M Pvt	—		0	—	
Creanor, Jacob	—	M Pvt	—		0	—	
Creighton, Charles	18	OS	17 May 03	Catarrhal fever	8	d/d	
Cress, Henry	25	S	7 Apr 03	Typhus fever	9	d/d	
			24 Oct 03	Catarrhal fever	2	d/d	
			4 Dec 03	Diarrhea	4	d/d	
Cross, Shubel	24	M Sergeant	20 Sep 02	Fever	4	D 24 Sep 02	
Crossman, John	21	OS	10 Nov 02	Rheumatismus	14	d/d	
			3 Dec 03	Catarrhal fever	3	d/d	sick idler from Oct 03
			21 Jan 03	Influenza	4	d/d	
Crow, Whipple	43	S	22 Dec 02	Catarrhal fever	8	d/d	
			15 Apr 03	Catarrhal fever	23	d/d	
			13 May 03	Catarrhal fever	33	d/d	hosp/Malta, 28 d
			11 Jul 03	Catarrhal → pulmonic f.	12	d/d	
Culverson, John	—	E	—		0	—	
Cumberland, James	40	OS; barber	27 Mar 03	Rheumatismus	3	d/d	
			3 Jul 03	Catarrhal fever	3	d/d	
			10 Jul 03	Typhus fever	2	d/d	
Curry, Anthony	35	S, Quarter gunner	5 Jan 03	Catarrhal fever	2	d/d	
			14 Jan 03	Knee abscess	37	d/d	

Name	Age	Rank or Position	Entered on Sick List	Diagnosis	Days Sick	Outcome	Notes & Remarks
DAILEY/DAYLEY	24	E	21 Apr 03	Catarrhal fever	20	d/d	prisoner
Dale, William	20	OS	11 Sep 02	Dysentery, intermit. f.	5	d/d	
			4 Oct 02	Dysentery, intermit. f.	40	*D* 12 Nov 02	
Dana, James	31	OS	21 Apr 03	Catarrhal fever	5	d/d	
Davis, John	—	Wardrm cook	—	—	0	—	
Davis, Robert	—	OS	—	—	0	—	
Dawling, William	21	Landsman	2 Sep 02	Liver obstruction	27	*d/c* 28 Sep 02	liver disease, debility; soon *D*
Dawson, David	—	E, holder	—	—	0	—	
Decatur, Stephen, Jr.	23	1st Lieutenant	—	—	0	—	left *N-Y* 5 Apr 03; *D* 1820
Decker, John	—	E	—	—	0	-	
Denning, Jesse	26	OS; Surgeon's aide	29 May 03	Lost 2 fingers in explosion	28	d/d	
Dennis, James	24	S	2 Sep 02	Bilious fever	7	d/d	
Derant (?), Gregory	—	E	—	—	0	—	
Dewhurst, James	—	OS	—	—	0	—	
Dirburn, Assa	19	OS	5 Sep 02	Dysentery	36	*d/c* 6 Oct 02	invalid
Donaldson, George	—	E	—	—	0	—	
Doran/Doring/ Dunham, John	23	S	20 Feb 03	Tumor of maxilla	3	d/d	
			3 Oct 03	Catarrhal fever	9	d/d	
Dorff/Doorfe, Samuel	19	M Pvt	19 Jul 03	Catarrhal fever	9	d/d	
			7 Aug 03	Catarrhal fever	5	d/d	

Name	Age	Rank or Position	Entered on Sick List	Diagnosis	Days Sick	Outcome	Notes & Remarks
Downes, John	18	Midshipman	5 Dec 02	Intermittent fever	21	d/d	
			21 Jul 03	Intermittent fever	4	d/d	D 1854
Doyle, John	40	OS	10 Sep 02	Intermittent fever	18	d/d	
			11 Mar 03	Catarrh, rheumatismus	51	d/d	
			31 Aug 03	Diarrhea	6	d/d	
			11 Sep 03	Catarrhal fever	1	d/d	
			12 Oct 03	Catarrh, rheumatismus	14	d/d	
			3 Nov 03	Scurvy	36+	hosp/US	
Driscoll, Richard	39	M Pvt	30 Sep 02	Intermittent fever	4	d/d	
			25 May 03	Catarrhal fever	3	d/d	
EIGART, Charles L.	—	E, Mids. Sidney Smith's steward	—	—	0	—	
Eliot, James	26	M Pvt	9 Jul 03	Typhus fever	19	d/d	
Elliott, Benjamin	—	M Corporal	—	—	0	—	
Evans, Samuel	24	Lieutenant	—	—	0	—	? passenger home
FEENEY/FINNEY, Bartholomew	40	OS	9 Sep 02	Diarrhea	16	d/d	
			29 Oct 02	Intermittent fever	13	d/d	
			19 May 03	Intermittent fever	6	d/d	
			8 Jul 03	Intermittent fever	4	d/d	
Fenner/Tenner, John	22	OS → S	1 Sep 02	Dysentery	3	d/d	
			7 Nov 02	Catarrh; diarrhea; rheumatismus	45	d/d	
			20 Jan 03	Rheumatismus	19	d/d	
			17 Feb 03	Rheumatismus	60	d/d	
			15 Oct 03	Catarrhal → typhus f.	19	D 2 Nov 03	

Name	Age	Rank or Position	Entered on Sick List	Diagnosis	Days Sick	Outcome	Notes & Remarks
Fink, Samuel	—	E	—	—	0	—	
Fox, James	29	Boatswain's Mt	11 Sep 02	Intermittent fever	7	d/d	
			30 Sep 02	Intermittent fever	9	d/d	
			18 Oct 02	Intermittent fever, rheumatismus	4	d/d	
			19 Nov 02	Intermittent fever	6	d/d	
			8 May 03	Catarrh, rheumatismus	4	d/d	
Francis, Matthew	—	Boy	—	—	0	—	
Frazier, James	—	Cook	—	—	0	—	
Fuller, Bartholomew	17	OS	6 Dec 02	Catarrhal fever	5	d/d	
			26 Mar 03	Catarrhal fever	3	d/d	
			3 Jul 03	Catarrhal fever	4	d/d	
Fullerton, Charles	—	E	—	—	0	—	
GABRIEL, Jacob	24	OS	5 Dec 03	Pleurisy, scurvy	4+	hosp/US	
Gadsden, Christopher, Jr.	21	Midshipman	19 May 03	Intermittent fever	10	d/d	left N-Y 16 Sep 03; D 1812
Galvin, Joseph	37	M Pvt	24 Feb 03	Catarrh	2	d/d	
Gardner, Benjamin	20	OS	20 Nov 02	Diarrhea, scurvy	40+	hosp/Malta, 30 Dec 02	did not return to N-Y
Garlick, John	—	Boy	—	—	0	—	
Garretson, Isaac	36	Purser	—	—	0	—	D 1830
Garvin, Hugh	28	M Pvt	2 Dec 03	Catarrhal fever	7+	hosp/US	

Name	Age	Rank or Position	Entered on Sick List	Diagnosis	Days Sick	Outcome	Notes & Remarks
Getting/Gittings, William	20	OS → Carpenter's Mt	26 Dec 02	Catarrhal fever	4	d/d	
			7 Jun 03	Catarrhal fever	2	d/d	
Giles, Edward	22	Midshipman	29 May 03	Catarrhal fever	9	d/d	
Gill, Jonas	30	S; Quarter gunner	4 Nov 03	Scurvy	35+	hosp/US	
Gleason/Glisson, Joseph	22	S	11 Sep 02	Dysentery	7	d/d	
			10 Nov 02	Diarrhea	3	d/d	
			19 Nov 02	Dysentery	4	d/d	
			10 Feb 03	Diarrhea	2	d/d	
			25 Feb 03	Catarrhal fever	4	d/d	
			9 Apr 03	Catarrhal fever	33	d/d	
			17 May 03	Slow fever; debility	40	d/d	
			7 Jul 03	Cachexia	10	d/d	
			1 Aug 03	Consumption	129+	hosp/US	
Gold, Charles	—	E	—	—	0	—	
Gold/Gould, John	—	M Pvt	—	—	0	—	
Gordon, Charles	25	2nd Lieutenant	26 Sep 02	Catarrhal fever	2	d/d	left *N-Y* 16 Sep 03; D 1816
Gough/Goff, William	18	OS	24 Nov 02	Catarrhal fever	2	d/d	
			11 Sep 03	Catarrhal fever	34	d/d	
			3 Nov 03	Catarrh, diarrhea	9	d/d	
Gould/Gold, William	38	S → Carpenter's Mt	15 Sep 02	Dysentery	6	d/d	
			3 May 03	Scurvy	6	d/d	
Grady, William	—	Carpenter's Mt	—	—	0	—	

Name	Age	Rank or Position	Entered on Sick List	Diagnosis	Days Sick	Outcome	Notes & Remarks
Grant, Peter	17	OS	14 Sep 02	Intermittent fever	1	d/d	
			7 May 03	Abscess	9	d/d	
Green, Samuel	26	Sailmaker	14 Apr 03	Catarrhal fever	4	d/d	
Gunter, Stephen	24	S	3 Feb 03	Catarrhal fever	4	d/d	
			14 Aug 03	Catarrhal fever	8	d/d	
			8 Oct 03	Catarrh, rheumatismus	26	d/d	
HALFPENNY, John	20	OS, Armorer's Mate	5 Nov 02	Catarrhal fever	5	d/d	
Hall, James	—	E	—	—	0	—	
Hamilton, David	—	Loblolly boy	25 Apr 03	Hurt in explosion	1	D 25 Apr 03	
Handy, Sewel	23	Midshipman	9 Sep 02	Diarrhea; catarrhal f.	3+	d/c 11 Sep 02	hosp/ Portsmouth, VA
Hanna, Edward	30	S	20 Apr 03	Catarrh	3	d/d	
			3 May 03	Rheumatismus	43	d/d	hosp/Malta
			10 Jul 03	Rheumatismus	28	d/d	
Hannibal, Joseph	28	OS	27 Aug 03	Diarrhea	7	d/d	
Harrison, Alexander Contee	24	Midshipman	28 Sep 02	Bilious fever	3	d/c 6 Apr 03	for debility; D 1809
Harvey, James	—	E	—	—	0	—	
Harvey, Samuel	28	OS	21 Sep 03	Lues	6	d/d	
			3 Oct 03	Scurvy; lues	10	d/d	
Harvey, William	24	S	28 May 03	Intermittent fever	4	d/d	

Name	Age	Rank or Position	Entered on Sick List	Diagnosis	Days Sick	Outcome	Notes & Remarks
Heath, Daniel C.	c. 24	Acting Lieutenant	—	—	0	—	
Hebron, William	24	M Pvt	6 Oct 02	Bilious fever	11	d/d	
			14 Mar 03	Catarrhal fever	1	d/d	
			6 Sep 03	Intermittent fever	5	d/d	
Henderson, —	—	M Sergeant	—	—	0	—	
Henderson, Francis	—	Armorer	—	—	0	—	
Henderson, John	—	Midshipman	—	—	0	—	passenger home
Henderson, William	—	M Pvt	—	—	0	—	
Hendrick, Francis	—	E	—	—	0	—	
Hendricks, Landus	—	E	—	—	0	—	
Heurex/Ury, Peter	13	Boy	26 Sep 02	Intermittent fever	5	d/d	
			17 May 03	Catarrhal fever	12	d/d	
Hewes, William	16	Boy	18 Sep 02	Rheumatismus	9	d/d	
			26 Sep 02	Intermittent fever	5	d/d	
			17 May 03	Catarrhal fever	12	d/d	
Higinbothom, James Semphill	24	Midshipman	23 Nov 03	Catarrhal fever	16+	hosp/US	D 1807
Hilton, William	26	S	4 Oct 02	Intermittent fever	2	d/d	
			27 Dec 02	Catarrhal fever, lues, rheumatismus	33	d/d	
			7 May 03	Scurvy	3	d/d	
			20 May 03	Catarrhal fever	4	d/d	

Name	Age	Rank or Position	Entered on Sick List	Diagnosis	Days Sick	Outcome	Notes & Remarks
Hins/Hoins, John	26	S	29 Dec 02	Catarrhal fever	1	d/d	
Hirwick/Hinwick, Francis	28	S	1 Dec 03	Scurvy	8+	hosp/US	
Hobbett, William	—	E	—	—	0	—	
Hodge/Hodges, Aaron	22	M Pvt	19 Jan 03	Influenza → Dysentery	72+		from *N-Y* 31 Mar 03 to hospital ship at Gibraltar
Holand/Holland, John	31	S	9 Sep 02	Dysentery	5	d/d	
			9 Dec 02	Flagellation	12	d/d	
			19 Apr 03	Catarrhal fever	8	d/d; lame list	
			2 May 03	Scurvy; ulcers	17	ulcers list	
			27 Nov 03	Scurvy	11+	hosp/US	
Holland, Peter	22	S	19 Jul 03	Catarrhal fever	10	d/d	
Holston, Christian	22	OS	4 Sep 03	Diarrhea	5	d/d	
Holt, James	23	S	8 Aug 03	Dysentery	35	d/d	
			28 Oct 03	Consumption	41+	hosp/US	
Hooper, Thomas Woodbridge	32	1st Lieutenant	—	—	0	—	? passenger home; D 1816
Horton, Patrick	50	OS	29 Jan 03	Diarrhea	55	*D* 24 Mar 03	
Howard, Isaac	—	E	—	—	0	—	
Hugh/Hughes, James	—	S	—	—	0	—	
Hugh/Hughes, John	29	M Sergeant	2 Mar 03	Catarrhal fever	3	d/d	
Hughes, William #1	16	Boy	—	—	0	—	

Name	Age	Rank or Position	Entered on Sick List	Diagnosis	Days Sick	Outcome	Notes & Remarks
Hughes, William #2	—	Midshipman	—	—	0	—	passenger home
Hummell, Michael	—	E	—	—	0	—	
Huston/Hewitson, Robert	22	OS, Scavenger	1 Dec 02	Intermittent f.; catarrh	4	d/d	
			4 Jan 03	Intermittent fever	13	d/d	
			15 Mar 03	Intermittent f.; catarrh	15	d/d	
			23 May 03	Intermittent fever	5	d/d	
			24 Aug 03	Intermittent fever	1	d/d	
			11 Sep 03	Diarrhea	5	d/d	
			28 Oct 03	Scurvy	40	hosp/US	
Hutchinson, Isaac	—	E	—	—	0	—	left N-Y 6 Oct 03
ISRAEL, Joseph	—	Midshipman	—	—	0	—	left N-Y 16 Sep 03; D 1804
JACKSON, James	—	Sailmaker's Mt	—	—	0	—	
Jackson, John	—	E, holder	—	—	0	—	
Jackson, William	—	M Pvt	—	—	0	—	
Jennings, Henry	—	E	—	—	0	—	
Jennings, John	—	Commodore's Secretary	—	—	0	—	boarded N-Y 6 Apr 03
Jennison, James	—	Captain's Clerk	25 Apr 03	Hurt in explosion	12	D 7 May 02	at Malta hosp
Johnston, John #1	29	S	1 Sep 02	Slow fever	20	d/d	
			6 Nov 02	Dysentery	35	d/d	
			24 Jan 03	Diarrhea	8	d/d	19 Jan 03; too sick for more than 12 lashes

Name	Age	Rank or Position	Entered on Sick List	Diagnosis	Days Sick	Outcome	Notes & Remarks
Johnston, John #1 (cont.)			20 Feb 03	Catarrhal fever	3	d/d	
			18 Mar 03	Catarrhal f., diarrhea	29	d/d	
			9 Jun 03	Debility → Scurvy	47	D 26 Jul 03	
Johnston, John #2	—	E	—	—	0	—	
Johnston, Robert	—	Quarter Master	—	—	0	—	
Johnston, Samuel	29	S	11 Sep 02	Intermittent fever	22	d/d	hosp/schooner
			9 Oct 02	Intermit. f., dysentery	14	d/d	
			3 Nov 03	Scurvy	19	D 22 Nov 03	
Johnston, William #1	36	S	12 Sep 02	Dysentery	13	d/d	
Joinner, William	18	OS	8 Nov 02	Catarrhal f., diarrhea	2	d/d	
			22 Nov 02	Bilious fever	4	D 25 Nov 02	at Mahon
Jolly, John	—	E	—	—	0	—	
Jones, Edward	24	S	7 Apr 03	Catarrhal fever	7	d/d	
			18 Nov 03	Catarrhal fever, scurvy	14	D 1 Dec 03	
Jones, Henry	21	OS	7 Jan 03	Catarrhal fever	3	d/d	
Jones, Richard	18	OS	14 Apr 03	Catarrhal fever	5	d/d	
			21 Apr 03	Catarrhal fever	2	d/d	
			21 Nov 03	Catarrhal f. → Scurvy	19+	hosp/US	
Jones, William	—	E	—	—	0	—	
KEARNEY, Archibald K.	18	Midshipman	27 Sep 02	Intermittent fever	3	d/d	
Kelly, James	—	S	—	—	0	—	
Kelly, Thomas	—	E	—	—	0	—	

Name	Age	Rank or Position	Entered on Sick List	Diagnosis	Days Sick	Outcome	Notes & Remarks
Kennedy, Patrick	—	Purser's steward	25 Apr 03	Hurt in explosion	7+	hosp/Malta	
King, Joseph	21	OS	12 Jan 03	Catarrhal fever	2	d/d	
King, Thomas	—	E	—	—	0	—	
Knapp, Stephen	26	M Pvt	19 Jul 03	Catarrhal fever	3	d/d	
Knowland/Nolen, Christopher	24	OS	16 Apr 03	Catarrhal fever	2	d/d	
			24 Apr 03	Catarrhal fever	7	d/d	
			4 Oct 03	Catarrhal fever	7	d/d	
			28 Nov 03	Scurvy	10+	hosp/US	
Knutson/Newton, Knut	22	S	31 Oct 02	Intermittent fever	9	d/d	
			19 Nov 02	Intermittent fever	8	d/d	
LANE, Enoch S.	30	M 2nd Lt.	16 Jun 03	Lues	11	d/d	D 1804
Large/Larde, John	23	Carpenter's Mt	21 Dec 02	Catarrhal f, severe	130	d/d	hosp/Malta 30 Dec 02, 16 d
Lee, Charles	20	OS, gunroom	5 Jan 03	Catarrhal fever	4	d/d	
Lee, William	29	OS	7 Jan 03	Catarrhal fever	3	d/d	
			13 Apr 03	Catarrhal fever	20	d/d	
			29 Nov 03	Catarrhal fever	5	d/d	
Leidster, John	36	S, Quarter Master	8 Sep 02	Catarrhal fever	5	d/d	
			8 Oct 02	Bilious fever	42	d/d	
			15 Feb 03	Rheumatismus	58	d/d	
			4 Sep 03	Catarrhal fever	3	d/d	
Leonard, James T.	c. 24	Midshipman	—	—	0	—	

Name	Age	Rank or Position	Entered on Sick List	Diagnosis	Days Sick	Outcome	Notes & Remarks
Lewis, Leven	18	OS	10 Sep 02	Intermittent f., dysentery	11	d/d	
			22 Nov 02	Intermittent f., diarrhea	12	d/d	
			15 Mar 03	Catarrhal fever	3	d/d	
			18 Apr 03	Typhus fever	9	d/d	
			27 Oct 03	Scurvy	7	d/d	
Lewis, William	??	Midshipman	25 Apr 03	Hurt in explosion [burns and blisters]	7	d/d	left N-Y 25 Sep 03; D 1815
Lightner, Michael	—	E	—	—	0	—	
Lingraham/Linger, August	24	OS → S	14 Sep 02	Dysentery	6	d/d	
			6 Dec 02	Catarrhal fever	5	d/d	
			15 Apr 03	Catarrhal fever	3	d/d	
			2 May 03	Scurvy	18	d/d	
			8 Oct 03	Catarrhal f. → Scurvy	47	hosp/US	
Little, James	34	OS	4 Sep 02	Catarrhal fever	1	d/d	
			14 Sep 02	Bilious f.; intermit. f.; rheumatismus	23+	d/c 6 Oct 02	as invalid
Llewellyn, Samuel	—	M 2nd → 1st Lieutenant	—	—	0	—	
Lockwood, Nathaniel	21	M, fifer	21 Sep 02	Intermittent fever	13	d/d	
			1 Dec 03	Scurvy; rheumatismus	8+	hosp/US	D 1806
Lovell, John Pittman	25	Sailing Master	23 May 03	Pain in side	2	d/d	
			9 Aug 03	Liver obstruction; lues	11	d/d	
Lowman, John	—	S	—	—	0	—	

Name	Age	Rank or Position	Entered on Sick List	Diagnosis	Days Sick	Outcome	Notes & Remarks
MAHOY (?), William	—	E	—	—	0	—	
Mann, John	24	OS	12 Sep 02	Intermittent fever	4	d/d	
			1 Dec 02	Slow fever	49	d/d	hosp/Malta 19 d
			27 Nov 03	Scurvy	11+	hosp/US	
Marsh, Benjamin	—	E, gun room	—	—	0	—	
Martin, James #1	28	M Pvt	19 Nov 02	Catarrhal fever	20	d/d	
Martin, James #2	—	S	—	—	0	—	
Matthews, Archibald	30	S, Qtr Gunner	21 Apr 03	Catarrhal fever	1	d/d	
Mayhew, Thomas	22	OS	4 Sep 02	Catarrhal fever	9	d/c 6 Oct 02	for debility
McAllister, James/John	39	M Pvt	21 Feb 03	Catarrhal fever	5	d/d	
			3 Dec 03	Diarrhea	6+	? hosp/US	
McCrosker, Alexander	36	OS	7 Oct 02	Dysentery	15	D 21 Oct 02	
McDade/McDead, John	30	S	8 May 03	Catarrhal fever	5	d/d	
			1 Dec 03	Scurvy	8+	hosp/US	
McDaniel, John	30	OS	27 Jan 03	Scurvy	12+	d/d	
			27 Aug 03	Scurvy	5	d/d	
McDaniels, Benjamin	—	E	—	—	0	—	
McDonald, Donald	—	E	—	—	0	—	
McDonald, Major	—	E	—	—	0	—	
McDonough, John	—	E	—	—	0	—	
McFarland, Alexander	—	Chaplain	—	—	0	—	
McFarland, Andrew	26	OS	2 Nov 03	Scurvy	32+	hosp/US	

Name	Age	Rank or Position	Entered on Sick List	Diagnosis	Days Sick	Outcome	Notes & Remarks
McGee, James	—	M Pvt	—	—	0	hosp/Malta	
McGee, William	—	M Pvt	25 Apr 03	Hurt in explosion	6+	?	hosp/Malta
McGill, Charles	36	OS	6 Sep 02	Invalid	36+	d/c 6 Oct 02	
McGrath, David	—	E	—	—	0	—	
McGregor, Peter	25	OS	28 May 03	Hurt in explosion	8	d/d	
			23 Nov 03	Catarrhal fever	5	d/d	
McGue, Daniel	24	OS	11 May 03	Catarrhal fever; scurvy; sores	9	d/d	
McGuire, John	36	OS	12 Sep 02	Diarrhea	4	d/c 6 Oct 02	for debility
McKenley, Michael	30	OS	14 Sep 02	Intermittent fever	5+	d/c 6 Oct 02	for debility
McLean, Michael	—	M Pvt	—	—	0	—	
McMahan, Bryan	—	E	—	—	0	—	
Mecroy/Megrou, David	22	OS	23 May 03	Catarrhal fever	4	d/d	
			25 Nov 03	Catarrhal fever	4	d/d	
Merrill/Morrill, Richard	24	Gunner	25 Sep 02	Bilious fever	4	d/d	
			25 Apr 03	Hurt in explosion	1	D 25 Apr 03	
Millett, Thomas	24	S	13 Sep 02	Dysentery	2	d/d	
			6 May 03	Catarrhal fever	3	d/d	
Mister, Stephen	22	S	9 Sep 02	Catarrhal fever	1	d/d	
			18 Apr 03	Catarrhal fever	2	d/d	
			28 Nov 03	Catarrhal fever	5	d/d	

Name	Age	Rank or Position	Entered on Sick List	Diagnosis	Days Sick	Outcome	Notes & Remarks
Mitchell, Aaron	18	OS	5 Oct 02	Dysentery	40	d/d	hosp/Malta
			2 Dec 02	Dysentery	75	d/d	30 Dec 02, 16 d
			26 May 03	Catarrhal fever	8	d/d	
			10 Oct 03	Catarrhal fever	24	d/d	
Morris, John	—	E	—	—	0	—	
Morris, Richard Valentine	35	Commodore	28 May 03	Intermittent fever	7	d/d	on *New-York*
			16 Jun 03	Diarrhea	2	d/d	6 Apr to 17 Sep 03; D 1815
Morris, Mrs. Richard V. & infant son Gerard	*Commodore's wife*		10 Jun 03	*Delivers second son [14 Jun 03 at Malta]*	—	—	*on N-Y 13 Aug 03; not attended by Dr. St. Medard*
Morris, William	21	Boy, gun room	23 Mar 03	Catarrhal fever	2	d/d	
Morrison, Robert	40	S, Quarter Master	7 Sep 02	Catarrhal fever	4	d/d	
			5 Oct 02	Catarrhal fever	7	d/d	
			23 Nov 02	Catarrhal fever	4	d/d	
			21 Apr 03	Catarrhal fever	5	d/d	
			17 Aug 03	Catarrhal fever	6	d/d	
			31 Aug 03	Diarrhea	4	d/d	
			7 Oct 03	Catarrhal fever; rheumatismus	24	d/d	
Mulloney, Michael	40	Carpenter's Mt	20 Apr 03	Catarrhal fever	3	d/d	
Myers, Frederick	20	S	1 Sep 02	Catarrhal fever	2	d/d	
NEWSON, Christian	—	E	—	—	0	—	
Nicholson, Jonathan	—	OS	—	—	0	—	

Name	Age	Rank or Position	Entered on Sick List	Diagnosis	Days Sick	Outcome	Notes & Remarks
Nicholson, Lawrence	26	S	3 Dec 03	Catarrhal fever	4	D 7 Dec 03	
Nicholson, Peter	—	E	—	—	0	—	
Niely, John	26	OS	6 Sep 02	Invalid	ca. 36	d/c 6 Oct 02	for debility
Nottingham, John	24	OS	8 Sep 02	Biliary colic; lues; rheumatic gout	131	d/d	hosp/Malta 30 Dec 02, for ? d
			15 Nov 03	Scurvy	22	D 7 Dec 03	
OATES, William	—	Boy	—	—	0	—	
Oldford, Peter	28	S → OS	3 Oct 03	Diarrhea	7	d/d	
			28 Oct 03	Scurvy	40+	hosp/US	
Osborn, Nehemiah	—	S	—	—	0	—	
Osborne, William S.	—	M 1st Lt.	—	—	0	—	D 1817
Otis, William	21	OS	9 Sep 02	Biliary colic	16	d/d	
			20 May 03	Catarrhal fever	3	d/d	
			25 Jun 03	Diarrhea	8	d/d	
			24 Nov 03	Scurvy	14+	hosp/US	
Owen, John	40	M Pvt	20 Jul 03	Catarrhal fever	5	d/d	
PARNALL, Thomas	19	OS, Steward's Mate	—	—	0	—	
Peterson, Frederick	23	S	8 Sep 02	Dysentery	39	d/d	
			30 Oct 02	Dysentery; vomiting blood	38+	deserted 6 Dec 02	
Phoenix, Thomas	—	E	—	—	0	—	

Name	Age	Rank or Position	Entered on Sick List	Diagnosis	Days Sick	Outcome	Notes & Remarks
Picknell, Richard	24	Carpenter's yeoman	19 Oct 02	Catarrhal fever	8	d/d	
Pierce, Joseph	22	OS	26 Nov 02	Catarrhal fever	1	d/d	
Pitchman, Charles	—	Gunner's yeoman	—	—	0	—	
Pitt, John	—	S	—	—	0	—	
Pittman, William	16	Boy	5 Mar 03	Catarrhal fever	5	d/d	
			4 Oct 03	Multiple fractures from fall	66	d/c 10 Dec 03	crippled for life
Plashman (?), Charles	—	E	—	—	0	—	
Ponel (?), Thomas	19	OS	15 Apr 03	Catarrhal fever	2	d/d	
Porter, David	23	1st Lieutenant	26 May 03	Catarrhal fever	2	d/d	on *N-Y* 7 Apr 03 to 16 Sep 03;
			2 Jun 03	Shot in thighs	9	d/d	D 1843
Poston, William	36	M Pvt	21 Sep 02	Intermittent fever	7	d/d	
			7 Nov 02	Intermittent fever	4	d/d	
			21 Nov 02	Diarrhea	2	d/d	
Poulston, Richard	21	OS	9 Apr 03	Catarrhal fever	7	d/d	hosp/Malta
			22 Apr 03	Nervous colic; consumption; strangury	26+	d/d?	
Powell, William	23	OS	2 Sep 02	Trauma to testes	8	d/d	
Prichard, Joseph	20	M Pvt	13 Oct 02	Intermittent fever	12	d/d	
			15 Oct 03	Catarrh → Typhus	37+	d/d ?	

Name	Age	Rank or Position	Entered on Sick List	Diagnosis	Days Sick	Outcome	Notes & Remarks
QUINN, John	16	OS	28 Dec 02	Catarrhal f.; intermit. f.	21	d/d	
			15 Feb 03	Intermittent fever	8	d/d	
			8 Aug 03	Dysentery	3	d/d	
			3 Sep 03	Intermittent fever	3	d/d	
			13 Dec 03	Intermittent fever	4	d/d	
RAMSEY, Charles	28	S → OS; hog feeder	5 Oct 02	Dysentery	1	d/d	
			4 Aug 03	Catarrhal fever	2	d/d	
Reed, James	23	M Pvt	15 Nov 02	Bilious fever	4	D 18 Nov 02	
Reilly, Thomas	33	OS	8 Sep 02	Dysentery	1	d/d	
Reynolds, Goldsbury	—	Carpenter	—	—	0	—	
Reynolds, Henry	28	S, Capt's head	18 Aug 03	Catarrh	3	d/d	
Reynolds, John	40	S, Qtr Master	3 Dec 03	Scurvy	6+	hosp/US	
Rhumstram, John	26	S	1 Sep 02	Dysentery	19	D 19 Sep 02	
Ridgeley, Charles Goodwin	19	Midshipman	—	—	0	—	left N-Y 16 Sep 03; D 1848
Rigby/Rigsby, Francis/Arthur	22/ 26	M Pvt	13 Dec 02	Catarrh; rheumatismus	8	d/d	
			27 Dec 02	Catarrhal fever	3	d/d	
			23 Feb 03	Catarrhal fever	4	d/d	
Ripp, William	18	OS	11 Mar 03	Hurt ankle	22	d/d ?	
Roberts, Charles	25	S	30 Dec 02	Catarrhal fever	5	d/d	
			8 Feb 03	Diarrhea	4	d/d	
Robertson, Samuel	23	Captain's clerk	2 Oct 02	Bilious fever	21	d/d	left N-Y 5 Apr 03; D 1820

Name	Age	Rank or Position	Entered on Sick List	Diagnosis	Days Sick	Outcome	Notes & Remarks
Robinson, James	34	S	23 Nov 03	Catarrhal fever	6	d/d	
Rodgers, John	30	Captain	—	—	0	—	on *N-Y* 7 Oct 03; to 9 Dec 03; D 1838
Roody, Lewis	—	E	—	—	0	—	
Rooney, Bernard	25	OS	26 Oct 03	Scurvy	44+	hosp/US	
Rowley, Edward	—	E	—	—	0	—	
ST. MEDARD, Peter	47	Surgeon	26 Dec 02	Contusion in fall	2	d/d	D 1822
Scott, Hugh	24	S	12 Oct 02	Catarrhal fever	2	d/d	
			21 Nov 02	Catarrhal fever	5	d/d	
			22 Dec 02	Rheumatismus	9	d/d	
			6 Jan 03	Rheumatismus	17	d/d	
			11 Feb 03	Rheumatismus	1	d/d	
			19 Mar 03	Rheumatismus	7	d/d	
			10 Apr 03	Catarrhal fever	3	d/d	
			13 Jun 03	Catarrhal fever	9	d/d	
			21 Jul 03	Catarrh; rheumatismus	5	d/d	
			29 Nov 03	Catarrh; rheumatismus	3	*d/c* 2 Dec 03	
Scott, John	21	OS, Capt's sweeper	4 Oct 02	Catarrhal fever	2	d/d	
			23 Jul 03	Catarrhal fever	3	d/d	
			7 Oct 03	Catarrhal fever	3	d/d	
Sellick, Thomas	—	M Pvt	—	—	0	—	
Shinney, John	21	M Pvt	16 Jan 03	Bilious fever	11	d/d	
			10 Jul 03	Typhus fever	38	d/d	
			1 Dec 03	Scurvy	8+	hosp/US	

Name	Age	Rank or Position	Entered on Sick List	Diagnosis	Days Sick	Outcome	Notes & Remarks
Shultz, John	—	Commodore's Secretary	25 Apr 03	Hurt in explosion	3	D 28 Apr 03	
Simmons, Willis	—	E	—	—	0	—	
Simms, William	—	Midshipman	—	—	0	—	
Sinclair/St. Clair, Peter	26	S	22 Aug 03	Diarrhea	27	d/d	
			3 Dec 03	Catarrhal fever	3	d/d	
Smith, Alexander	—	E	—	—	0	—	
Smith, Daniel	21	OS	2 Oct 03	Catarrhal fever	8	d/d	
Smith, John	—	E	—	—	0	—	
Smith, Patrick	36	M Pvt	18 Feb 03	Catarrhal fever	8	d/d	
			9 May 03	Catarrh; scurvy; rheumatismus	8	d/d	
			17 Oct 03	Catarrhal f.; scurvy; rheumatismus	7	d/d	
Smith, Sidney	—	Midshipman	—	—	0	—	D 1827
Smith, William #1	24	S	5 Oct 02	Dysentery	1	d/d	
			17 Jul 03	Typhus fever	11	d/d	
Smith, William #2	28	S	10 Oct 03	Catarrhal fever	2	d/d	
			29 Nov 03	Catarrhal f.; ? scurvy	3	D 1 Dec 03	
Spickman, John	22	OS	1 Dec 03	Scurvy	8+	hosp/US	
Sponset, Joseph	20	S	9 Sep 02	Catarrhal fever	1	d/d	
			4 Feb 03	Catarrhal fever	3	d/d	

Name	Age	Rank or Position	Entered on Sick List	Diagnosis	Days Sick	Outcome	Notes & Remarks
Spry, Francis	41	Boatswain's Mt	8 Sep 02	Catarrhal fever	7	d/d	
			4 Jan 03	Catarrhal fever	5	d/d	
			29 May 03	Concussion in explosion	21	d/d	
			17 Jul 03	Catarrhal fever	4	d/d	
			11 Aug 03	Dysentery	7	d/d	
Staines, John	26	S → Qtr Gunner	21 Jan 03	Influenza	8	d/d	
Staines, Nancy	*19*	*Supernumerary*	*21 Apr 03*	*Angina [sore throat]*	*2*	*d/d*	
			15 Sep 03	*Abortion*	*12*	*D 26 Sep 03*	
Stone, Jonathan	26	S	5 Oct 02	Catarrhal fever	5	d/d	
Strick/Strike, William	23	Ship's Cook	10 Sep 02	Catarrhal fever	1	d/d	
TAYLOR, Persifer	—	Carpenter	—	—	0	—	
Terrell, Edward	28	M Pvt	16 Nov 02	Scurvy	3	d/d	
			26 Nov 02	Scurvy; diarrhea	35+	?	hosp/Malta 30 Dec 02
Thomas, Henry	23	OS	9 Feb 03	Catarrhal f. → Dysuria & dropsy	51	d/d	
Thomas, James	30	S	16 Nov 02	Diarrhea	10	d/d	
Thomas, John	22	S	10 Sep 02	Diarrhea	6	d/d	
			5 Oct 02	Diarrhea	4	d/d	
Thomas, William #1	29	M Corporal	13 Mar 03	Hurt left leg	3	d/d	
Thomas, William #2	32	S, Qtr Gunner	8 Sep 02	Diarrhea	2	d/d	
			16 Jan 03	Rheumatismus	19	d/d	

Name	Age	Rank or Position	Entered on Sick List	Diagnosis	Days Sick	Outcome	Notes & Remarks
Thompson, John #1	24	S	11 Mar 03	Jaundice	5	d/d	
			5 Oct 03	Catarrhal fever	3	d/d	
Thompson, John #2	28	Boatswain's Mt	14 Jan 03	Catarrhal fever	2	d/d	
			11 Jul 03	Catarrhal fever	8	d/d	
			29 Jul 03	Debility	7	d/d	
Thompson, William	30	M Corporal	30 Oct 02	Diarrhea	3	d/d	
			27 Nov 02	Dysentery; debility; phthisis	39	D 7 Jan 03	hosp/Malta 30 Dec 02
Thurston, Samuel	23	Boy	30 May 03	Catarrhal fever	3	d/d	
Trowson, Canute	—	E		—	0	—	
Tyler, William	—	E		—	0	—	
VAN BIBBER, James	30	OS	29 Sep 02	Catarrhal fever	5	d/d	
			22 Oct 02	Bilious fever	7	d/d	
			1 Jan 03	Diarrhea; scurvy	18	d/d	hosp/Malta 2 Jan 03, 16 d
			9 Jun 03	Slow fever	7	d/d	
			26 Jun 03	Debility	12	d/d	
Vandyke, Henry	24	3rd Lieutenant	3 Jan 03	Shot in thighs and perineum	17	D 29 Jan 03	
Vaughan, George	—	E		—	0	—	
Vitry, Henry	—	E		—	0	—	

Name	Age	Rank or Position	Entered on Sick List	Diagnosis	Days Sick	Outcome	Notes & Remarks
WADSWORTH, Henry	18	Midshipman	9 Jul 03	Typhus fever	6	d/d	on N-Y 7 Apr 03 to 25 Sep 03; D 1804
Walker, James	—	E			0	—	
Walker, Noel	22	S	11 Sep 02	Diarrhea; lues	5	d/d	
			10 Oct 02	Dysentery; lues	2	d/d	
			19 Apr 03	Catarrhal fever; lues	2	d/d	
			15 May 03	Catarrhal fever	2	d/d	
			2 Oct 03	Catarrhal fever	10	d/d	
Wall, William	—	M Pvt			0	—	
Walsh/Welsh, John	26	S, Quarter Gunner	17 Dec 02	Catarrh; rheumatismus	4	d/d	
			8 Feb 03	Rheumatismus	4	d/d	
			8 Jun 03	Rheumatismus; debility	3	d/d	
			29 Jun 03	Intermit. f.; rheumatis.	4	d/d	
Warrington, Lewis	21	Midshipman			0	—	? passenger home; D 1851
Watkins, James	—	S			0	—	
Watt/Watts, William	20	M Pvt	11 Mar 03	Catarrhal fever	1	d/d	
Weatherhead, Thomas	23	OS	1 Sep 02	Dysentery	3	d/d	
Webster, Stephen	21	OS → S	4 Sep 02	Diarrhea	6	d/d	
			21 Nov 02	Catarrhal fever	3	d/d	
			21 Dec 02	Catarrhal fever	16	d/d	
			7 May 03	Scurvy	4	d/d	
			6 Oct 03	Catarrh, rheumatismus	20	d/d	
			4 Nov 03	Scurvy	28	D 1 Dec 03	

Name	Age	Rank or Position	Entered on Sick List	Diagnosis	Days Sick	Outcome	Notes & Remarks
Weems, Nathaniel	—	Surgeon's Mt	25 Apr 03	Hurt in explosion [arm & ear injuries; umbilical hernia]	24	d/d	hosp/Malta; back to N-Y 8 Sep 03; to *Constitution* 18 Oct 03
Wells, William	20	S	6 May 03	Catarrhal fever	7	d/d	
Wheeling, Oliver	22	S	15 Jan 03	Bilious fever; catarrh	54	d/d	
			17 May 03	Catarrhal fever	21	d/d	
			29 Jun 03	Diarrhea	5	d/d	
			2 Oct 03	Catarrhal fever	11	d/d	
			29 Nov 03	Scurvy	10+	hosp/US	
White, Luther	25	Gunner	16 Jun 03	Catarrhal fever	2	d/d	to N-Y 26 Apr 03
White, Robert	38	S	21 Oct 02	Catarrhal fever	1	d/d	
Whitny, Henry	23	OS	12 Sep 02	Dysentery	13	d/d	
			17 Jan 03	Dislocated femur	81+	lame list	
Williams, Abraham	—	M Pvt	—	—	0	—	
Williams, Isaac	32	S	19 Jul 03	Catarrhal fever	11	d/d	
			8 Aug 03	Catarrhal fever	9	d/d	
			29 Nov 03	Catarrh; rheumatismus	10+	hosp/US	
Williams, John	26	S, Qtr Master	9 May 03	Catarrhal fever	2	d/d	
Williams, Jotham	—	E	—	—	0	—	
Williams, Owen	32	Boatswain's Mt	18 Oct 02	Beaten, bruised, pains	5	d/d	
Williamson, John	24	OS	1 Dec 03	Scurvy	8+	hosp/US	
Wilson, John #1	28	S	16 Jul 03	Catarrhal f. → Diarrhea	58	d/d	

Name	Age	Rank or Position	Entered on Sick List	Diagnosis	Days Sick	Outcome	Notes & Remarks
Wilson, John #2	—	E	—	—	0	—	
Windless, Christian	25	M Pvt	29 Mar 03	Diarrhea	3	d/d	
Winds, Direct	25	M Pvt	2 Jun 03	Shot in thigh	7	D 8 Jun 03	
Winner, Peter	23	S	7 Sep 02	Catarrhal fever	1	d/d	
			5 Oct 02	Dysentery	8	d/d	
			6 Feb 03	Catarrhal fever	4	d/d	
			19 May 03	Catarrhal fever	3	d/d	
			31 Aug 03	Diarrhea	3	d/d	
			24 Oct 03	Catarrhal fever	4	d/d	
			31 Oct 03	Scurvy	39+	hosp/US	
Wolman, George	—	E	—	—	0	—	
Woolsey, Melanchton T.	22	Midshipman, aide to Comm. Rodgers	—	—	0	—	on N-Y 7 Oct 03
YOUNG, Thomas	20	OS	7 Oct 03	Rheumatismus	3	d/d	
Unknown	—	Shipwright	8 Sep 02	[fell from maintop gallant yard into chains]	—	D 8 Sep 02	
Ury, Peter See: Heurex, Peter							

PATIENTS SENT TO *NEW-YORK* FROM OTHER SHIPS,
SEPTEMBER, 1803, AT GIBRALTAR

A. From *Constitution* or *Philadelphia*, at Gibraltar

Name	Age	Rank or Position	Entered on Sick List	Diagnosis	Days Sick	Outcome	Notes & Remarks
Cherry, John	E	—	18 Sep 03	Lues	4	d/d	returned to *Philadelphia*
Cox, John S. H.	—	Lieutenant	18 Sep 03	Debility	4	?	
Debney, William	—	E	20 Sep 03	Foul stomach	2	d/d	returned to *Philadelphia*
Farnsworth, James	34	S → OS	18 Sep 03	Leg ulcers	38	d/d	returned to *Constiton*
Green, Thomas	—	E	18 Sep 03	Strangury	4	d/d	returned to *Philadelphia*
Harden, William	—	E	18 Sep 03	Rheumatismus	5	d/d	returned to *Philadelphia*
Hassan/Hyson, John	20	OS	18 Sep 03	Scurvy; ulcerated exostoses	38+	d/d	
Hawes, William	—	E	18 Sep 03	Rheumatismus	4	d/d ?	
Herald, Roger	34	S	18 Sep 03	Sores	1+	d/d	returned to *Constitution*
Johnston, William #2	36	S	18 Sep 03	Nervous headache	30+	d/d	on hosp/ship 30 d returned to *Phila.*

Name	Age	Rank or Position	Entered on Sick List	Diagnosis	Days Sick	Outcome	Notes & Remarks
Leecraft, —	—	E	20 Sep 03	Lues	2	d/d	returned to *Philadelphia*
Ludlow, Charles	—	Lieutenant	16 Sep 03	—	0	—	returned to *Philadelphia*; D 1839
McCracken, John	26	S	18 Sep 03	Leg ulcers	48	?	on hosp ship 32 d
Morgan, John	—	E	18 Sep 03	Phthisis	4+	?	
Redding, William R.	24	S	18 Sep 03	Rheumatismus	8	d/d	
Stillwell, John	30	S	18 Sep 03	Diarrhea; lues	48	d/d	
Tuttle, Jesse	28	S	18 Sep 03	White swelling; scurvy	77	D 3 Dec 03	
Warren, David	30	S	18 Sep 03	Dropsy; scurvy	52+	? hosp/US	on hosp ship 27 d

B. Enemy prisoners seen by Surgeon's Mate Nathaniel Weems on *Meshouda*

Name	Age	Rank or Position	Entered on Sick List	Diagnosis	Days Sick	Outcome	Notes & Remarks
Ahmed	—	—	20 Sep 03	Sore	2	?	
Assan	—	—	20 Sep 03	Costive	1	d/d	
Memet	—	—	20 Sep 03	Foul stomach	2	?	
Unknown #1	—	—	21 Sep 03	Pain in bowels	1 ?	?	
Unknown #2	—	—	21 Sep 03	Pain in bowels	1 ?	?	

Index

For the full range of drugs that Dr. St. Medard requisitioned for *New-York*, see the alphabetized list in section A of Appendix I, and for the surgical equipment he considered necessary, see section B. Italicized entries are ship names. Names in bold face are those of several of his patients on *New-York*; for more on these, for the illnesses and accidents of others, and for those not known to have become sick, see the alphabetized list in Appendix II.